10

The Biology
of
Mycoplasmas

CELL BIOLOGY: A Series of Monographs

EDITORS

D. E. BUETOW

*Department of Physiology
and Biophysics
University of Illinois
Urbana, Illinois*

I. L. CAMERON

*Department of Anatomy
University of Texas
Medical School at San Antonio
San Antonio, Texas*

G. M. PADILLA

*Department of Physiology and Pharmacology
Duke University Medical Center
Durham, North Carolina*

G. M. Padilla, G. L. Whitson, and I. L. Cameron (editors). THE CELL CYCLE: *Gene-Enzyme Interactions*, 1969

A. M. Zimmerman (editor). HIGH PRESSURE EFFECTS ON CELLULAR PROCESSES, 1970

I. L. Cameron and J. D. Thrasher (editors). CELLULAR AND MOLECULAR RENEWAL IN THE MAMMALIAN BODY, 1971

I. L. Cameron, G. M. Padilla, and A. M. Zimmerman (editors). DEVELOPMENTAL ASPECTS OF THE CELL CYCLE, 1971

P. F. Smith. THE BIOLOGY OF MYCOPLASMAS, 1971

The Biology of Mycoplasmas

Paul F. Smith

Department of Microbiology
University of South Dakota
Vermillion, South Dakota

ACADEMIC PRESS   New York and London

1971

ACADEMIC PRESS, INC.
111 Fifth Avenue, New York, New York 10003

United Kingdom Edition published by
ACADEMIC PRESS, INC. (LONDON) LTD.
Berkeley Square House, London W1X 6BA

LIBRARY OF CONGRESS CATALOG CARD NUMBER: 71-154397

PRINTED IN THE UNITED STATES OF AMERICA

To my wife, Marie,
and our children,
Rebecca, Leigh Ann, Laurie,
and Graham

Contents

Preface

The primary purpose of this book is to acquaint the general biological scientist with an interesting group of microorganisms, the relative simplicity of which makes them excellent candidates for studies of basic biological mechanisms. No recent treatise exists encompassing all aspects of these organisms in an integrated fashion. It is my intent to satisfy this need. One subject, the relationship of mycoplasmas to bacteria and bacterial L-forms, is absent from other books about mycoplasmas. A critical examination of this problem precedes any discussion of mycoplasmas as a distinct entity in order to orient the uninitiated. The central theme of the main body of the book stresses the interrelationships between structure and function, whether they concern the organisms themselves or their interactions with their environment including host habitats. A short final chapter presents my assessment of the importance of these microorganisms as well as areas for future research. This book is not intended to be a reference text although it may find use for this purpose. Conceivably it could be used as a text for a specialized graduate course.

Any work by a single author does not reflect solely his endeavor. Certainly I have had generous assistance. I must thank Dr. Harry E. Morton for introducing me to these microorganisms and to Difco Laboratories and Dr. C. W. Christensen for financing and encouraging my graduate studies some twenty years ago. I must thank my family for persevering during numerous absences from normal family life in order to pursue research and write this book. Grateful acknowledgment is made to the many workers in the field who generously supplied illustrations and the results of unpublished work. The names are numerous and are found in the appropriate portions of the text. I also wish to acknowledge the generosity of the various holders of copyrights. The financial assistance of several agencies has been sincerely appreciated. Without this aid very little of my contributions would have been possible. These include the National Institute for Arthritis and Metabolic Diseases (1F03AM38586), National Institute of Allergy and Infectious Diseases (E2179, AI04410, and 5R01AI232), the National Science Foundation (G3026), and the Office of Naval Research [Nonr 551(04), 551(31), and 4898]. Last, recognition is due to the several co-workers whose names appear with mine on publications. Completion of this book occurred during my sabbatical leave. Thanks are extended to Professor L. L. M. van Deenen for use of the facilities of his laboratory in Utrecht, The Netherlands.

PAUL F. SMITH

The Biology
of
Mycoplasmas

A. HISTORICAL

Bovine pleuropneumonia appeared as a recognizable contagious disease in Europe in the early 1700's. According to Nocard *et al.* (1898),

"La lésion essentielle de la péripneumonie contagieuse des bêtes bovines consiste dans la distension des mailles du tissu conjonctif interlobulaire, par une grande quantité de serosite albumineuse, jaunâtre et limpide. Cette sérosité est très virulente."

Repeated attempts to cultivate an infectious agent on the common bacteriological culture media of that day met with failure. Successful cultivation finally was achieved by inoculating bouillon with infectious fluid, placing this in a colloidion sac, and inserting it into the peritoneal cavity of rabbits. Subsequently *in vitro* propagation was possible on a medium composed of twenty parts of the "bouillon-peptone de Martin" and one part serum from cow or rabbit. The authors concluded,

"L'agent de la virulence péripneumonique est constitué par un microbe d'une extrême ténuité; ses dimensions, très inférieures à celles des plus petits microbes connus, ne permettent pas, même après coloration, d'en déterminer exactment la forme."

Although the infectious agent was considered for many years to be a virus, Nocard, Roux, and collaborators actually described the first isolation of the prototype of a group of microorganisms now known as *Mycoplasma*.

Spurred on by this initial success, other workers (Dujardin-Beaumetz, 1906; Borrel *et al.*, 1910; Bordet, 1910) studied the morphology and infectivity of this microbial agent. Bordet described the variable morphology

1

stating that in some cases it looked like the "virus of syphilis" and that it could be stained with Giemsa stain. Borrel *et al.* (1910) observed the characteristic pleomorphism at 5000 × magnification, describing asterococcal, round and ovoid granular, tetrad, ring, pseudovibrio, and filamentous forms. For 25 years the organism of bovine pleuropneumonia occupied a unique class unto itself. Then Bridre and Donatien (1923, 1925) isolated a filterable organism, which was culturally and morphologically identical, from sheep and goats suffering from agalactia or mastitis.

The lag phase of studies with mycoplasmas continued through the 1930's and 1940's. Morphological examination of the organism of bovine pleuropneumonia was extended by Turner (1933, 1935a,b) and Ørskov (1938, 1939). They described in detail the filamentous nature of the organism and noted that these filaments fragmented into small spherules from which new filaments were extruded. The initial studies on the immunology and physiology were reported. Kurotchkin (1939) and Kurotchkin and Benaradsky (1938) observed the protective effect of attenuated cultures of the bovine pleuropneumonia organism. They isolated a crude carbohydrate fraction which was useful in serological diagnosis of the disease. Holmes and Pirie (1932) and Holmes (1937) performed the first metabolic experiments showing the reduction of methylene blue by suspensions of this organism in the presence of lactic acid and measuring the disappearance of glucose from cultures. They found neither proteolytic activity nor liberation of ammonia. They observed that growth was limited by the exhaustion of H^+ donors in the medium. Tang *et al.* (1935, 1936) examined in detail the conditions required for artificial cultivation of the bovine pleuropneumonia organism. They confirmed the requirement for a serum supplement and the filterability of the organisms. Further it was shown that an alkaline pH was required, that growth occurred both aerobically and anaerobically, that 37°C was the optimal temperature, and that the organism could ferment a variety of carbohydrates. The organisms were found to reduce hemoglobin, to be bile soluble, and to be relatively resistant to ultraviolet irradiation. Virulence was restricted to cattle, and the natural transmission of the disease occurred by the aerosol route. It is ironic that so much information recorded by these early workers, albeit qualitative in most instances, is rediscovered today. Even the culture media used in the present day are mere modifications of the first used by Nocard and Roux.

Organisms with the cellular and colonial morphology of the bovine pleuropneumonia organism were sought and found in a variety of sources. The lack of an acceptable classification scheme led to their being called pleuropneumonia-like organisms or PPLO. Shoetensack (1934, 1936a,b) successfully recovered such organisms from dogs suffering from distemper. Nelson

(1935, 1936, 1939a,b) described coccobacilliform bodies in poultry with infectious fowl coryza. Nasal exudates were infectious and the organisms appeared both intra- and extracellularly in infected birds. Cultivation was successful both in serum supplemented broth and in chick embryo tissue cultures. These findings prompted the search for and discovery of organisms in mice suffering from infectious catarrh (Nelson, 1937a,b,c). Subsequently Sabin (1939b) demonstrated that normal mice were carriers of potentially pathogenic mycoplasmas, the mucous membranes of the respiratory tract being the normal habitat. The first hint of the existence of different species of mycoplasmas occurring in the same animal came with the demonstration by Sabin (1938a,b, 1939b) and Findlay et al. (1938) of a neurolytic syndrome called rolling disease and of a polyarthritis. The neurolytic disease was shown to be produced by an exotoxic-like substance which was thermolabile and antigenic. Polyarthritis was produced by an organism lacking the exotoxin but possessing an affinity for the soft tissues of joints. These organisms possessed species specificity producing disease only in mice. Findlay et al. (1939) and Woglom and Warren (1938a,b, 1939) isolated a filterable pyogenic agent from white rats. The organism of Findlay produced a polyarthritis which underwent remission upon treatment with organic gold salts. The agent of Woglom and Warren produced abscesses and widespread necrosis when injected into susceptible rats. It is of interest that this organism initially was discovered associated with sarcoma in rats. The organism was quite susceptible to heat and ultraviolet irradiation, passed through Berkfeld W filters, and retained viability and virulence upon drying. These organisms were specifically infective for rats. Nelson (1940a,b, 1946a,b) extended his studies of respiratory diseases to white rats showing that mycoplasmas were responsible agents. Normal animals became carriers as a result of exposure shortly after birth. The entire adult population of many colonies were asymptomatic carriers. The disease could be precipitated by stressing the animals.

Normal guinea pigs were found to harbor mycoplasmas in the respiratory tract (Klieneberger, 1935). Organisms similar to mycoplasmas were isolated from abscesses of guinea pigs by Klieneberger (1940) and Findlay et al. (1940). The agent of a fatal febrile disease of guinea pigs described by Nelson (1939b) probably was a mycoplasma.

The first isolation of mycoplasmas from the human was made by Dienes and Edsall (1937) who found it as the apparent cause for suppuration of the Bartholin's gland. Subsequently mycoplasmas were found in the genitourinary tract of humans by many workers including Klieneberger-Nobel (1945), Schaub and Guilbeau (1949), W. E. Smith (1942), Melen and Odeblad (1951), Ruiter and Wentholt (1950), Dienes et al. (1948), and Morton et al. (1951a). The role of these organisms in producing disease was equivocal. Then in 1956 Shepard discovered the T strains (T meaning tiny colonies) which appear to produce pathological reactions in the genito-urinary tract of man. During this period Eaton and co-workers (1944) were studying primary atypical pneumonia in humans and successfully cultivated the agent in cotton rats. Unknown to them at the time, they had found *Mycoplasma pneumoniae*. Artificial cultivation of this organism was achieved by Chanock *et al.* (1962). Other infections of humans were shown to be associated with mycoplasmas in the late 1940's and early 1950's. They were isolated in pure culture from a brain abscess resulting from an altercation in which a pipe stem was thrust into the brain through the eye (Paine *et al.*, 1950). This first suggestion of their presence in the human oral cavity was later proven by Morton *et al.* (1951b). They were first implicated in Reiter's disease by Harkness (1949).

Detection of mycoplasmas was not restricted to animals. In 1936 Laidlaw and Elford isolated a new group of mycoplasmas by cultivation of the gradacol membrane filtrates of raw London sewage. These were found to grow in culture media without supplementation and at room temperature. Under anaerobic conditions the medium became pigmented. It was later shown that this yellow pigmentation was due to the synthesis of carotenoids by the organisms (Smith, 1960; Rothblat and Smith, 1961). Seiffert (1937a,b) found mycoplasmas of similar nature to the saprophytes of Laidlaw and Elford in soil, compost, leaves, and manure. These mycoplasmas are now called *M. laidlawii*. Edward and Freundt (1969b) have suggested their inclusion in a separate family. The ease of their cultivation and the higher cell yields have encouraged significantly more biochemical and biological experimentation with them than any other species. Thus *M. laidlawii* of the order Mycoplasmatales is the counterpart of *Escherichia coli* of the order Eubacteriales. Known sources of mycoplasmas are listed in Table I.1.

Concurrent with this upsurge of research with the mycoplasmas was the discovery of the L phase of bacteria. Klieneberger (1935) noted what she concluded was symbiotic growth of mycoplasmas with *Streptobacillus moniliformis* isolated from guinea pigs. Dienes (1939) arrived at a different conclusion, i.e., these "mycoplasmas" really were variants of the bacterium. After many years of study and controversy, Klieneberger-Nobel (1949) conceded that these organisms arose from the bacterium. The L designation given to these bacterial variants originated from the laboratory strain coding used by Klieneberger. It stands for the Lister Institute in London where the initial discovery was made. For many years mycoplasmas also were designated L which caused considerable confusion. The L terminology now is used solely to refer to the L-phase variants of bacteria.

The early workers were not content merely to demonstrate the existence

TABLE I.1

Sources of Mycoplasmas

Source	Reference to initial isolation
Cat	Cole *et al.* (1967)
Cattle	Nocard *et al.* (1898)
Chicken	Nelson (1935)
Dog	Shoetensack (1934)
Goat	Bridre and Donatien (1923)
Guinea pig	Klieneberger (1935)
Hamster	Ito (1960)
Horse	Beller (1944)
Insects	Carrere (1952)
Man	Dienes and Edsall (1937)
Mouse	Nelson (1937a)
Monkey	Taylor-Robinson *et al.* (1963)
Parakeet	Adler (1957)
Pigeon	Mathey *et al.* (1956)
Plants	Heimbeck (1954)
Rabbit	Ito (1960)
Rat	Klieneberger and Steabbin (1937)
Sewage	Laidlaw and Elford (1936)
Sheep	Bridre and Donatien (1923)
Soil	Seiffert (1937a)
Swine	Switzer (1955)
Turkey	Markham and Wong (1952)

of these organisms in a variety of sources. In addition to those already mentioned others developed techniques still in vogue today and initiated physiological studies. Klieneberger (1934) devised her impression smear technique which allowed microscopic visualization of the fragile cells at the colony surface. Dienes developed his *in situ* staining technique whereby a coverslip containing a film of methylene blue–Azur II mixture in buffered maltose is overlaid on an agar block containing colonies of mycoplasmas. Nonmaltose fermenting species retain the blue coloration, whereas the fermenting species and most bacteria reduce the dye to a colorless state. Warren (1942), Edward (1940), and Warren and Sabin (1942) examined in detail the biological and immunological characteristics of a variety of species. They demonstrated immunologically specific agglutination, the effects of chemical agents, the stimulatory effect on growth of carbon dioxide, the loss of virulence upon multiple transfers on artificial culture media and the ability of the organisms to reduce methylene blue in the presence of specific substrates. Edward (1947) devised the first selective culture medium employing thallium acetate.

Critical examination of the nutrition and physiology of mycoplasmas was begun in the 1950's. Rodwell and Rodwell (1954a,b,c) demonstrated the existence of the Embden-Meyerhof pathway in *M. mycoides* as well as showing specific nutritional requirements. Edward and Fitzgerald (1951) established the requirement for sterol by species requiring serum supplementation. Smith and Morton (1951, 1952) and Smith *et al.* (1954) found that a specific type of protein together with lipid was the component from serum required by certain mycoplasmas. A variety of amino acid transformations and the oxidation of fatty acids as mechanisms of energy production by nonfermentative species were described (Smith, 1955, 1957a,b,c; Lynn, 1960). Quantitative techniques for assessment of growth were developed (Smith, 1956). Freundt (1958) ushered in the use of newer techniques for the study of morphology. All these studies accumulated enough information to allow the derivation of a classification scheme by Edward and Freundt (1956). Until this time the organisms were referred to as pleuropneumonia-like organisms. One can find other terminology in the early literature such as *Coccobacillus*, *Micromyces*, *Asteromyces*, *Borrelomyces*, *Bovimyces*, and *Asterococcus*. The organisms now are known as *Mycoplasma*.

The 1960's saw a rapid upsurge in research on the mycoplasmas. Their acceptance as a group of organisms of practical as well as theoretical interest materialized. Their ubiquitous nature and their probable role as agents of infectious disease of man and animals aroused the interest of physicians and veterinarians. Serious studies on the mechanisms of pathogenesis, diagnostic procedures, and immunochemical analysis were instituted. Their small size and their lack of a rigid cell wall offer a model system for studies on molecular biology and the nature and function of biological membranes. Although many species are difficult to cultivate and cell yields are of the order of 1/100th that of *Eubacteria*, the probability of discovering new fundamental biological mechanisms by their examination has encouraged ever increasing interest.

B. BASIS FOR CLASSIFICATION AS A SEPARATE GROUP

Recognition of the agent of bovine pleuropneumonia and the pleuropneumonia-like organisms as a group distinct from and unrelated to bacteria generally is accepted. Yet for obvious reasons there remains some scepticism. These reasons will be examined in Section C. Several early attempts at classification (Ledingham, 1933; Turner, 1935a; Sabin, 1941) failed to achieve general acceptance due in part to the paucity of knowledge concerning these organisms and in part to lack of interest. Furthermore some of the nomenclature was invalid. Upon persuasion by the trustees of "Bergey's Manual of Determinative Bacteriology," Edward and Freundt (1956) prepared a system of classification and nomenclature which expressed the tentative agreements of workers in the field. Subsequently a subcommittee on the taxonomy of Mycoplasmatales recognized by the International Committee on Nomenclature of Bacteria was formed.

The organisms of the pleuropneumonia group now are classified under the proposed new class Mollicutes (derived from the Latin adjective *mollis* meaning soft or pliable and the Latin noun *cutis* meaning skin). Under this class the order Mycoplasmatales or alternatively Mollicutales has been established. The former term derived from the Greek noun *myces* meaning fungus and the Greek noun *plasma* meaning something formed or molded has gained common acceptance. Although only one family, Mycoplasmataceae, presently is recognized, additional separations are considered appropriate in order to encompass those organisms already known. Two genera, *Mycoplasma* and *Acholeplasma*, have been formed. Over thirty species have been named.

All workers in this field acknowledge the value of an orderly nomenclature as contrasted to symbolism. Scepticism is retained by many in fear that the finality of decision inherent in classification will retard the objective search for a relationship to bacteria. The fundamental question requiring an answer is whether sufficient distinction exists between these organisms and the bacteria. An examination of this point deserves scrutiny.

1. Diversity of the Organisms

Organisms with similar colonial and cellular morphology that exhibit great diversity with respect to nutritional requirements, metabolic activities, DNA composition, protein components, and ubiquity of their occurrence suggest the existence of a separate class. They occur as parasites or commensals in most mammalian species. Frequently mycoplasmas contaminate cultured tissue cells. Sewage, compost, and leaves have yielded these organisms. The guanine plus cytosine content varies too greatly, i.e., 23 to 39%, for mycoplasmas to be considered simply one genus, although the composition of DNA alone is an insufficient criterion for such a conclusion.

2. Morphological Evidence

Colonial morphology is distinctive and constitutes the primary criterion for initial identification. The colonies, which may vary from 10 to 500 μm in diameter, typically present an umbonate shape, i.e., the appearance of a fried egg. The central portion is more dense due in part to penetration of organisms into the interstices of agar gel and in part to heaping up. The peripheral area is less dense being more confined to the surface and representing the growing sites. Variations occur: sometimes no peripheral area is seen, and occasionally the colonies exhibit a lacy network. Although colonial morphology can be modified by alteration of cultural conditions, no true bacterial colony displays this form or size.

Cellular morphology is governed in part by the absence of a rigid cell wall. Electron micrographs of thin sections clearly show that the limiting envelope is a trilaminar unit membrane and that no vestige of an outer rigid wall exists. On this account mycoplasmas exhibit complete refractivity to the agents which interfere with bacterial cell wall biosynthesis. The resultant plasticity of the organisms undoubtedly is the cause for disagreement on the true morphology of individual cells. Multiple varieties of forms have been described but only a few are considered typical. Some species produce filamentous and even mycelial-like structures which appear to fragment into small coccoidal forms. Others appear to bud at one or more loci giving the appearance of yeast-like forms or teardrops. Yet others suggest binary fission as seen in the coccal forms of bacteria.

Early morphologists alluded to the similarities of mycoplasmas to viruses (Nocard et al., 1898; Seiffert, 1937a; Schauwecker, 1947). Their filterability resulted in their being considered viruses for many years. Pleomorphism during growth and development suggested a possible relationship to infectious ectromelia virus of mice (Schauwecker, 1947) and *Bacterium tularense*(Hesselbrock and Foshay, 1945). More recent morphological examination by electron microscopy clearly shows distinction from the rickettsia, which possess a cell wall (Anderson et al., 1965). Although mycoplasmas tend to be much more pleomorphic, an ultrastructure comprising a trilaminar outer envelope enclosing DNA strands and ribosomes is found not only in the mycoplasmas but also in the ornithosis virus (Anderson et al., 1965) and *Haemobartonella muris* and *Eperythrozoon coccoides* (Tanaka et al., 1965).

3. Nutritional Requirements

Several nutritional requirements and such growth conditions as pH, temperature, and gaseous environment have proven useful in distinguishing one species of *Mycoplasma* from another. Only the need for some sterol with structural similarity to cholesterol has been singled out to demonstrate the uniqueness of mycoplasmas. The absence of sterols in bacteria is generally recognized. However recent claims of finding a variety of sterols in trace amounts in some strains of *Escherichia coli* and *Azotobacter chroococcum* appear to have legitimacy. The use of the sterol requirement to distinguish mycoplasmas from other microorganisms is incorrect. Strains exist, some of which have been classified as *Mycoplasma laidlawii*, that possess no requirement for sterol. Evidence is available supporting the idea that the sterol requirement reflects an enzymic deficiency for the biosynthesis of polyterpenes. Until recently all sterol nonrequiring mycoplasmas were considered to contain carotenoid pigments. There now appear to be some organisms with many of the characteristics of mycoplasmas but possessing neither a sterol requirement nor significant amounts of carotenoid pigments. Since the sterol requirement has been compromised it can no longer be seriously considered a distinguishing trait of mycoplasmas.

4. Metabolic Activities

The mycoplasmas as a group display a rather wide diversity of metabolic activities. Many degrade sugars with the production of lactic and acetic acids similar to the lactic acid bacteria. Some oxidize short-chain fatty acids by the β-oxidative pathway and utilize the tricarboxylic acid cycle for acetate metabolism. Others convert arginine to ornithine by the arginine desimidase pathway. Glycerides are hydrolyzed by a variety of mycoplasmas. A special group called T strains hydrolyzes urea. No common metabolic character has been found that will distinguish mycoplasmas from other microorganisms. Yet these metabolic traits are useful in differentiating members of the group. A peculiar property associated primarily with mycoplasmas is the inhibition of growth by specific antisera. In one particular test, the metabolic inhibition test, absence of growth is measured by degree of inhibition of some utilizable substrate, such as glucose, arginine, or urea. Whether the metabolic inhibition reflects interference with the specific enzymes involved in substrate utilization or whether some more general phenomenon occurs has never been established. Some effect on the cytoplasmic membrane resulting in impaired permeability or cell lysis is the most likely explanation.

5. DNA Composition and Homology

The wide variation in base composition of DNA suggests that mycoplasmas are heterogeneous. Even those organisms with similar guanine + cytosine ratios need not be related. DNA-DNA and DNA-RNA homology studies are more revealing. Two techniques have been used most extensively. One is the Denhardt technique for DNA-DNA, the other the Nygaard-Hall technique for DNA-RNA hybridizations. Similar heterogeneity among the mycoplasmas using these techniques has been found. Classification based on nucleic acid homology closely parallels classification schemes devised using other biological characteristics. For example, mycoplasmas isolated from humans could be divided into seven different species. No significant homology has been detected between mycoplasmas and certain bacteria selected because of similarities in guanine + cytosine (G + C) composition or because of recurring appearance in mycoplasmal cultures. The bacterial–mycoplasmal pairs examined include *M. arthritidis* (*M. hominis,* type 2) and certain diphtheroids, *M. gallinarum* and *Hemophilus gallinarum,* *M. gallisepticum* and *H. gallinarum,* and *M. pneumoniae* and *Streptococcus* MG. Homology data support the classification of mycoplasmas as distinct from bacteria.

Some criticism can be directed toward too great a reliance on homology results if taken as the primary evidence for nonrelatedness. The technique depends upon binding by single-stranded DNA of fragmented single-stranded nucleic acid. This demands random contact of matching regions. Obviously, imperfect matching can occur. Some regions of the DNA may be more accessible to hybridization than others by reason of the orientation of binding to membrane filters or the completeness of initial strand separation. The conditions under which the hybridization is conducted can have an effect. The thermal stability of double helical areas is directly related to the G + C composition. The higher the G + C content the higher the temperature required for strand separation. Nonspecific binding can result. The ionic strength of buffers used in washing also can lead to nonspecific binding. If the radiolabeling of the nucleic acid *in vivo* or *in vitro* is not random and the more heavily labeled regions exhibit greater ease in melting or hybridization anomolous results could be obtained. Thorough studies of these parameters have not been performed with mycoplasmal nucleic acids. Homology studies have employed arbitrarily selected conditions. Although it is unlikely that a great degree of relatedness would be shown between those mycoplasmas and bacteria thus far examined, some degree of similarity might exist.

A possible example of such similarity is the finding of satellite DNA in *M. arthritidis* and an associated diphtheroid. The DNA isolated from several cultures of *M. arthritidis* exhibited two different buoyant densities, the major component having a density of 1.695, the minor a density of 1.723. The reverse situation was found with the DNA of a diphtheroid originally isolated from the mycoplasmal culture. Contamination and DNA fragmentation have been rigorously eliminated as possible explanations for this finding. Although a relationship between these two organisms is suggested, additional evidence is needed which must include homology studies of the purified DNA's with equivalent buoyant densities.

6. Protein Composition

Electrophoretic patterns of the total cellular or membrane proteins on polyacrylamide gels have proven useful in differentiating species of mycoplasmas. Each species gives a distinctive pattern none of which match patterns of bacteria. There is a paucity of comparative studies with bacteria and mycoplasmas. Neither nonidentity nor identity of electrophoretic bands can certify relatedness or nonrelatedness. The patterns portray the electrophoretic mobilities of proteins solubilized by rather drastic methods which could result in denaturation. Identification of the separated proteins would be necessary, preferably by immunological techniques. When coupled with other characteristics, gel-electrophoretic patterns of similar organisms is a valuable taxonomic tool, but the technique cannot with certainty exclude some relationship between presumably different microorganisms.

7. Serological Characteristics

It should be emphasized initially that a large number of attempts by many investigators to demonstrate meaningful serological cross relationships between bacteria and mycoplasmas have failed. Examples of such efforts include those of Freundt (1958) using *Streptobacillus moniliformis* and various mycoplasmas and of Shifrine and Gourlay (1967) using *M. mycoides* and ten different bacterial species. The negative nature of the results of most such studies has precluded publication making the literature on this aspect scarce.

Reflection on the morphological nature of bacteria and mycoplasmas calls to mind the fact that bacteria possess outer walls which constitute much of their dry weight and their antigenic characters. Removal of the walls results not only in loss of antigens but also reduction in the specificity of antigens. Mycoplasmas which have no cell walls exhibit less immunological specificity as well as poorer antigenicity. Therefore the many reports of cross reactivity between mycoplasmas and other microorganisms cannot be dismissed without some consideration even though this evidence shows that any relationships probably are distant.

a. *Mycoplasma mycoides*

Serological cross reactivity occurs with vaccinia virus (Provost, 1958), *Diplococcus pneumoniae*, types I and II (Kurotchkin and Benaradsky, 1938; Plackett *et al.*, 1963), *Actinobacillus ligneresi* (Turner, 1956), *Escherichia coli*, *Aeromonas hydrophila*, and *Corynebacterium xerosis* (Shifrine and Gourlay, 1967), and *Agrobacterium tumefaciens* (Plackett *et al.*, 1963). Generally the antigen-antibody interaction is manifested only by the precipitin reaction. The common antigenic component(s) are polysaccharides. This is either a galactan (*M. mycoides*) or a glucan (bovine arthritis strain) (Plackett *et al.*, 1963). Glucose is a necessary component of the polysaccharide for demonstration of cross precipitation. Specific cross reactivity has been related to the β-D-(1 → 2)-glucopyranosyl structure found in the polysaccharides of both a bovine arthritis strain of mycoplasma and *Agrobacterium tumefaciens*. It can be assumed that the common structural component responsible for cross-precipitin reactions between pneumococci and *M. mycoides* is an α-D-(1 → 4)-glucopyranosyl segment. The significance of these relationships might be questioned as many plants contain polysaccharides with identical structures and some have been shown to cross react, e.g., barley glucan (Plackett *et al.*, 1963) which contains equal numbers of β-D-(1 → 3) and β-D-(1 → 4) linkages (Horton and Wolfrom, 1963). The nature of the polysaccharides of other bacteria which exhibit common precipitin lines with *M. mycoides* has not been established although the common antigens in *E. coli* have been partially purified by density gradient centrifugation (Stone and Shifrine, 1968).

b. *Mycoplasma pneumoniae*

Recognition of *M. pneumoniae* as a causative agent of primary atypical pneumonia of man was obscured by the finding in patients' sera of cold agglutinins which were relatable to *Streptococcus* MG (Eaton, 1950). Subsequent isolation of *M. pneumoniae* (Chanock *et al.*, 1962) led to the discovery that infection by this organism likewise can give rise to the production of cold agglutinins (Chanock *et al.*, 1961; Clyde and Denney, 1963; Cook *et al.*, 1960; Grayston *et al.*, 1965; Liu *et al.*, 1959; van der Veen and van Nunen, 1963). Early studies concluded that the reduction in immunofluorescence by absorption of *M. pneumoniae* antiserum with *Streptococcus* MG was due to removal of complement (Liu *et al.*, 1956) since no cross agglutination was apparent using rabbit antisera (Liu *et al.*, 1959). Slight reaction between these two organisms in complement-fixation and immunofluorescence tests were noted by Marmion and Hers (1963). Carefully performed cross-absorption experiments by Lind (1968) failed to demonstrate cross reactivity using rabbit antisera in agglutination and fluorescent antibody tests. However, sera from patients with primary atypical pneumonia exhibited precipitin lines of identity between *M. pneumoniae* and *Streptococcus* MG. Marmion *et al.* (1967) found precipitin lines of identity and cross reactivity by complement fixation using *M. pneumoniae* antigen and *Streptococcus* MG antiserum. The reciprocal reactions did not occur nor did absorption of *Streptococcus* MG antiserum with *M. pneumoniae* antigens reduce agglutinating activity against the bacterium. Resolution of this problem was suggested (Plackett *et al.*, 1969) upon discovery in *M. pneumoniae* of two lipid fractions containing glucose and galactose which exhibited complement-fixing activity with *Streptococcus* MG antiserum. The diglucosyl diglyceride of *Streptococcus* MG served as an antigenic hapten in complement fixation with both *M. pneumoniae* and *Streptococcus* MG antisera. The structure of the haptenic lipids of *M. pneumoniae* have not been fully characterized but are known to include digalactosyl and trigalactosyl diglycerides, a diglycosyl diglyceride containing glucose and galactose, and trihexosyl diglycerides containing both of these sugars.

c. *Mycoplasma laidlawii*

Glycolipids of this mycoplasma also serve as haptens in both kaolin agglutination and complement-fixation tests. Similar end points are seen in these serological reactions using the glycolipids of either *M. laidlawii* or *Streptococcus* MG and the antiserum of either organism (Plackett and Shaw, 1967). The glycolipids of *M. laidlawii* have been identified as O-α-D-glucopyranosyl (1 → 1) diglyceride and O-α-D-glucopyranosyl (1 → 2)-O-α-D-glucopyranosyl (1 → 1) diglyceride (Shaw *et al.*, 1968). Since these lipids appear to serve as specific antigenic determinants, cross reactivity between *M. laidlawii* and *Streptococcus faecalis* and *Streptococcus pyogenes* is to be expected. Both of these streptococci contain diglucosyl diglycerides with structures identical to those of *M. laidlawii* (Brundish *et al.*, 1966; Cohen and Panos, 1966). The prevalence of identical lipids in mycoplasmas and bacteria and their behavior as antigenic determinants may be circumstantial or they may have evolutionary significance. Another example is found with an avian mycoplasmal species, *M. gallinarum*, strain J, which contains a 3,4,6-triacyl-β-D-glucopyranose (Smith and Mayberry, 1968) and *Streptococcus faecalis* which contains a 3,4,6-tri-O-acetyl-2-O-lauryl-glucopyranose (Welsh *et al.*, 1968). Some importance may be attached to the nature of the glycolipids of microorganisms in determining their taxonomic position. Among those bacteria examined thus far, grouping as to glycolipid structure compares favorably with their classification by traditional taxonomic parameters (Shaw and Baddiley, 1968).

d. *Mycoplasma arthritidis*

Diphtheroids have been isolated from presumably pure cultures of *M. arthritidis* (Minck, 1953; Smith *et al.*, 1957; Wittler *et al.*, 1956; Smith and Rothblat, 1960; Pease and Laughton, 1962, 1965). Agglutination of the mycoplasmas with the diphtheroid antiserum was observed (Smith and Rothblat, 1960). Lack of significant agglutination of the intact diphtheroids by antimycoplasmal serum was explained as masking of antigenic sites by the cell wall of the diphtheroid. Cross precipitation reactions occurred but only weak interaction was noted between the mycoplasmal antigen and the bacterial antiserum. Such a result would be expected since the wall antigens would be most abundant and most antigenic, resulting in a competitive masking of internal antigens. Pease and Laughton (1965) reported the existence of common antigens in *M. arthritidis* and *Hemophilus* and *Corynebacterium* although on further study they concluded that any antigenic relatedness between mycoplasmas and *Corynebacterium* is superficial or nonexistant. A definite but weak antigenic relationship has been confirmed between *M. arthritidis* and diphtheroids isolated from mycoplasmal cultures (Lynn and Haller, 1968a). Cross reactivity was demonstrated using complement fixation, latex agglutination, and gel precipitation. In the latter test, one to three common lines were observed using mycoplasmal antigen and bacterial antiserum. The chemical nature of these common antigens is not known. Their existence cannot be denied but their significance is open to challenge. Designation of the bacteria as diphtheroids was made on the basis of morphology. In actual fact they may not be corynebacteria as the G + C ratios of their DNA's are more akin to those of the nocardia.

e. *Mycoplasma hominis* and *Mycoplasma salivarium*

Antigens common to these species of mycoplasma and Group D streptococci and *Hemophilus influenzae*, *H. gallinarum*, *H. haemolyticus*, "*H. vaginalis*," and some unclassified *Hemophilus* have been demonstrated by use of agar gel diffusion and antibody absorption techniques (Pease, 1965, 1967). Placing too much confidence in the existence of common antigens as indicative of similarity or evolutionary origin is risky. Generally the further removed from the surface a cellular component is found, the less specific its antigenic character. The wall-less mycoplasmas by their nature would be less distinct immunologically than walled microorganisms. Thus is seen the cross reactivity of *M. mycoides* polysaccharide and barley glucan and the immunological similarity of protoplast membrane of Group A streptococci and the human sarcolemma, the cell membrane of cardiac muscle (Freimer and Zabriskie, 1968). If these serological relationships exist as rightly claimed, the question must be asked why DNA homology studies do not reveal any relatedness. A possible explanation may be that mutations occurred changing the base composition of DNA sufficiently to preclude hybridization. A suggestion of such a change has been reported by Gause *et al.* (1964).

8. Isolation of Bacteria from Mycoplasmal Cultures

The old bacteriological literature is filled with claims and refutations of filterable forms which give rise to typical bacteria. Isolation of a bacterium from a mycoplasmal culture can be ridiculed as contamination, aseptic technique, mixed cultures, or that the mycoplasma was not really a mycoplasma but a bacterial L form. Mycoplasmal cultures have yielded *Hemophilus* (McKay and Truscott, 1960), diphtheroids (Wittler *et al.*, 1956; Smith *et al.*, 1957), and gram-positive cocci (Kelton *et al.*, 1960; van Iterson and Ruys, 1960). Although extreme care was taken in most cases and contamination was ruled out statistically, no proof can ever be given that the bacteria did arise from the mycoplasmas. If it were shown to occur beyond any doubt, it could easily be discounted on the basis of definition, i.e., L forms are L forms because the bacterial parentage is known; a mycoplasma is a mycoplasma because it has no known bacterial parentage.

A few futile attempts have been made to induce reversion of mycoplasmas to bacteria by incorporating bacterial DNA and cell wall polymers into the culture medium (Smith and Rothblat, 1960). Reported reversions of mycoplasmas to bacteria in cultured tissue cells or chick embryos are easily compromised by the known existence of microorganisms residing inapparently in these biological systems.

9. Conclusions

No rational student of the mycoplasma can deny that these organisms are distinct from the bacteria. Yet no objective scientist can dismiss the possibility that some relationship exists which will require future resolution. The best evidence favoring taxonomic classification is the DNA homology and serology. Yet both of these refined methods have produced unanswered questions. Diversity of organisms, nutritional requirements, and metabolic characteristics are too broad to be useful in distinguishing mycoplasmas as a group from other microorganisms. The greatest similarity of mycoplasmas, if one were to choose only the majority of them, lies with the gram-positive bacteria, in particular the streptococci. Here is found a resemblance in complex nutritional requirements, metabolic and respiratory activities (homolactic fermentation of glucose and the absence of a cytochrome pathway), specific glycolipids, and in some instances the base composition of DNA. Distinction of mycoplasmas from bacteria alone is not sufficient for there exists the L phase of bacteria, those wall-less bacteria capable of independent reproduction and growth.

C. RELATIONSHIP OF MYCOPLASMAS TO THE BACTERIAL L PHASE

The simplest definition of the L phase of bacteria is a pleomorphic wall-less microorganism which occurs spontaneously in bacterial cultures or is induced with some bacteriotoxic agent and which is capable of growth and reproduction in this wall-less state. The discovery of these forms was made by Klieneberger (1935) who observed mycoplasmal like colonies growing in association with *Streptobacillus moniliformis* (Fig. 1.1). She gave the designation L form to these colonies. Dienes, in a lengthy series of studies (1938, 1939, 1940, 1943, 1946b, 1947a,b), conclusively proved that the L form arose from and could revert to *Streptobacillus moniliformis*. After many years and many counterarguments Klieneberger-Nobel relinquished her symbiotic theory and accepted the L forms as bacterial variants (1949). During this interim and subsequently, Dienes and co-workers produced the L phase in a score or more of bacterial genera. Through his stimulus new bacterial genera are being added to the list by other workers with such regularity that it is safe to assume the phenomenon to be typical of bacteria.

The subject of this volume is *Mycoplasma*, so that a detailed account of the L phase of bacteria must be left for another author. Certain aspects must be considered as they relate closely to the biology of mycoplasmas. Hence a comparison of the pertinent similarities and dissimilarities of the two types of organisms will be examined. But this comparison must be prefaced with a short account of the changes which occur in a bacterium upon transformation to the L phase.

L Forms arise spontaneously in cultures of *S. moniliformis* and *Bacterioides* (Dienes, 1941) although their production probably is the result of accumulation of toxic metabolic end products. Production of L forms from other bacterial genera has required the exposure of the bacterial culture to some toxic agent. L Transformation requires interference with cell wall synthesis and has been induced with penicillin (Dienes, 1947b), methicillin (Kagan *et al.*, 1962), cycloserine (Ward and Martin, 1962), ristocetin, bacitracin, and vancomycin (Roberts, 1968), high concentrations of the amino acids, glycine, methionine, phenylalanine, and carboxylamine (Dienes *et al.*, 1950; Dienes and Zamecnik, 1952), specific antisera (Dienes and Weinberger, 1951), murolytic enzymes (Gooder, 1968), ultraviolet irradiation (Rubio-Huertos and Cabezas de Herrera, 1966), and

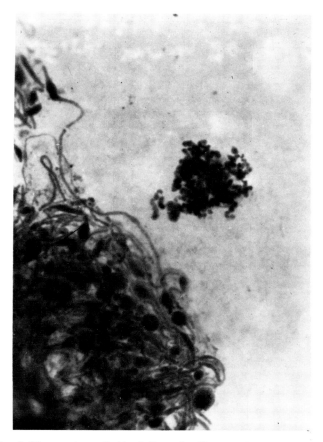

FIG. 1.1.   L-Phase colony (L-1) of *Streptobacillus moniliformis* growing next to a colony of the parent bacterium. ✕ 2000. Courtesy of S. Madoff and L. Dienes.

interstrain incompatibility as in *Proteus* (Dienes, 1946b). During the course of L transformation a variety of intermediate forms appear (Dienes, 1946a; 1949). Among these are the so-called large bodies which may (*1*) lyse, (*2*) multiply by fragmentation to form the so-called B type colony in which reversion to the bacterial form occurs upon removal of the inducing agent, or (*3*) develop into small umbonate colony (3A type) in which the L phase is maintained in the absence of inducing agent (Fig. 1.2). Another type (C), with characteristics similar to the 3A type differs from the latter by being completely devoid of α,ϵ-diaminopimelic acid (Kandler and Ze-hender, 1957). It is this latter type which requires comparison with the mycoplasmas.

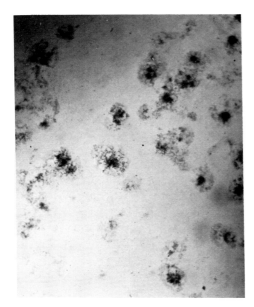
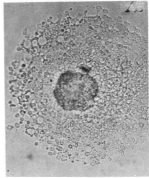

FIG. 1.2.   L-Phase colonies of *Proteus*. *Left*, A type; *right*, B type. × 100. Courtesy of S. Madoff and L. Dienes. Copyright by American Society for Microbiology. Frames 7 and 2 of Fig. 2, Dienes (1949).

The nonreverting L form is considered the L phase. Generally the gram-positive bacteria give rise to osmotically unstable or salt-requiring L forms (Dienes and Sharp, 1956) while the L phase of gram-negative bacteria are osmotically stable. When the complexity of the ultrastructure of the walls of gram-negative bacteria is contrasted to the relative simplicity of the gram-positive bacterial wall, osmotic stability upon removal of the peptidoglycan from the two types of bacteria becomes more obvious. However this explanation of residual wall material rendering osmotic stability to gram-negative L forms probably is an oversimplification because spheroplasts produced from gram-negative bacteria by rupture or removal of the peptidoglycan are osmotically labile. It would appear that a more deep-rooted change has occurred. The requirement for a high concentration of electrolyte by the L phase of gram-positive bacteria is not met in entirety by nonelectrolytes. The necessity for electrolyte has been postulated to reflect stabilization of phospholipid orientation in the cytoplasmic membrane (Smith and Rothblat, 1962; Smith, 1964).

The nature of the change(s) occurring during the transformation from bacterium to the nonrevertable L phase is disputed. Quantitative conversion to the revertable 3B form has been shown with *Proteus* and *Escherichia* (Landman *et al.*, 1958). The degree of reversion to the bacterial state of these forms and spheroplasts of *Proteus* likewise is high (Altenbern, 1963). Obviously this phase of the phenomenon is nonmutational. This conclusion has been extended to include the 3A type forms (Landman *et al.*, 1958) based upon the high frequency of conversion. The diaminopimelic acid-less C type is considered mutational in origin (Kandler and Kandler, 1956). Inspection of available evidence reveals points favoring both mutational and nonmutational mechanisms.

The nucleic acid content (both RNA and DNA) of the L phase differs little from the bacterial parent when adjustment is made for dry weight loss due to the absence of cell wall in the L phase (Kandler *et al.*, 1956a; Panos *et al.*, 1959; Langenfeld and Smith, 1963; Bader-Hirsch *et al.*, 1964). DNA hybridization studies have shown significant homology between the parent bacterium and its L form (Rogul *et al.*, 1965; Haller and Lynn, 1969). However, competition experiments suggest a loss of a portion of the base sequence in DNA of *Streptococcus faecalis* during L transformation (Hoyer and King, 1969). DNA fragments from the L form do not compete as effectively as those from the parent bacterium in parent–parent reassociations while DNA fragments of both L form and parent compete equally well in L form–L-form reassociations.

The occurrence of vestigial cell walls is suggested for some L forms. The 3A type of *Proteus vulgaris* L form contains small amounts of hexosamine and diaminopimelic acid yet the C type lacks the latter compound which is distinctive for bacterial cell walls. (Kandler and Zehender, 1957). Sharp and Dienes (1959) also found an hexosamine in *Pr. morgani*. L Forms of group A streptococci contain trace quantities of rhamnose and glucosamine (Panos, 1964; Panos *et al.*, 1959) but no muramic acid (Sharp, 1963). Occasionally a streptococcal L form is capable of biosynthesis of M protein, a wall constituent of the parent bacterium (Sharp *et al.*, 1957) and hyaluronic acid, a capsular polysaccharide (Mortimer and Vastine, 1967). An enzymic block in the pathway to peptidoglycan synthesis occurs in streptococcal (J. Edwards and Panos, 1962) and staphylococcal (Fodor and Toth, 1965) L forms since both accumulate uridine diphosphate–muramic acid peptides. Streptococcal L forms also are incapable of transferring rhamnose from d-thymidine diphosphate rhamnose to the polymeric rhamnose-membrane acceptor (Panos and Cohen, 1966; Panos, 1967). L Forms of *Proteus* (Weibull *et al.*, 1967; Kotelko *et al.*, 1965), *Salmonella* (Dasinger and Suter, 1962; Diena *et al.*, 1963), and *Vibrio* (Tulasne and Lavillaureix, 1954) retain the capacity to produce endotoxin. Loss of O antigens occurs in bacteria of the alkalescens-dispar group of enteric organisms upon L transformation (Aksoycan and Aktan, 1962). A variety

of surface or extracellular enzymes of bacteria appear in cultures of their
L forms: coagulase in staphylococci (Mattman et al., 1961), neuraminidase
in Vibrio cholerae (Madoff et al., 1961), and deoxyribonuclease and hemolysin in group A streptococci (Freimer et al., 1959). Some L forms of Clostridium tetani produce typical tetanus toxin (Rubio-Huertos and Gonzalez-
Vazquez, 1960; Scheibel and Assandri, 1959). Salmonella lose their H antigens upon L transformation (Weinberger et al., 1950) but some Proteus
L forms retain this antigen (Kirn et al., 1962; Minck et al., 1961).

Quantitative changes occur in lipids associated with the cytoplasmic
membranes of the L forms and their bacterial parents. The total lipid content increases twofold or greater over the bacterial parent or its protoplast
(Rebel et al., 1960, 1964; Smith and Rothblat, 1962; Cohen and Panos, 1966;
Ward and Perkins, 1968; Rebel and Mandel, 1969; Nesbitt and Lennarz,
1965). Qualitatively the lipids have not changed although shifts in ratios
of various lipids are seen. In streptococcal L forms, glycolipid, identifiable
as diglucosyl diglyceride, increases dramatically while there is a reduction
in phospholipid. cis-Vaccenic acid is the predominating monoethenoid
fatty acid of the bacterial protoplast while its isomer, oleic acid predominates in the L form (Cohen and Panos, 1966; Panos et al., 1967). The
L form of Proteus morgani, grown in serum-containing medium exhibits
an increase in cholesterol and phospholipids and a decrease in glycolipids
(Rebel et al., 1960). Nesbitt and Lennarz (1965) observed a drastic drop
in C^{17} and C^{19} cyclopropane ring containing fatty acids. The glycolipid
of staphylococcal L forms increases relative to the parent and diphos-
pahtidyl glycerol predominates contrasted to phosphatidyl glycerol in
the bacterium (Ward and Perkins, 1968).

Usually only quantitative changes are observed in the metabolic character of the two types of organisms. A reduction in oxidative activity is
seen in the L form of Proteus (Weibull and Beckman, 1960a; Kandler and
Kandler, 1955; Kandler et al., 1956b). Related to this phenomenon is the
loss of catalase and cytochromes during L transformation of staphylococci
and a diphtheroid but the retention of the cytochromes of the gram-
negative Pr. mirabilis (Weibull and Gyllang, 1965). Panos (1962) noted a
lower efficiency in utilization of acetylhexosamines by the L form of streptococcus. Further, the L form displayed greater activity in utilizing galactose, rhamnose, ribose, glucose 6-phosphate, fructose 1,6-diphosphate,
glyceraldehyde, and dihydroxyacetone but less activity than the parent
bacterium toward glucose, glucosamine, N-acetylglucosamine, mannose,
and fructose. The L form exhibited an adaptive response to glucose while
the parent did not. The lack of selectivity by the L form toward increasing
levels of glucose suggested the loss of a repression mechanism found in the
parent. A Proteus L form retained the parent's capacity to metabolize

nitrogen-containing compounds with the exception of loss in proteolytic and urease activities (Kandler and Kandler, 1955). Reduction in metabolic activity results in a reduction in growth rates following L transformation (Panos et al., 1965; Kandler and Kandler, 1955). This reduction in growth rate is reflected by a reduction of RNA content (Panos et al., 1965).

Antigens common to both L form and parent have been found. Differences usually can be explained by the absence of surface antigens associated with the wall or capsule of the bacterium but absent in the L form. Antibody against both bacterium and L form are removable by absorption of antisera with the bacterium; absorption of the antibacterial serum with the L form does not remove all the antibacterial antibodies (Dienes et al., 1950; Klieneberger, 1942). Occasionally antisera against the L form contains antibody nonreactive with the parent, for example in streptococcal L forms (Lynn and Muellenberg, 1964). This difference may be more apparent than real as certain antigenic sites common to both types of organism may be available only in the L form. Serological data supporting differences or similarities between a bacterium and its L form must be carefully scrutinized. Certain problems are apparent. The use of intact bacteria as immunogens may result in antibody formation against only surface antigens none of which may occur in the L form. The greater structural lability of L forms could result in their lysis upon injection into an animal, thereby unmasking hitherto unavailable antigenic sites. The specificity and immunogenicity of various antigens may vary. Those of the L form, being more internal, would be expected to be less specific and immunogenic than many of the bacterial antigens. The nature of the antigens used in performing serological tests can alter the results. Bacterial antigens anticipated to exist in the L form can be detected with L form antiserum upon removal of the bacterial wall or total lysis of the bacterium. Examples of these problems are seen in work with streptococcal L forms (Lynn and Haller, 1968b) and with diphtheroid L forms (Smith et al., 1957; Smith and Rothblat, 1960).

Transitional forms capable of almost quantitative conversion from and reversion to the bacterial state probably are not mutational in origin. The bulk of evidence denoting fundamental phenotypic change supports a mutational mechanism for the development of the true L phase, i.e., those which do not revert readily to the bacterial form in the absence of the inducing agent.

The true L phase more closely approximates the characteristics of mycoplasmas. These are the organisms which are the subject of the controversy as to whether they possess any relationship to the mycoplasmas. A pertinent assessment of comparative characteristics of mycoplasmas and the bacterial L phase is warranted.

1. Comparative Morphology and Development

A bacterium under the influence of an appropriate inducing agent starts
to divide, but division does not proceed to completion. Rather the segments
fuse, and swelling occurs at the site of fusion resulting in the formation
of a "large round body" several micrometers in diameter. (Dienes, 1960,
1963; Dienes and Weinberger, 1951). Transfer of a round body to a medium
devoid of inducing agent results in its fragmentation into several typical
parent bacteria. This evidence is considered indicative of multiplication
without separation inside a common envelope rather than a simple physical
imbibition of water. Upon transfer to culture medium containing inducing
agent many of these fragile bodies lyse being transformed by vacuolization
into empty blebs. Some fragment into granular elements 0.3 to 2 μm in
diameter which swell into round bodies (Fig. 1.3). These are the 3B type
of L form which retain the ability to revert almost quantitatively to bac-

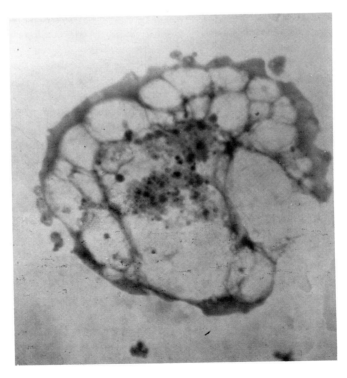

FIG. 1.3.   Large bodies of an L form filled with granules. $\times$ 3500. Courtesy of S.
Madoff and L. Dienes.

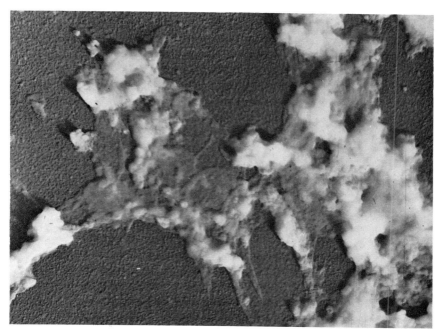

FIG. 1.4.   Granular elements of the L form from *Streptobacillus moniliformis* lying in a matrix. Courtesy of E. Klieneberger-Nobel and R. M. Lemcke. Copyright by Academic Press, Inc. Figure 36, Klieneberger-Nobel (1962).

teria. This reversion occurs only from the round bodies and not from the granular elements.

The mode of reproduction of the 3A type form is less clear. Colonial development occurs from small granules initially derived from lysed large bodies. Some of these granules retain the ability to form the round bodies. However, these large bodies may represent granular elements embedded in a matrix and therefore may be unable to separate. The arrangement of these small organisms in rows or branching strands is indicative of reproduction by binary fission or budding, not by swelling and fragmentation. Growth of these forms in liquid culture appears granular, clumpy, stringy, or sometimes as puffballs. Electron micrographs of these clumps show small (200 to 300 nm) organisms held together in a matrix (Fig. 1.4) (Klieneberger-Nobel, 1962). Organisms floating free in liquid appear as small spheres connected by filaments (Weibull and Lundin, 1963). The matrix and filaments may be composed of DNA which conceivably can leak out of the fragile wall-less cells. Support for this contention is the ability of DNase to dissolve the matrix allowing for even suspension of the organisms. The capacity of the small granular elements to reproduce has been proven by their separation by differential centrifugation with *Proteus* L forms (Weibull and Beckman, 1960b) and sonication plus filtration with streptococcal L forms followed by demonstration of viability (Panos *et al.*, 1960). The mechanism of reproduction of the 3A type organisms would appear to be binary fission or budding with filament formation. Rarely are these forms capable of reversion to the parent bacterium. Reversion probably occurs as a result of the random development of granular elements into a true round body which then fragments into the parent bacteria. The mechanism and the cause of such a reversion is unknown. It occurs

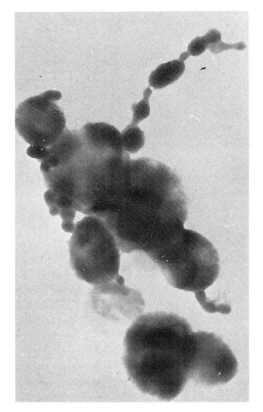 

FIG. 1.5.   Electron micrographs of individual cells of the L phase of *Proteus* (*left*, × 16,000) and of *M. mycoides* (*right*, × 8600). L-Form photograph courtesy of C. Weibull. Copyright by American Society for Microbiology. Figure 2, Weibull (1965). *Mycoplasma* photograph courtesy of A. W. Rodwell. Copyright by *J. Gen. Microbiol.* From Rodwell and Abbot (1961).

best in liquid culture (Klieneberger-Nobel, 1962; Dienes and Weinberger, 1951) and is stimulated by removal of blood serum from the medium, by increasing the concentration of agar (Hamburger and Carleton, 1966); and by the addition of yeast extract to the medium (Marston, 1961).

The pleomorphism generated by the absence of a rigid cell wall has interfered with proper comparison of the morphology of mycoplasmas and the bacterial L phase (Fig. 1.5). Individual mycoplasmal cells have been described as coccoid, coccobacillary, teardroplike, starlike, ringlike, and filamentous in shape (Freundt, 1958; Klieneberger-Nobel, 1962). The more refined techniques of recent years tend to show them as teardrop-shaped or filamentous cells (Freundt, 1960; Rodwell, 1965; Maniloff et al., 1965; Domermuth et al., 1964a,b; Weibull and Lundin, 1962). The cells of M. arthritidis, M. orale and M. pneumoniae appear to divide by binary fission (Furness, 1968; Furness et al., 1968a,b; Maniloff, 1969; Kelton, 1962). Division by binary fission in some mycoplasmal species is supported by the synchronous doubling produced by withholding serum from the culture medium or cold shocking. Most cells of M. gallisepticum appear to form single budlike structures at one pole which eventually constrict and separate. Occasionally these budlike projections are seen at both poles of the cell (Maniloff et al., 1965; Maniloff and Morowitz, 1967) and are considered to arise in cells which initially developed a single protrusion. This sequential budding has been advanced as the typical life cycle of this mycoplasma. Other morphologists consider the budlike protrusions as evidence for filamentous growth (Edward and Freundt, 1969a). The potential to produce filamentous or mycelial structures is used as a characteristic to distinguish mycoplasmas as a separate group. General acceptance of filamentous growth as the normal morphology occurs only with M. mycoides and possibly M. agalactia. There are claims and counterclaims that both filaments and coccoid forms are involution forms of aged or nutritionally deficient cells or that they are the result of physical damage during preparation for microscopic study (Freundt, 1958; Liebermeister, 1960). Certainly there is adequate experimental evidence to show that M. mycoides develops from small coccoid elements by outgrowth of single or multiple filaments which branch. These nonseptate filaments appear homogeneous except for terminal swollen club-shaped formations. After several hours growth, small spherical refractile bodies appear uniformly distributed within the filaments giving an appearance of a chain of beads. Fragmentation then occurs giving rise to single small coccoid elements (Freundt, 1958, 1960; Klieneberger-Nobel, 1962). Gourlay and Thrower (1968) have examined these threadlike filaments connecting the coccoidal mycoplasmal cells and found them to be homogeneously electron transparent and to be stainable with periodate–Schiff reagent. They concluded that this material

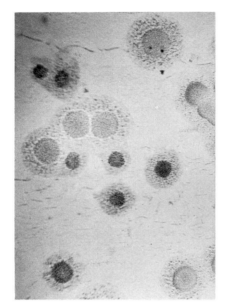 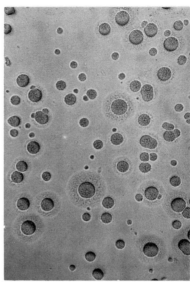

FIG. 1.6.   Colonies of the L phase of *Salmonella* (*left*) and *Mycoplasma* sp. (*right*). X 100. L-Colony photograph courtesy of S. Madoff and L. Dienes. Photograph of mycoplasmal colony courtesy of Y. E. Crawford; official U. S. Navy photograph.

was the galactan shown to occur extracellularly in *M. mycoides* cultures by Buttery and Plackett (1960). Although this interpretation probably is correct, nucleic acids which would also be periodate–Schiff positive were not ruled out. Freundt (1960) contends that under optimal conditions for growth most mycoplasmas can be induced to form at least vestigial filaments. Stimulation of filamentous growth can be achieved by providing sufficient concentration of metabolizable substrate, control of pH, making available a proper concentration of cholesterol (Freundt, 1958), and supplying preformed unsaturated fatty acids in the culture medium (Razin *et al.*, 1966). Needless to say there exists little agreement on modes of development that is useful in differentiating mycoplasmas from the typical L phase of bacteria.

The colonial morphology of mycoplasmas and the bacterial L phase bear striking similarities. Both are umbonate or more descriptively appear as fried eggs (Fig. 1.6). This typical shape is due to the growth of the plastic organisms into the pores of the agar gel and to heaping up in the central portion and to surface growth at the periphery (Razin and Oliver, 1961). Young colonies do not present this appearance because of the absence of peripheral surface growth (Madoff, 1960). Variations of this "typical" morphology are seen occasionally, primarily upon initial isolation or under suboptimal growth conditions such as nutritional deficiency, too high concentration of agar, or the presence of toxic substances. The deep central growth may be absent or the peripheral portions may appear vacuolated due to cell lysis or lipid accumulations. Although most experienced investigators can usually distinguish an L phase from a mycoplasmal colony, none had adequately described a tangible difference (Edward and Freundt, 1956). Relative differences include the larger size of L colonies, slight differences in smoothness of colony outline, and in granularity. A tangible difference which can be noted frequently is the sliminess or stringiness of the L colonies probably due to nucleic acid which has leaked from the cells.

Pleomorphism is a quality of individual cells of both types of organisms. The L phase organisms, although filterable are somewhat larger (200 to 300 nm) than mycoplasmal cells (100 to 200 nm). But this difference is relative as smaller and larger cells of both have been described. The fine structure is no more differentiating. Both organisms are bounded by a trilaminar membrane with no evidence for cell wall. Internally ribosomes and fibrillar DNA are seen (Weibull, 1965; Dannis and Marston, 1965; Domermuth et al., 1964b; Maniloff et al., 1965; Anderson and Barile, 1965). (Fig. 1.7) Occasionally in both types, internal vacuoles bounded by a trilaminar membrane are observed. These may represent some type of reproductive elementary body, some involution form, the consequence of a pinocytotic process, or a mesome. A more complicated internal structure has been described in M. gallisepticum at the sites of reproductive development (Maniloff et al., 1965). Diffuse nuclear material is seen in some staphylococcal L forms (Dannis and Martson, 1965). This nucleic acid may be related to the extracellular nucleic acid which imparts the stringiness to these L forms grown either on solid or in liquid medium.

2. Comparison of DNA Composition and DNA Hybridization

Reported values for total nucleic acid vary widely, ranging from 2 to 15% of the dry weight. Most of the discrepancies can be explained by the loss of nucleic acid resulting from cell lysis during handling and by variations in RNA content with the age of cells when harvested (Smith, 1964). Another explanation may be the degree of synthesis of diffuse nucleic acid found in some L forms. DNA constitutes about 4% of the dry weight of both mycoplasmas and L forms. As with the bacteria it remains relatively constant throughout the growth cycle. (Kandler et al., 1956a; Lynn and Smith, 1957; Panos et al., 1959; Weibull, 1958). The G + C content varies widely. The values for the L-phase organisms closely approximates those

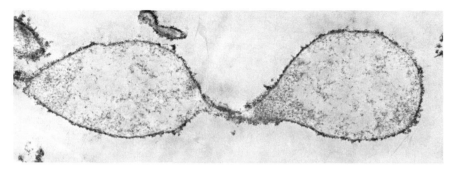

FIG. 1.7.   Electron micrographs of thin sections of *Corynebacterium* L form (*left*, × 51,000) and *Mycoplasma* sp. (*right*, × 60,000) showing trilaminar membrane, ribosomes and fibrillar nuclear material. Courtesy of C. Weibull and S. Madoff. Electron micrograph of L form. Copyright by American Society for Microbiology. Figure 3, Weibull (1965).

TABLE I.2

Relationship of Mycoplasmas and Bacterial L Forms to their Real or Postulated Bacterial Parents Based upon DNA Hybridizations

Source of donor DNA	% G + C (donor DNA)	Source of recipient DNA	% G + C (recipient DNA)	% Relative homology
M. hominis 2[a]	32	*M. hominis* 2	32	100
M. hominis 2[a]	32	Diphtheroid D-5	62	0
M. hominis 2[a]	32	Diphtheroid L form	66	0
M. gallisepticum[a]	32	Gram-positive coccus	33	0
M. hominis 1[b]	29	Diphtheroid	60	0
Diphtheroid[b]	60	*M. hominis* 1	29	0
Streptococcus MG[c]	39	*Streptococcus* MG	39	100
Streptococcus MG[c]	39	*M. pneumoniae*	39	0
M. pneumoniae[c]	39	*M. pneumoniae*	39	100
H. gallinarum[d]	42	*H. gallinarum*	42	100
H. gallinarum[d]	42	*M. gallinarum*	28	0
H. gallinarum[d]	42	*M. gallisepticum*	33	1
M. gallisepticum[d]	33	*M. gallisepticum*	33	100
Pr. mirabilis[d]	40	*Pr. mirabilis*	40	100
Pr. mirabilis L form[d]	40	*Pr. mirabilis*	40	101

[a] McGee *et al.* (1967).

[b] Somerson *et al.* (1967).

[c] McGee *et al.* (1965).

[d] Rogul *et al.* (1965).

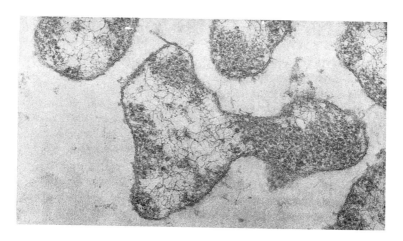

of the parent bacteria (McGee, Rogul and Wittler; Haller and Lynn, 1969). The values for mycoplasmas range from 23 to 40% (McGee et al., 1967; Neimark, 1967). The G + C values of the L forms range higher than the mycoplasmas while those of the mycoplasmas range lower than in the L forms. This difference may be of consequence or it may reflect the existence of undetected organisms in both groups.

DNA hybridization studies present the strongest evidence for a distinction between mycoplasmas and L forms. Table I.2 summarizes the existing data. Efforts at hybridization have been restricted to mycoplasmas and L forms derived from bacteria claimed to have arisen in mycoplasmal cultures or which possess similar G + C ratios. In no case has significant homology been demonstrated. Diphtheroids and their L forms (Haller and Lynn, 1969) and group A streptococci and their L forms (Somerson et al., 1967) show almost complete homology.

3. Chemical Composition

A typical bacterial cell wall component, α,ϵ-diaminopimelic acid, is absent from mycoplasmas (Kandler and Zehender, 1957; Plackett, 1959; Smith and Rothblat, 1960) and most bacterial L forms (Kandler and Zehender, 1957; Panos et al., 1959). Exceptions are seen in some *Proteus* L forms which contain trace amounts (Weibull and Beckman, 1960b, 1961). Muramic acid is absent from mycoplasmas and its occurrence in polymeric form has not been detected in bacterial L forms. UDP–muramyl peptides accumulate in streptococcal (J. Edwards and Panos, 1962) and in staphylococcal L forms (Fodor and Toth, 1965). Hexosamines occur in mycoplasmas (Naide, 1963). Two small peptides ostensibly are synthesized by *M. gallisepticum*. They are comprised of alanine, glutamic acid, glycine, and lysine, amino acids typical of peptidoglycan (Gill, 1962). Bovine mycoplasmal strains synthesize galactans or glucans (Buttery and Plackett, 1960; Plackett *et al.*, 1963) which may be compared to bacterial slime or capsular polysaccharide. L Forms from streptococci whose walls contain polymeric rhamnose are incapable of transferring this sugar from dTDP-rhamnose to the polymeric membrane acceptor (Panos and Cohen, 1966). Lysine and ornithine are formed by the pathways common to bacteria in both mycoplasmas and L forms (Smith, 1966). D-Amino acids are found as the acyl esters of phosphatidyl glycerol in some mycoplasmas (Koostra and Smith, 1969). The L forms of many enteric bacteria retain the capacity to synthesize endotoxins. *M. mycoides* has been reported to exhibit endotoxic activity but the purity of the preparation examined is questionable (Villemot *et al.*, 1962). These random findings do not prove but only suggest that mycoplasmas and L forms alike make thwarted efforts to synthesize components characteristic of bacterial cell walls. The refractivity of both types of organisms to antibiotics and chemical agents which interfere with bacterial wall biosynthesis confirms their nonnecessity for a wall.

Lipid composition gives a greater implication of some possible relatedness. Lipids comprise 8 to 20% of the dry weight of mycoplasmas (Smith, 1968) and 3 to 15% of the dry weight of L forms (Smith and Rothblat, 1962; Smith, 1964; Nesbitt and Lennarz, 1965). The lower values among L forms occur in the salt-requiring type indicating that the greater lipid content plays some role in maintenance of the structural integrity of the cells. Polar lipids constitute about half of the total lipids in all but the L forms of gram-negative bacteria, which contain a preponderance of polar lipids (Rebel and Mandel, 1969). The major phospholipid of *Proteus* L forms is phosphatidyl ethanolamine, as in the parent bacterium. Phosphatidyl glycerol and diphosphatidyl glycerol also are found (Rebel *et al.*, 1964; Krembel, 1966). When grown in the presence of cholesterol, the *Proteus* L forms but not the bacteria absorb the sterol similar to mycoplasmas but in less quantity (Rebel *et al.*, 1963). The L forms grown under this condition exhibit an increase in relative percentage of phospholipids and a decrease in glycolipids. The nature of the glycolipids has not been established (Rebel *et al.*, 1960). Although cholesterol is found in the L forms, they are incapable of its biosynthesis. Phospholipids from L forms of gram-positive bacteria and mycoplasmas are acidic in nature. Diphosphatidyl glycerol and phosphatidyl glycerol occur in streptococcal (Cohen and Panos, 1966) and staphylococcal L forms (Ward and Perkins, 1968). A shift to greater concentration of diphosphatidyl glycerol is seen in the staphylococcal L form as compared with its parent. Glycerophospholipids account for all of the phospholipids of mycoplasmas (Smith, 1968).

Recently the existence of sphingolipid (Plackett and Smith, unpublished) was discovered in an unclassified mycoplasma that differs from others both by its lack of sterol requirement and its relative nonpigmentation (Tully and Razin, 1969). Only one bacterial genus is known to contain sphingolipids, the *Bacterioides* (LaBach and White, 1969). Although possibly coincidentally, this bacterial genus gives rise to L forms spontaneously.

The glycolipids of staphylococcal L forms are principally diglucosyl diglycerides with a $\beta(1 \rightarrow 6)$ linkage between the sugar residues (Ward and Perkins, 1968). Those of streptococcal L forms and *M. laidlawii* are mono- and diglucosyl diglycerides with an $\alpha(1 \rightarrow 2)$ linkage. *M. gallinarum*, strain J (Smith and Mayberry, 1968) contains an acylated glucose, as does *Streptococcus faecalis* (Welsh *et al.*, 1968). The glycolipids of *M. mycoides* are galactofuranosyl diglycerides, primarily the monogalactofuranosyl diglyceride (Plackett, 1967). Galactosyl diglycerides are common to photosynthetic organisms but their occurrence in nonphotosynthetic bacteria has been detected (Walker and Bastl, 1967). *Mycoplasma pneumoniae* contains galactosyl and glucosylgalactosyl diglycerides (Plackett *et al.*, 1969). Lactobacilli and pneumococci, both of which give rise to L forms, also have mixed glycosyl diglycerides containing glucose and galactose (Shaw and Baddiley, 1968). The diglycosyl diglycerides predominate in the L forms but the monoglycosyl diglycerides are preponderant in the mycoplasmas. Further identification of glycolipids from bacteria, their L forms, and mycoplasmas would be intriguing as a means of establishing the origins of mycoplasmas, especially in view of the taxonomic implications of these lipids.

4. Nutrition and Metabolism

Mycoplasmas or L forms taken as a group display diversity with respect to both nutrition and metabolism. It can be argued that diversity among the mycoplasmas favors their classification as a distinct group or that it reflects the diversity of their possible bacterial origin. One nutritional requirement that has been singled out to distinguish them from bacteria and their L forms is sterol. Acceptance of this requirement as distinctive is fallacious for several reasons, namely (*1*) *M. laidlawii* and a newly characterized mycoplasma, referred to previously as containing sphingolipid, do not require sterol; (*2*) the sterol requirement of all mycoplasmas examined to date can be explained as enzymic blocks in the pathway to polyterpene biosynthesis (Smith, 1968). The absorption of sterol as a basis for distinction likewise is unacceptable because L forms also possess this capability (Smith and Rothblat, 1962; Rebel *et al.*, 1963).

The osmotic requirements of L forms are different depending upon their source. Usually those derived from gram-positive bacteria require an environment of higher osmotic strength than those derived from gram-negative bacteria. The former type grow in a range of sodium chloride concentrations from 0.25 to 1.1 M (Sharp, 1954). Osmolality is not the sole need for a high salt concentration (Panos and Barkulis, 1959) as sucrose cannot replace it completely. Di- and trivalent cations are effective at lower concentrations than monovalent cations. Stabilization of the membranes by bridging phospholipid molecules has been forwarded as a possible explanation for the necessity of cations and the greater efficacy of polyvalent cations (Smith and Rothblat, 1962). The L forms of gram-negative bacteria are capable of survival and multiplication in the osmotic environment of the usual bacteriological culture media, i.e., 5 to 10 atmospheres. The optimal osmotic pressure for growth of mycoplasmas lies between 6.8 and 14.0 atmospheres although some grow over a very wide range (Leach, 1962). Those organisms containing absorbed cholesterol appear to resist osmotic changes to a greater degree than those without sterol (Smith, 1964). Other differences in osmotic lability can be attributed to differences of origin and in size, the smaller organisms being the least sensitive (van Boven, 1969).

In order to propagate L forms in broth some particulate matter must be added to which the organisms can attach (Dienes, 1960). This requirement is seen only upon initial adaptation from growth on solid medium to growth in liquid medium. Some mycoplasmas exhibit the same phenomenon.

There are no distinguishing metabolic features which can be used to differentiate mycoplasmas from L forms. In both types there are found organisms capable of glucose utilization, homolactic fermentation, flavine terminated respiration, oxidative respiration, fatty acid oxidation and the like. An L form or bacterial counterpart can be found for every metabolic type of mycoplasmas.

5. Serological Relationships

Unlike the parent bacteria, mycoplasmas exhibit few antigens common to L forms. However, most of the studies have been restricted to comparisons of mycoplasmas and bacteria. Obviously random selection of bacterial L forms and mycoplasmal species for comparison could lead only to chance recognition of antigenic similarities. L Forms from *Proteus* and *Strepto-*

bacillus moniliformis exhibit one to two immunoelectrophoretic precipitin bands similar to those in several mycoplasmal species (Fowler *et al.*, 1967). Components of the culture media were ruled out as the cause for these similarities. Some cross reactivity has been observed between *M. arthritidis* and the L forms of diphtheroids found associated with this mycoplasma. Cross reactivity was seen by complement fixation, latex agglutination, and immunodiffusion tests (Lynn and Haller, 1968a). Growth of one of four strains of *M. arthritidis* was inhibited by anti–L form serum and one L form was inhibited by antiserum to *M. arthritidis*. These are minor serological similarities but they do connote some common antigens which cannot be ignored. Glycolipids behave as haptens in immunogenic and serological phenomena. The identity of glycolipids in some mycoplasmas and L forms could lead to the production of antibodies of identical specificity. Although such identity has been demonstrated only with the glycolipids of *M. laidlawii* and *Streptococcus* MG (Plackett and Shaw, 1967) it can be presumed in other instances.

Growth inhibition by specific antibody, originally considered characteristic for mycoplasmas (Edward and Fitzgerald, 1954), has been shown to occur with bacterial L forms from *Proteus, Streptococcus*, and diphtheroids (Lynn, 1967).

6. Pathogenic Properties

Pathogenicity has been selected as a distinguishing feature of mycoplasmas in an effort to differentiate them from L forms (Edward, 1967; Klieneberger-Nobel, 1962). Critical examination of current evidence disproves this point. All mycoplasmas are not pathogenic. Many L forms retain pathogenic properties of the parent bacterium. As previously documented, they can exhibit endotoxic activity, excrete exotoxin, and produce coagulase and neuraminidase. Pathogenicity should be rare with L forms as most pathogenic properties of bacteria are associated with cellular components, such as the wall and capsule, which are lost during L transformation. Many L forms are infective without eliciting disease. There are increasing authentic reports of the *in vivo* existence and production of L forms (Guze, 1968).

7. Miscellaneous Characteristics

Transformation of *Proteus mirabilis* to its L phase results in loss of ability to adsorb bacteriophage (Taubeneck, 1961). However, if the bacterium is lysogenic prior to L transformation, phage is capable of maturation in the L form (Taubeneck, 1963). The inability of the L form to adsorb phage is understandable as it lacks the bacterial wall with the phage receptor sites. Phage capable of infecting mycoplasmas has been found. Gourlay (1970) isolated a filterable lytic agent from mycoplasmal cultures which is capable of multiplication. In their study of the structure of mycoplasmas G. A. Edwards and Fogh (1960) suggested the possibility that dense particles found attached to the cytoplasmic membrane or in the cytoplasm may be phage and account for the ghost forms of mycoplasmas in colonies and infected tissue cells. The satellite DNA in *M. arthritidis* (Haller and Lynn, 1969) and in *M. laidlawii* (Dugle and Dugle, 1971) may represent viral DNA.

Sensitivity to antibiotics and chemical agents is variable among both mycoplasmas and L forms. The susceptibility of L forms parallels the pattern of the parent bacteria (Dienes and Weinberger, 1951). A common feature of mycoplasmas and L forms is their complete resistance to agents which interfere with cell wall biosynthesis.

The ability to revert to a bacterial form occurs infrequently in the typical L phase. When it occurs the resultant bacterium is identical to the starting parent (Mortimer, 1965; Dienes, 1947a; Dienes and Weinberger, 1951). The reports documenting the appearance of possible bacterial revertants from mycoplasmas has been mentioned previously. None of these can be proven beyond question.

The conclusion can be drawn from present knowledge that enough distinction exists to warrant separation of the bacterial L phase from the mycoplasmas. On the other hand there are enough similarities in properties and sufficient doubt as to the reliability of the procedures which produce the most distinctive results, e.g., nucleic acid homologies and serological tests, to conjecture that mycoplasmas may have arisen from bacteria and represent an evolutionary form. The purists should tread with caution in claiming no relationship, and the radicals should not let their efforts be deterred.

REFERENCES

Adler, H. E. (1957). *J. Amer. Vet. Med. Ass.* **130,** 408.
Aksoycan, N., and Aktan, M. (1962). *Zentralbl. Bakteriol. Abt.* 1 *Orig.* **187,** 208.
Altenbern, R. A. (1963). *J. Bacteriol.* **85,** 269.
Anderson, D. R., and Barile, M. F. (1965). *J. Bacteriol.* **90,** 180.
Anderson, D. R., Hopps, H. E., Barile, M. F., and Bernheim, B. C. (1965). *J. Bacteriol.* **90,** 1387.
Bader-Hirsch, A. M., Sensenbrenner, M., and Mandel, P. (1964). *Bull. Soc. Chim. Biol.* **46,** 495.

Beller, K. (1944). *Arch. Wiss. Prakt. Tierheilk.* **79,** 197.

Bordet, J. (1910). *Ann. Inst. Pasteur* Paris **24,** 161.

Borrel, M. M., Dujardin-Beaumetz, Jeantet, and Jouan (1910). *Am. Inst. Pasteur Paris* **24,** 168.

Bridre, J., and Donatien, A. (1923). *C. R. Acad. Sci. Paris* **177,** 841.

Bridre, J., and Donatien, A. (1925). *Ann. Inst. Pasteur Paris* **39,** 925.

Brundish, D. E., Shaw, N., and Baddiley, J. (1966). *Biochem. J.* **99,** 546.

Buttery, S. H., and Plackett, P. (1960). *J. Gen. Microbiol.* **23,** 357.

Carrere, L. (1952). *C. R. Soc. Biol.* **146,** 522.

Chanock, R. M., Mufson, M. A., Bloom, H. H., James, W. D., Fox, H. H., and Kingston, J. R. (1961). *J. Amer. Med. Ass.* **175,** 213.

Chanock, R. M., Hayflick, L., and Barile, M. F. (1962). *Proc. Nat. Acad. Sci. U.S.* **48,** 41.

Clyde, W. A., Jr., and Denney, F. W. (1963). *Med. Clin. N. Amer.* **47,** 1201.

Cohen, M., and Panos, C. (1966). *Biochemistry* **5,** 2385.

Cole, B. C., Golightly, L., and Ward, J. R. (1967). *J. Bacteriol.* **94,** 1451.

Cook, M. K., Chanock, R. M., Fox, H. H., Huebner, R. J., Buescher, E. L., and Johnson, R. T. (1960). *Brit. Med. J.* **1,** 905.

Dannis, D. C., and Marston, J. H. (1965). *Tex. Rep. Biol. Med.* **23,** 729.

Dasinger, B. L., and Suter, E. (1962). *Proc. Soc. Exp. Biol. Med.* **111,** 399.

Diena, B. B., Wallace, R., and Greenberg, L. (1963). *Can. J. Microbiol.* **10,** 555.

Dienes, L. (1938). *Proc. Soc. Exp. Biol. Med.* **39,** 365.

Dienes, L. (1939). *J. Infec. Dis.* **65,** 24.

Dienes, L. (1940). *Proc. Soc. Exp. Biol. Med.* **43,** 703.

Dienes, L. (1941). *Proc. Soc. Exp. Biol. Med.* **47,** 385.

Dienes, L. (1943). *Proc. Soc. Exp. Biol. Med.* **53,** 84.

Dienes, L. (1946a). *Cold Spring Harbor Symp. Quant. Biol.* **11,** 51.

Dienes, L. (1946b). *Proc. Soc. Exp. Biol. Med.* **63,** 265.

Dienes, L. (1947a). *J. Bacteriol.* **54,** 231.

Dienes, L. (1947b). *Proc. Soc. Exp. Biol. Med.* **64,** 166.

Dienes, L. (1949). *J. Bacteriol.* **57,** 529.

Dienes, L. (1960). *Ann. N. Y. Acad. Sci.* **79,** 356.

Dienes, L. (1963). *In* "Recent Progress in Microbiology" (N. E. Gibbons, ed.), pp. 511–517. Univ. of Toronto Press, Toronto.

Dienes, L., and Edsall, G. (1937). *Proc. Soc. Exp. Biol. Med.* **36,** 740.

Dienes, L., and Sharp, J. T. (1956). *J. Bacteriol.* **71,** 208.

Dienes, L., and Weinberger, H. J. (1951). *Bacteriol. Rev.* **15,** 245.

Dienes, L., and Zamecnik, P. C. (1952). *J. Bacteriol.* **64,** 770.

Dienes, L., Ropes, M. W., Smith, W. E., Madoff, S., and Bauer, W. (1948). *N. Eng. J. Med.* **238,** 509.

Dienes, L., Weinberger, H. J., and Madoff, S. (1950). *J. Bacteriol.* **59,** 755.

Domermuth, C. H., Nielsen, M. H., Freundt, E. A., and Birch-Anderson, A. (1964a). *J. Bacteriol.* **88,** 1428.

Domermuth, C. H., Nielsen, M. H., Freundt, E. A., and Birch-Anderson, A. (1964b). *J. Bacteriol.* **88,** 727.

Dugle, D. L., and Dugle, J. R. (1971). *Can. J. Microbiol.* **17,** 433.

Dujardin-Beaumetz (1906). *Ann. Inst. Pasteur Paris* **20,** 449.

Eaton, M. D. (1950). *Handbuch Virusforschung II. Erganizugband* **87,** 140.

Eaton, M. D., Meiklejohn, G., and van Herick, W. (1944). *J. Exp. Med.* **79,** 649.

Edward, D. G. ff. (1940). *J. Pathol. Bacteriol.* **50,** 409.

Edward, D. G. ff. (1947). *J. Pathol. Bacteriol.* **59,** 209.

Edward, D. G. ff. (1967). *Ann. N. Y. Acad. Sci.* **143,** 7.

Edward, D. G. ff., and Fitzgerald, W. A. (1951). *J. Gen. Microbiol.* **5,** 576.

Edward, D. G. ff., and Fitzgerald, W. A. (1954). *J. Pathol. Bacteriol.* **68,** 23.

Edward, D. G. ff., and Freundt, E. A. (1956). *J. Gen. Microbiol.* **14,** 197.

Edward, D. G. ff., and Freundt, E. A. (1969a). *In* "The Mycoplasmatales and the L-Phase of Bacteria" (L. Hayflick, ed.), pp. 147–200, Appleton, New York.

Edward, D. G. ff., and Freundt, E. A. (1969b). *J. Gen. Microbiol.* **57,** 391.

Edwards, G. A., and Fogh, J. (1960). *J. Bacteriol.* **79,** 267.

Edwards, J., and Panos, C. (1962). *J. Bacteriol.* **84,** 1202.

Findlay, G. M., Klieneberger, E., MacCallum, F. O., and Mackenzie, R. D. (1938). *Lancet* **2,** 1511.

Findlay, G. M., Mackenzie, R. D., MacCallum, F. O., and Klieneberger, E. (1939). *Lancet* **237,** 7.

Findlay, G. M., Mackenzie, R. D., and MacCallum, F. O. (1940). *Brit. J. Exp. Pathol.* **21,** 13.

Fodor, M., and Toth, B. (1965). *Acta Microbiol. Acad. Sci. Hungary* **12,** 173.

Fowler, R. C., Coble, D. W., Kramer, N. C., Pai, R. R., Serrano, B. A., and Brown, T. McP. (1967). *Ann. N. Y. Acad. Sci.* **143,** 641.

Freimer, E. H., and Zabriskie, J. B. (1968). *In* "Microbial Protoplasts, Spheroplasts and L-Forms" (L. B. Guze, ed.), pp. 356–371. Williams & Wilkins, Baltimore, Maryland.

Freimer, E. H., Krause, R. M., and McCarty, M. (1959). *J. Exp. Med.* **110,** 853.

Freundt, E. A. (1958). "The Mycoplasmataceae," 147 pp. Munksgaard, Copenhagen.

Freundt, E. A. (1960). *Ann. N. Y. Acad. Sci.* **79,** 312.

Furness, G. (1968). *J. Infect. Dis.* **118,** 436.

Furness, G., Pipes, F. J., and McMurtrey, M. J. (1968a). *J. Infect. Dis.* **118,** 1.

Furness, G., Pipes, F. J., and McMurtrey, M. J. (1968b). *J. Infec. Dis.* **118,** 7.

Gause, G. G., Lashkareua, N. P., Zbrozsky, I. B., and Gause, G. F. (1964). *Nature London* **203,** 598.

Gill, J. W. (1962). *J. Bacteriol.* **83,** 213.

Gooder, H. (1968). *In* "Microbial Protoplasts, Spheroplasts and L-Forms" (L. B. Guze, ed.), pp. 40–51. Williams & Wilkins, Baltimore, Maryland.

Gourlay, R. N. (1970). *Nature (London)* **225,** 1165.

Gourlay, R. N., and Thrower, K. J. (1968). *J. Gen. Microbiol.* **54,** 155.

Grayston, J. T., Alexander, E. R., Kenny, G. E., and Clarke, E. R. (1965). *J. Amer. Med. Ass.* **191,** 369.

Guze, L. B., ed. (1968). "Microbial Protoplasts, Spheroplasts and L-Forms," 523 pp. Williams & Wilkins, Baltimore, Maryland.

Haller, G. J., and Lynn, R. J. (1969). *Bacteriol. Proc.* p. 33.

Hamburger, M., and Carleton, J. (1966). *J. Infec. Dis.* **116,** 544.

Harkness, A. H. (1949). *Brit. J. Vener. Dis.* **25,** 185.

Heimbeck, L. S. (1954). "On the Etiology of Brown Roots, Yellowing and Wilt due to 'B Type (Dienes) L (Klieneberger) Forms' of Bacteria with Special Reference to Pea Wilt," 40 pp. Dreyers Forlag, Oslo.

Hesselbrock, W., and Foshay, L. (1945). *J. Bacteriol.* **49,** 209.

Holmes, B. E. (1937). *Brit. J. Exp. Pathol.* **18,** 103.

Holmes, B. E., and Pirie, A. (1932). *Brit. J. Exp. Pathol.* **13,** 364.

Horton, D., and Wolfrom, M. L. (1963). *In* "Comprehensive Biochemistry" (M. Florkin and E. H. Stotz, eds.), Vol. 5, p. 185. Elsevier, Amsterdam.

Hoyer, B. H., and King, J. R. (1969). *J. Bacteriol.* **97**, 1516.
Ito, S. (1960). *Jap. J. Bacteriol.* **15**, 1193.
Kagan, B. M., Molander, C. W., and Weinberger, H. J. (1962). *J. Bacteriol.* **83**, 1162.
Kandler, O., and Kandler, G. (1955). *Zentralbl. Bakteriol. Abt.* **2 180**, 383.
Kandler, O., and Kandler, G. (1956). *Z. Naturforsch. B* **11**, 252.
Kandler, O., and Zehender, C. (1957). *Z. Naturforsch. B* **12**, 725.
Kandler, O., Zehender, C., and Müller, J. (1956a). *Arch. Mikrobiol.* **24**, 219.
Kandler, O., Zehender, C., and Müller, J. (1956b). *Arch. Mikrobiol.* **24**, 209.
Kelton, W. H. (1962). *J. Bacteriol.* **83**, 948.
Kelton, W. H., Gentry, R. F., and Ludwig, E. H. (1960). *Ann. N. Y. Acad. Sci.* **79**, 410.
Kirn, A., Fleck, J., and Minck, R. (1962). *Ann. Inst. Pasteur Paris* **102**, 113.
Klieneberger, E. (1934). *J. Pathol. Bacteriol.* **39**, 409.
Klieneberger, E. (1935). *J. Pathol. Bacteriol.* **40**, 93.
Klieneberger, E. (1940). *J. Hyg.* **40**, 204.
Klieneberger, E. (1942). *J. Hyg.* **42**, 485.
Klieneberger, E., and Steabben, D. B. (1937). *J. Hyg.* **37**, 143.
Klieneberger-Nobel, E. (1945). *Lancet* **2**, 46.
Klieneberger-Nobel, E. (1949). *J. Gen. Microbiol.* **3**, 434.
Klieneberger-Nobel, E. (1962). "Pleuropneumonia-Like Organisms (PPLO) Myco-plasmataceae," 157 pp. Academic Press, New York.
Koostra, W. L., and Smith, P. F. (1969). *Biochemistry* **8**, 4794.
Kotelko, K., Lüderitz, O., and Westphal, O. (1965). *Biochem. Z.* **343**, 227.
Krembel, J. (1966). *Bull. Soc. Chim. Biol.* **48**, 1305.
Kurotchkin, T. J. (1937). *Proc. Soc. Exp. Biol. Med.* **37**, 21.
Kurotchkin, T. J., and Benaradsky, C. V. (1938). *Chin. Med. J. Suppl.* **2**, 269.
LaBach, J. P., and White, D. C. (1969). *J. Lipid Res.* **10**, 528.
Laidlaw, P. P., and Elford, W. J. (1936). *Proc. Roy. Soc. London Ser. B* **120**, 292.
Landman, O. E., Altenbern, R. A., and Ginoza, H. S. (1958). *J. Bacteriol.* **75**, 567.
Langenfeld, M. G., and Smith, P. F. (1963). *J. Bacteriol.* **86**, 1216.
Leach, R. H. (1962). *J. Gen. Microbiol.* **27**, 345.
Ledingham, J. C. G. (1933). *J. Pathol. Bacteriol.* **37**, 393.
Liebermeister, K. (1960). *Ann. N. Y. Acad. Sci.* **79**, 326.
Lind, K. (1968). *Acta Pathol. Microbiol. Scand.* **73**, 237.
Liu, C., Eaton, M. D., and Heyl, J. T. (1956). *Bull. N. Y. Acad. Med.* **32**, 168.
Liu, C., Eaton, M. D., and Heyl, J. T. (1959). *J. Exp. Med.* **109**, 545.
Lynn, R. J. (1960). *Ann. N. Y. Acad. Sci.* **79**, 538.
Lynn, R. J. (1967). *Ann. N. Y. Acad. Sci.* **143**, 654.
Lynn, R. J., and Haller, G. J. (1968a). *Antonie van Leeuwenhoek J. Microbiol. Serol.* **34**, 249.
Lynn, R. J., and Haller, G. J. (1968b). *In* "Microbial Protoplasts, Spheroplasts and L-Forms," (L. B. Guze, ed.), pp. 270–278. Williams & Wilkins, Baltimore, Maryland.
Lynn, R. J., and Muellenberg, M. B. (1964). *Antonie van Leeuwenhoek J. Microbiol. Serol.* **31**, 15.
Lynn, R. J., and Smith, P. F. (1957). *J. Bacteriol.* **74**, 811.
McGee, Z. A., Rogul, M., Falkow, S., and Wittler, R. G. (1965). *Proc. Nat. Acad. Sci. U.S.* **54**, 457.
McGee, Z. A., Rogul, M., and Wittler, R. G. (1967). *Ann. N. Y. Acad. Sci.* **143**, 21.
McKay, K. A., and Truscott, R. B. (1960). *Ann. N. Y. Acad. Sci.* **79**, 465.

Madoff, M., Annenberg, S. M., and Weinstein, L. (1961). *Proc. Soc. Exp. Biol. Med.* **107,** 776.
Madoff, S. (1960). *Ann. N. Y. Acad. Sci.* **79,** 383.
Maniloff, J. (1969). *J. Bacteriol.* **100,** 1402.
Maniloff, J., and Morowitz, H. J. (1967). *Ann. N. Y. Acad. Sci.* **143,** 59.
Maniloff, J., Morowitz, H. J., and Barrnett, R. J. (1965). *J. Bacteriol.* **90,** 193.
Markham, F. S., and Wong, S. C. (1952). *Poultry Sci.* **31,** 902.
Marmion, B. P., and Hers, J. F. (1963). *Amer. Rev. Resp. Dis.* **88,** 198.
Marmion, B. P., Plackett, P., and Lemcke, R. M. (1967). *Aust. J. Exp. Biol. Med. Sci.* **45,** 163.
Marston, J. (1961). *J. Bacteriol.* **81,** 832.
Mathey, W. J., Jr., Adler, H. E., and Siddle, P. J. (1956). *Amer. J. Vet. Res.* **17,** 521.
Mattman, L. H., Tunstall, L. H., and Rossmore, H. W. (1961). *Can. J. Microbiol.* **7,** 705.
Melen, B., and Odeblad, E. (1951). *Scand. J. Clin. Lab. Invest.* **3,** 47.
Minck, R. (1953). *C. R. Acad. Sci. Paris* **236,** 250.
Minck, R., Kirn, A., and Fleck, M. (1961). *Ann. Inst. Pasteur Paris* **101,** 178.
Mortimer, E. A., Jr. (1965). *Proc. Soc. Exp. Biol. Med.* **119,** 159.
Mortimer, E. A., Jr., and Vastine, E. L. (1967). *J. Bacteriol.* **94,** 268.
Morton, H. E., Smith, P. F., and Leberman, P. R. (1951a). *Amer. J. Syph. Gonor. Vener. Dis.* **35,** 14.
Morton, H. E., Smith, P. F., Williams, N. B., and Eickenberg, C. F. (1951b). *J. Dent. Res.* **30,** 415.
Naide, Y. (1963). *Jap. J. Microbiol.* **7,** 135.
Neimark, H. (1967). *Ann. N. Y. Acad. Sci.* **143,** 31.
Nelson, J. B. (1935). *Science* **82,** 43.
Nelson, J. B. (1936). *J. Exp. Med.* **63,** 515.
Nelson, J. B. (1937a). *J. Exp. Med.* **65,** 833.
Nelson, J. B. (1937b). *J. Exp. Med.* **65,** 843.
Nelson, J. B. (1937c). *J. Exp. Med.* **65,** 851.
Nelson, J. B. (1939a). *J. Exp. Med.* **69,** 199.
Nelson, J. B. (1939b). *Proc. Third Int. Congr. Microbiol.* p. 180.
Nelson, J. B. (1940a). *J. Exp. Med.* **72,** 645.
Nelson, J. B. (1940b). *J. Exp. Med.* **72,** 655.
Nelson, J. B. (1946a). *J. Exp. Med.* **84,** 7.
Nelson, J. B. (1946b). *J. Exp. Med.* **84,** 15.
Nesbitt, J. A., III, and Lennarz, W. J. (1965). *J. Bacteriol.* **89,** 1020.
Nocard, E., Roux, E. R., Borrel, M. M., Salimbeniet, 00., and Dujardin-Beaumetz, 00. (1898). *Ann. Inst. Pasteur Paris* **12,** 240.
Ørskov, J. (1938). *Zentrblt. Bakteriol. Abt. 1 (Orig.)* **141,** 229.
Ørskov, J. (1939). *Proc. Third Int. Congr. Microbiol.* p. 179.
Paine, T. F., Jr., Murray, R., Perlmutter, I., and Finland, M. (1950). *Ann. Intern. Med.* **32,** 554.
Panos, C. (1962). *J. Bacteriol.* **84,** 921.
Panos, C. (1964). *Trans. N. Y. Acad. Sci.* **26,** 954.
Panos, C. (1967). *Ann. N. Y. Acad. Sci.* **143,** 152.
Panos, C., and Barkulis, S. S. (1959). *J. Bacteriol.* **78,** 247.
Panos, C., and Cohen, M. (1966). *Biochim. Biophys. Acta* **117,** 98.
Panos, C., Barkulis, S. S., and Hayashi, J. A. (1959). *J. Bacteriol.* **78,** 863.
Panos, C., Barkulis, S. S., and Hayashi, J. A. (1960). *J. Bacteriol.* **80,** 336.

Panos, C., Hynes, L. M., and Cohen, M. (1965). *Biochem. Biophys. Res. Commun.* **19,** 62.

Panos, C., Cohen, M., and Fagan, G. (1967). *J. Gen. Microbiol.* **46,** 299.

Pease, P. (1965). *J. Gen. Microbiol.* **41,** 299.

Pease, P. (1967). *J. Gen. Microbiol.* **49,** 433.

Pease, P., and Laughton, N. (1962). *J. Gen. Microbiol.* **27,** 383.

Pease, P., and Laughton, N. (1965). *J. Gen. Microbiol.* **41,** 293.

Plackett, P. (1959). *Biochim. Biophys. Acta* **35,** 260.

Plackett, P. (1967). *Biochemistry* **6,** 2746.

Plackett, P., and Shaw, E. J. (1967). *Biochem. J.* **104,** 61.

Plackett, P., Buttery, S. H., and Cottew, G. S. (1963). *In* "Recent Progress in Microbiology" (N. E. Gibbons, ed.), pp. 535–547. Univ. of Toronto Press, Toronto.

Plackett, P., Marmion, B. P., Shaw, E. J., and Lemcke, R. M. (1969). *Aust. J. Exp. Biol. Med. Sci.* **47,** 171.

Provost, A. (1958). *C. R. Acad. Sci. Paris* **246,** 1323.

Razin, S., and Oliver, O. (1961). *J. Gen. Microbiol.* **24,** 225.

Razin, S., Cosenza, B. J., and Tourtellotte, M. E. (1966). *J. Gen. Microbiol.* **42,** 139.

Rebel, G., and Mandel, P. (1969). *Ann. Inst. Pasteur Paris* **117,** 501.

Rebel, G., Bader, A. M., Sensenbrenner, M., and Mandel, P. (1960). *C. R. Acad. Sci. Paris* **250,** 3516.

Rebel, G., Bader-Hirsch, A. M., and Mandel, P. (1963). *Bull. Soc. Chim. Biol.* **45,** 1327.

Rebel, G., Sensenbrenner, M., Klein, F., and Mandel, P. (1964). *Bull. Soc. Chim. Biol.* **46,** 7.

Roberts, R. B. (1968). *In* "Microbial Protoplasts, Spheroplasts and L-Forms" (L. B. Guze, ed.), pp. 230–238. Williams & Wilkins, Baltimore, Maryland.

Rodwell, A. W. (1965). *J. Gen. Microbiol.* **40,** 227.

Rodwell, A. W., and Abbot, A. (1961). *J. Gen. Microbiol.* **25,** 201.

Rodwell, A. W., and Rodwell, E. S. (1954a). *Aust. J. Biol. Sci.* **7,** 18.

Rodwell, A. W., and Rodwell, E. S. (1954b). *Aust. J. Biol. Sci.* **7,** 31.

Rodwell, A. W., and Rodwell, E. S. (1954c). *Aust. J. Biol. Sci.* **7,** 37.

Rogul, M., McGee, Z. A., Wittler, R. G., and Falkow, S. (1965). *J. Bacteriol.* **90,** 1200.

Rothblat, G. H., and Smith, P. F. (1961). *J. Bacteriol.* **82,** 479.

Rubio-Huertos, M., and Cabezas de Herrera, E. (1966). *Nature (London)* **209,** 1262.

Rubio-Huertos, M., and Gonzalez-Vazquez, C. (1960). *Ann. N. Y. Acad. Sci.* **79,** 626.

Ruiter, M., and Wentholt, H. M. M. (1950). *J. Invest. Dermatol.* **15,** 301.

Sabin, A. B. (1938a). *Science* **88,** 189.

Sabin, A. B. (1938b). *Science* **88,** 575.

Sabin, A. B. (1939a). *Science* **90,** 18.

Sabin, A. B. (1939b). *Science* **89,** 228.

Sabin, A. B. (1941). *Bacteriol. Rev.* **5,** 1.

Schaub, I. G., and Guilbeau, J. A. (1949). *Bull. Johns Hopkins Hosp.* **84,** 1.

Schauwecker, R. (1947). *Schweiz. Z. Pathol. Bakteriol.* **10,** 714.

Scheibel, I., and Assandri, J. (1959). *Acta Pathol. Microbiol. Scand.* **46,** 333.

Seiffert, G. (1937a). *Zentralbl. Bakteriol. (Orig.)* **139,** 337.

Seiffert, G. (1937b). *Zentralbl. Bakteriol. (Orig.)* **140,** 168.

Sharp, J. T. (1954). *Proc. Soc. Exp. Biol. Med.* **87,** 94.

Sharp, J. T. (1963). *J. Bacteriol.* **86,** 692.

Sharp, J. T., and Dienes, L. (1959). *J. Bacteriol.* **78,** 343.

Sharp, J. T., Hijmans, W., and Dienes, L. (1957). *J. Exp. Med.* **105,** 153.

Shaw, N., and Baddiley, J. (1968). *Nature (London)* **217**, 142.
Shaw, N., Smith, P. F., and Koostra, W. L. (1968). *Biochem. J.* **107**, 329.
Shepard, M. C. (1956). *J. Bacteriol.* **71**, 362.
Shifrine, M., and Gourlay, R. N. (1967). *Ann. N. Y. Acad. Sci.* **143**, 317.
Shoetensack, H. M. (1934). *Kitasato Arch. Exp. Med.* **11**, 277.
Shoetensack, H. M. (1936a). *Kitasato Arch. Exp. Med.* **13**, 175.
Shoetensack, H. M. (1936b). *Kitasato Arch. Exp. Med.* **13**, 269.
Smith, P. F. (1955). *J. Bacteriol.* **70**, 552.
Smith, P. F. (1956). *Appl. Microbiol.* **4**, 254.
Smith, P. F. (1957a). *J. Bacteriol.* **73**, 91.
Smith, P. F. (1957b). *J. Bacteriol.* **74**, 75.
Smith, P. F. (1957c). *J. Bacteriol.* **74**, 801.
Smith, P. F. (1960). *Ann. N. Y. Acad. Sci.* **79**, 508.
Smith, P. F. (1964). *Bacteriol. Rev.* **28**, 97.
Smith, P. F. (1966). *J. Bacteriol.* **92**, 164.
Smith, P. F. (1968). *Adv. Lipid Res.* **6**, 69.
Smith, P. F., and Mayberry, W. R. (1968). *Biochemistry* **7**, 2706.
Smith, P. F., and Morton, H. E. (1951). *J. Bacteriol.* **61**, 395.
Smith, P. F., and Morton, H. E. (1952). *Arch. Biochem. Biophys.* **38**, 23.
Smith, P. F., and Rothblat, G. H. (1960). *Ann. N. Y. Acad. Sci.* **79**, 461.
Smith, P. F., and Rothblat, G. H. (1962). *J. Bacteriol.* **83**, 500.
Smith, P. F., Lecce, J. G., and Lynn, R. J. (1954). *J. Bacteriol.* **68**, 627.
Smith, P. F., Peoples, D. M., and Morton, H. E. (1957). *Proc. Soc. Exp. Biol. Med.* **96**, 550.
Smith, W. E. (1942). *J. Bacteriol.* **43**, 83.
Somerson, N. L., Reich, P. R., Chanock, R. M., and Weissman, S. M. (1967). *Ann. N. Y. Acad. Sci.* **143**, 9.
Stone, S. S., and Shifrine, M. (1968). *J. Bacteriol.* **95**, 1254.
Switzer, W. R. (1955). *Amer. J. Vet. Res.* **16**, 540.
Tanaka, H., Hall, W. T., Sheffield, J. B., and Moore, D. H. (1965). *J. Bacteriol.* **90**, 1735.
Tang, F. F., Wei, H., McWhirter, D. L., and Edgar, J. (1935). *J. Pathol. Bacteriol.* **40**, 391.
Tang, F. F., Wei, H., and Edgar, J. (1936). *J. Pathol. Bacteriol.* **42**, 46.
Taubeneck, U. (1961). *Z. Naturforsch. B* **16**, 849.
Taubeneck, U. (1963). *J. Bacteriol.* **86**, 1265.
Taylor-Robinson, D., Somerson, N. L., Turner, H. C., and Chanock, R. M. (1963). *J. Bacteriol.* **85**, 1261.
Tulasne, R., and Lavillaureix, J. (1954). *C. R. Acad. Sci. Paris* **148**, 2080.
Tully, J. G., and Razin, S. (1969). *J. Bacteriol.* **98**, 970.
Turner, A. W. (1933). *J. Council Sci. Ind. Res. Australia* **6**, 299.
Turner, A. W. (1935a). *J. Pathol. Bacteriol.* **41**, 1.
Turner, A. W. (1935b). *Aust. J. Exp. Biol. Med. Sci.* **13**, 149.
Turner, A. W. (1956). *Bull. Off. Int. Epizoot.* **46**, 382.
van Boven, C. P. A. (1969). *Antonie van Leeuwenhoek J. Microbiol. Serol.* **35**, 249.
van der Veen, J., and van Nunen, M. C. J. (1963). *Amer. J. Hyg.* **78**, 293.
van Iterson, W., and Ruys, A. C. (1960). *J. Ultrastruct. Res.* **3**, 282.
Villemot, J. M., Provost, A., and Queval, R. (1962). *Nature (London)* **193**, 906.
Walker, R. W., and Bastl, C. P. (1967). *Carbohyd. Res.* **4**, 49.
Ward, J. R., and Martin, C. H. (1962). *Proc. Soc. Exp. Biol. Med.* **111**, 156.

Ward, J. B., and Perkins, H. R. (1968). *Biochem. J.* **106,** 391.

Warren, J. (1942). *J. Bacteriol.* **43,** 211.

Warren, J., and Sabin, A. B. (1942). *Proc. Soc. Exp. Biol. Med.* **51,** 24.

Weibull, C. (1958). *Acta Pathol. Microbiol. Scand.* **42,** 324.

Weibull, C. (1965). *J. Bacteriol.* **90,** 1467.

Weibull, C., and Beckman, H. (1960a). *Nature (London)* **188,** 428.

Weibull, C., and Beckman, H. (1960b). *J. Bacteriol.* **79,** 638.

Weibull, C., and Beckman, H. (1961). *J. Gen. Microbiol.* **24,** 379.

Weibull, C., and Gyllang, H. (1965). *J. Bacteriol.* **89,** 1443.

Weibull, C., and Lundin, B. M. (1962). *J. Bacteriol.* **84,** 513.

Weibull, C., and Lundin, B. M. (1963). *J. Bacteriol.* **85,** 440.

Weibull, C., Bickel, W. D., Haskins, W. T., Milner, K. C., and Ribi, E. (1967). *J. Bacteriol.* **93,** 1143.

Weinberger, H. J., Madoff, S., and Dienes, L. (1950). *J. Bacteriol.* **59,** 765.

Welsh, K., Shaw, N., and Baddiley, J. (1968). *Biochem. J.* **107,** 313.

Wittler, R. G., Cary, S. G., and Lindberg, R. B. (1956). *J. Gen. Microbiol.* **14,** 763.

Woglom, W. H., and Warren, J. (1938a). *J. Exp. Med.* **68,** 513.

Woglom, W. H., and Warren, J. (1938b). *Science* **87,** 370.

Woglom, W. H., and Warren, J. (1939). *J. Hyg.* **39,** 266.

Structure of the Mycoplasmal Cell

2

A. MORPHOLOGY: ITS PHYSICAL AND CHEMICAL BASIS

1. Colonial Appearance

The typical mycoplasmal colony is round with a well-demarcated edge. Its average diameter is about 100 μm but may vary from 10 to 600 μm or greater. It exhibits a dense center and a translucent periphery, giving the so-called fried egg shape. The greater density of the central area is due primarily to growth into the agar but in some instances to heaping of the organisms. Early microscopists (Nocard et al., 1898; Bridre and Donatien, 1925; Klieneberger, 1934; Dienes, 1945; Kandler and Kandler, 1954) described this picture on the basis of finding organisms at focusing levels below the agar surface. Cross sectioning of the agar later confirmed these early descriptions (Razin and Oliver, 1961). As the fluid dries around the single organism it is drawn by capillary action into the interstices of the agar gel. There it begins to multiply and spread between the agar fibrils and onto the agar surface. The absence of resistance to spread on the surface results in a flat, thin periphery. The plasticity of the individual cells allows for penetration of the agar. Various conditions affect this type of colonial growth. If two cells fall in close proximity two centers and a confluent peripheral area is seen. Occasionally an entire line of centers with confluent peripheries occur. Except for a few species, especially those of avian origin, confluent growth is the exception. Even under crowded conditions well-demarcated colonies are the rule. Crowding appears to prevent the formation of peripheral growth. No experimental explanation has been given, but it probably is a result of depletion of nutrient rather than inter-

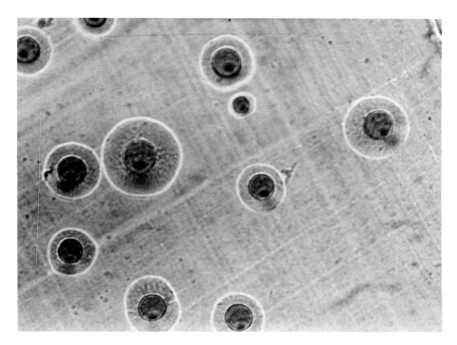

FIG. 2.1. Colony of *M. salivarium* showing the typical umbonate (fried egg) shape; 0.1 mm diameter. Courtesy of Y. E. Crawford. Official U. S. Navy photograph.

colonial antagonism. Crowded colonies are smaller as are those in a nutritionally deficient culture medium. Use has been made of this property to quantitate the growth response to various nutritional factors (Smith, 1956). An agar concentration greater than 1.5% impedes penetration by the organisms giving rise to surface growth and small colonies. The colonial appearance sometimes is characteristic of species or strain, although the degree of variation usually is too great to permit identification. The T strains have very small colonies about 10 μm in diameter and lack peripheral surface growth (Shepard, 1958, 1960). Use of newer piperazine buffers in the agar medium permits formation of typical fried egg colonies (Manchee and Taylor-Robinson, 1969) (Figs. 2.1 to 2.4). The diameter of the dense central area varies among the species inhabiting humans (Crawford and Kraybill, 1967). In some instances, particularly upon initial isolation on agar medium, no dense center appears. The periphery may appear granular or lacy. This lacework has been attributed to lipid accumulations (Morton *et al.*, 1954; Kandler and Kandler, 1954), to vacuolization as a result of lysis (Dienes, 1945) and to the presence of large flat cells which

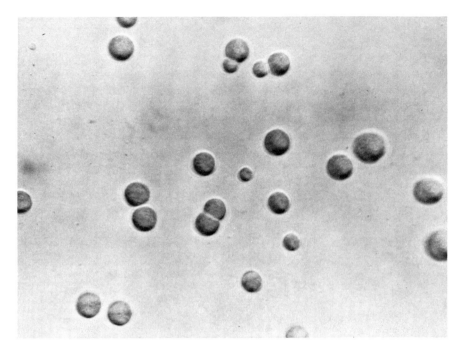

FIG. 2.2. Colony of *M. pneumoniae* showing no area of peripheral growth; 0.05 mm diameter. Courtesy of Y. E. Crawford. Official U. S. Navy photograph.

are very thin in the middle and contain condensed granules around the periphery (Klieneberger-Nobel, 1962). Increased vacuolization is characteristic of aging colonies. The fact that mycoplasmas can absorb large amounts of lipid (Smith and Rothblat, 1960b) to the extent that lipid droplets become associated with the organisms (Partridge and Klieneberger, 1941) suggests that the lacework is amorphous lipid. Extracellular polysaccharide produced by some species also could account for this lacework. Edward (1954) has described colonies of some species as forming "film and spots" and has used this characteristic for differentiation of species. In some cases this appearance can be ascribed to sterol accumulation. Others possess lipase activity (Smith, 1959) which can result in the production of magnesium and calcium salts of fatty acids. Precipitation of these insoluble soaps can account for the spots. Nonbiological formation of these insoluble soaps can create artifacts in solid culture medium and give the appearance of mycoplasmal colonies to the uninitiated. These forms, originally considered to be mycoplasmas (Swift and Brown, 1939),

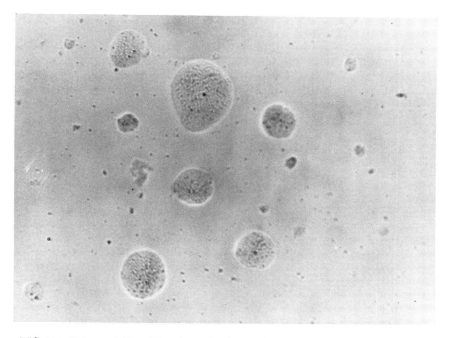

FIG. 2.3. Colony of *M. gallisepticum* showing no deep central area; 0.1 mm diameter. Courtesy of Y. E. Crawford. Official U. S. Navy photograph.

were shown to arise in uninoculated medium containing a variety of animal sera upon mechanical disturbance of the surface, such as rubbing or addition of liquid (Brown *et al.*, 1940). Microscopically these artifacts usually exhibit a dense granular central mass surrounded by a swirl of fibrillar chains emanating from the center, i.e., they give the fried egg appearance (Fig. 2.5). To further confuse the observer these artifacts appear to be "subculturable." Transfer of the artifacts results in mechanical disturbance of the fresh agar plate giving rise to more precipitated lipid. Their formation requires several days, thereby simulating mycoplasmal colony formation. Epithelial tissue cells with their nuclei surrounded by cytoplasm also have been mistaken as mycoplasmal colonies.

The typical colonial morphology is seen in infected tissue cells (Nelson, 1950; Shepard, 1960; Fogh and Fogh, 1964) (Fig. 2.6). Some further explanation than growth into the interstices of a gel may be needed to adequately explain this morphological appearance. Mycoplasmas possess the ability to attach themselves to glass (Somerson *et al.*, 1967) and plastic surfaces (Taylor-Robinson and Manchee, 1967). The mechanism of attach-

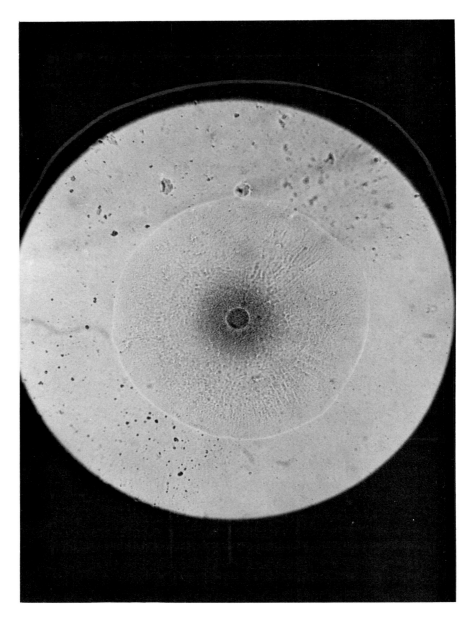

FIG. 2.4. Large colony of *M. salivarium* showing lacy peripheral area; 1.6 mm diameter. Courtesy of Y. E. Crawford. Official U. S. Navy photograph.

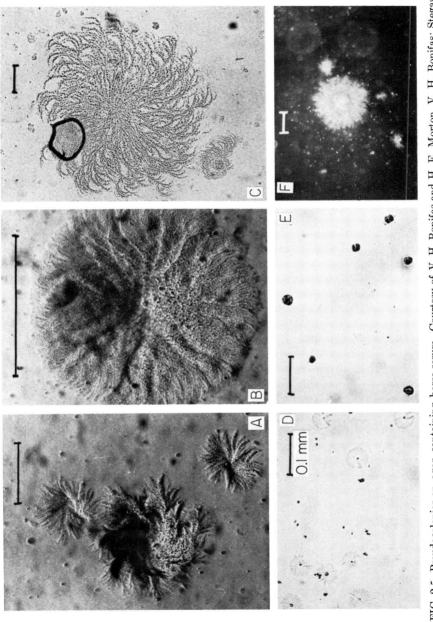

FIG. 2.5. Pseudocolonies on agar containing horse serum. Courtesy of V. H. Bonifas and H. E. Morton. V. H. Bonifas: Stegasma 'Organism' found in Sterile Serum from Warm Blooded Animals, PATHOLOGIA ET MICROBIOLOGIA **26**, pp. 696–711, figures 1, 2, 3, 7, 9, 10, (1963). Copyright by S. Karger AG, Switzerland

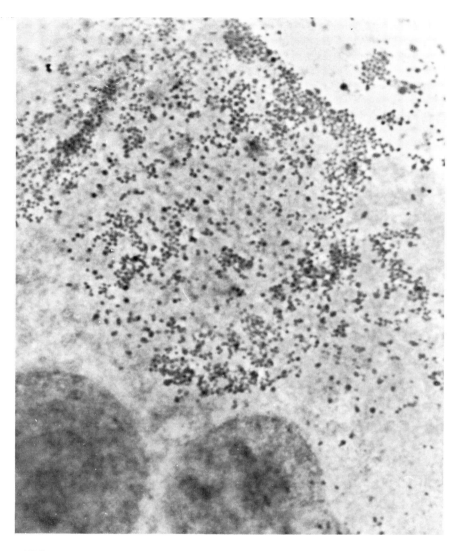

FIG. 2.6. Mycoplasmas growing in the cytoplasm of cultured tissue cells. Organisms tend to form colonies. × 4400. Courtesy of J. Fogh.

ment has not been established but it appears to bear no relationship to cations or to haemadsorption. Confluent growth results but areas of cellular concentration occur giving the appearance of contiguous fried egg shaped colonies.

2. Cellular Morphology

One feature common to all mycoplasmas is the plasticity brought about by the absence of a rigid outer wall. For this reason the early literature is replete with descriptions of all sorts of bizarre shapes ranging from coccobacilliform to ring to asteroid. Even today with more refined fixation and microscopic techniques unanimous agreement is lacking. The problem is accentuated by the variations among species and by changes which can be induced by cultural conditions. Sizing by filtration (Klieneberger-Nobel, 1962; Morowitz *et al.*, 1963) is subject to criticism as the organisms could change shape and pass through filters of pore size smaller than the actual organism. Sufficiently detailed studies have been performed with a selected number of species to justify some generalizations. Three species, *M. mycoides*, *M. laidlawii*, and *M. gallisepticum*, are singled out as examples.

a. MYCOPLASMA MYCOIDES

The smallest morphological unit, termed an elementary body, is coccoid shaped measuring 250 to 300 nm. Upon initiation of growth very thin optically homogeneous filaments are extruded which terminate in a tiny

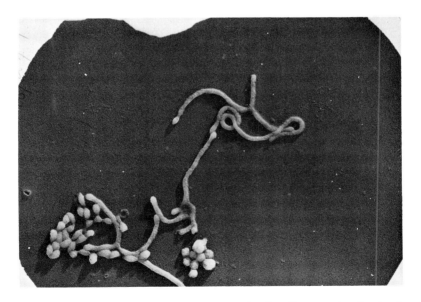

FIG. 2.7. Electron micrograph of *M. mycoides* showing filaments forming beadwork of coccal forms. × 8600. Courtesy of A. W. Rodwell. Copyright by J. Gen. Microbiol. From Rodwell and Abbot (1961).

refractile spherical or club shaped body of the same dimension as the elementary body. One or more filaments which are capable of branching can appear from a single elementary body. These filaments can become exceedingly long (Fig. 2.7). No transverse septa are discernible in these filaments. Subsequently there arise within the filaments regularly spaced, strongly refractile spherical elements of uniform size and shape. Constrictions appear in the cylindrical filament between the refractile masses giving rise to a chain of beads. The coccoid elements separate into elementary bodies (Freundt, 1952a,b, 1958, 1960). This morphology can be observed both in liquid and on solid culture media. Another type of morphological form is seen on solid medium which is not attributable to difference in species. In this form only short filaments are seen. Some swollen elementary corpuscles (large bodies) occur together with extracellular bodies embedded between filaments. Freundt considers these to be disintegration forms. Dienes (1960) and Klieneberger-Nobel (1962) are sceptical of this interpretation as applied to all mycoplasmal species.

Certainly the evidence favors Freundt's morphological description of *M. mycoides*. Growth of this organism in high glucose-containing medium without control of pH results in acid production and a preponderance of swollen elements (Freundt, 1952a, b). Deficiency in cholesterol, a nutritional requirement, or low oxygen tension and excessive CO_2 decrease the degree of filamentous growth (Freundt, 1958). Rodwell and Abbot (1961) have related nutritional sufficiency for long-chain fatty acids to filamentous growth. Deficiency gives rise to swollen, osmotically fragile forms. Hypertonicity of the surrounding environment maintains the filamentous state (Rodwell, 1965). Reexposure of hypotonically treated organisms to a hypertonic medium results in reformation of the filamentous state. Proof of the nature of the filamentous material is lacking. Gourlay and Thrower (1968) have described the amorphous nature of the threads connecting the elementary bodies. This substance is stainable with periodate–Schiff reagent and is assumed to be the galactan synthesized by this organism. It is possible that the filaments represent chains of elementary bodies produced as a result of fission or budding. These could be surrounded by galactan and because of their small size be obscured. Upon increase in size they would give rise to the beadlike chain. Galactan synthesis occurs at the greatest rate during the early stages of development (Plackett *et al.*, 1963) supporting such a thesis. Extracellular polysaccharide is found only in certain species and long filament formation is restricted to these organisms. The changes seen upon altering the tonicity of the suspending medium could fit this interpretation. If fission does not occur in a stepwise manner, it must be assumed that a coenocytic stage occurs. An alternate possibility could be some modification of the multiplication process seen in *M. ar-*

thritidis (Maniloff, 1969). The small coccal cell elongates and divides by binary fission. The daughter cells move apart but remain connected by a tubule of membrane-surrounding cytoplasm. This tubule becomes thinner and thinner until back-to-back membrane constitutes the tubule. Growing cells stick together and could form a beaded filament.

b. Mycoplasma Laidlawii

The primary morphological unit of young viable cultures is a coccoid element about 500 nm in diameter. The size can vary from 100 to 600 nm. These observations were made on freely moving organisms using electronic flash as a light source (Weibull and Lundin, 1962, 1963). Coccoidal and ellipsoidal forms around 500 nm in diameter are interspersed with smaller spheroidal elements averaging 125 nm (Cuckow and Klieneberger-Nobel, 1955). The viability of the smaller elements is questionable. Comparison of microscopic particle counts with viable cell counts shows a discrepancy amounting to 4 to 10 times as many particles as colonies (Weibull and Lundin, 1962; Anderson *et al.*, 1965). The difference is not explainable

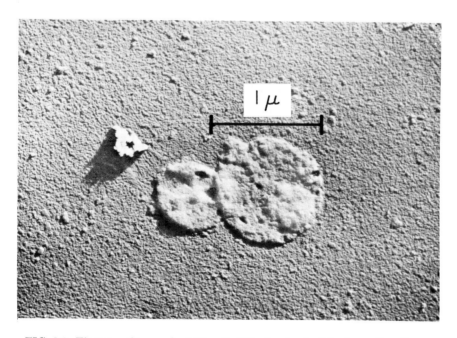

FIG. 2.8. Electron micrograph of *M. arthritidis* showing budlike formation. Courtesy of H. E. Morton.

by aggregation of individual cells. The small particles are reminiscent of the elevated knoblike structures lying within the flattened dried cells seen in the electron micrographs of Morton *et al.* (1954) (Fig. 2.8). Young colonies are composed almost entirely of the larger coccoidal forms. Some claim viability for the small particles, but until they are separated from the larger coccoidal forms this question will remain unanswered.

Like *M. mycoides* the cellular morphology of *M. laidlawii* can be altered by changes in environment. Growth in the presence of glucose without controlling pH results in a two- to fourfold enlargement of the cells which progressively deteriorate with presumed liberation of small particles (Anderson *et al.*, 1965). Freundt (1960) has presented electron micrographs of *M. laidlawii* showing the existence of small branching filaments. Provision of preformed long-chain unsaturated fatty acids in the culture medium induces the formation of long highly branched filaments (Razin *et al.*, 1966) composed of small coccoid bodies. These investigators consider the filamentous form as normal because of the increase in osmotic stability of mycoplasmas containing long-chain enoic fatty acids (Razin, 1964).

c. MYCOPLASMA GALLISEPTICUM

This species growing in colonial form possesses polygonal and teardrop shaped cells (Shifrine *et al.*, 1962; Domermuth *et al.*, 1964a,b) 500 to 800 nm in diameter (Fig. 2.9). In liquid medium and in areas where the cells are uncrowded the teardrop shape predominates. The cells possess a knoblike protrusion at one or both ends (Domermuth *et al.*, 1964a; Morowitz and Maniloff, 1966). These protrusions are believed to occur during the reproductive stage of the cells. First the protruding bleb appears at one end of the cell. Following development of this morphological feature at the

FIG. 2.9. Electron micrograph of *M. gallisepticum* showing teardrop-shaped forms. × 36,400. Courtesy of J. Maniloff. Copyright by American Society for Microbiology. Figure 1, Morowitz and Maniloff (1966).

opposite end a constriction appears in the center of the cell with the formation of two daughter cells.

The morphological features of *M. gallisepticum* appear more constant
and well defined than in other mycoplasmas. Close examination of phase
contrast and electron micrographs of all species reveal pear or teardrop
shaped cells. Even filaments can be construed to be chains of similar cellular shapes. Other bizarre forms can be attributed to distortions resulting
from handling or toxic effects of the suspending medium. The multiplicity
of shapes seen in species other than *M. gallisepticum* can be explained by
differences in rigidity of the cytoplasmic membrane. Hexosamines occur in
significant concentration in species of avian origin (Naide, 1963). The
appearance of small peptides containing amino acids common to the peptidoglycan of bacterial walls in the culture supernatant fluid of *M. gallisepticum* suggest an attempt to synthesize wall components. The inclusion
of some wall components in the outer structure could impart more rigidity
and hence less distortion of the true morphological form.

3. Gross Chemical Composition of Whole Cells

The principal differences of mycoplasmas from bacteria are the increased
lipid content and the absence of wall components. The cells are comprised
of 40 to 60% protein based on dry weight (Lynn and Smith, 1960; Razin
et al., 1963). Hydrolyzates of whole cells contain at least seventeen different
amino acids common to proteins (Kandler and Zehender, 1957; Morowitz
et al., 1962). There is a complete absence of α,ϵ-diaminopimelic acid
(Kandler and Zehender, 1957; Naide, 1963; Plackett, 1959; Smith and
Rothblat, 1960b). Starch-gel and polyacrylamide-gel electrophoresis have
shown a great multiplicity of protein bands which exhibit similar and dis-
similar mobilities among different species (Fowler *et al.*, 1963, 1967; Razin,
1968). Aside from their value as differentiating features for classification
purposes these electrophoretic patterns reveal little about the cell.

In most species carbohydrate contributes little to the total dry weight,
amounting to 0.1% or less (Morowitz *et al.*, 1962; Razin *et al.*, 1963; Smith
and Koostra, 1967). Exceptions are *M. mycoides* and strains associated
with bovine arthritis (Buttery and Plackett, 1960; Plackett *et al.*, 1963).
As much as 10% of the dry weight can be accounted for as the galactan of
M. mycoides and the glucan of the bovine arthritis organism. The amount
varies with age, the maximum yield occurring in cultures at the peak of
the logarithmic phase of growth. Greatest synthesis occurs during the
time of rapid multiplication. Other species contain detectable hexoses including galactose, glucose, and mannose but only in trace amounts. Hexosamines, measured as glucosamine, can comprise 1% or more of the dry

weight of *M. laidlawii*, strain B and *M. arthritidis* (Naide, 1963). It has been judged absent or present only in trace amounts in *M. laidlawii*, strain A, *M. mycoides*, and some avian and murine species (Kandler and Zehender, 1957; Plackett, 1959). It is present in *M. gallinarum* (Smith, 1967a). No muramic acid has been detected (Sharp, 1963; Plackett, 1959).

The DNA content ranges from 1.5 to 7% of the dry weight (Kandler *et al.*, 1956a,b; Lynn and Smith, 1957; Morowitz *et al.*, 1962; Razin *et al.*, 1963). The average value of 4% probably is the most realistic. No odd bases such as hydroxymethyl cytosine are found (Lynn and Smith, 1957). The amount of DNA varies little during growth.

The RNA content reflects the age and growth phase of the organisms. It varies from 3 to 17%. The amount increases during early logarithmic growth and then declines rapidly. Hence cells harvested during the stationary phase would be low in RNA. Handling of the organisms is a contributing factor in the variation of RNA content. Plackett (1957) has shown that as much as 80% of the RNA is liberated from the cells by freezing and thawing, indicating that if lysis occurs during manipulations low RNA values will result.

Lipid comprises 8 to 20% of the dry weight, the lower values being characteristic of sterol nonrequiring species (Smith and Rothblat, 1962; Razin *et al.*, 1963). About half of the lipids are neutral, consisting of unsaponifiable lipids, glycolipids, and possibly some glycerides; the other half are polar lipids, almost exclusively phospholipids. The lipid phosphorus content ranges from 0.12 to 0.44% and reflects the variations in types of phospholipids which occur (Langenfeld and Smith, 1963; Lynn and Smith, 1957). Although the total lipid does not vary during growth, changes do occur in the quantity of various types of lipids (Smith, 1968). Both the qualitative and quantitative lipid composition can be altered by varying the lipids in the culture medium.

The ash content of mycoplasmas has never been determined.

B. ULTRASTRUCTURE

The fine structure of the typical mycoplasmal cell consists of a trilaminar membrane surrounding a cytoplasm packed with ribosomes, fibrillar DNA, one or more electron dense areas and occasionally empty vesicles surrounded by a trilaminar membrane (Fig. 2.10). Species variations exist but an ultrastructure common to all can be deduced. Since the stability of the ultrastructure seems greater in *M. gallisepticum* this organism will serve best for a detailed description. The variations from this structure seen in other species can be related subsequently.

The cytoplasmic membrane is typical of the so-called unit membranes,

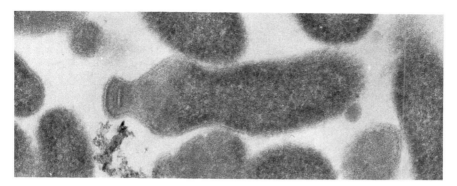

FIG. 2.10. Electron micrograph of *M. gallisepticum* showing internal structure.
× 117,000). Courtesy of J. Maniloff.

being composed of a light area about 5 nm thick bounded on either side
by electron dense regions about 3 nm thick giving a membrane with the
overall thickness of 11 nm (Domermuth *et al.*, 1964b; Maniloff *et al.*,
1965a,b). The outer layer is unlike the basement membrane of metazoan
organisms. Domermuth *et al.* consider the outer layer to be more dense
than the inner electron absorbing layer, presenting an asymmetrical appearance. Dense material absorbing to the outer layer is interpreted to be
a capsular substance (Domermuth *et al.*, 1964a).

The nuclear material consists of an unbounded fibrillar and granular
region. The fibrils are about 3 nm thick and are not contained within a
membrane reminiscent of the bacteria. The chromosome is circular (Fig.
2.11) and when replicating exhibits two Y forms consistent with the postulated mechanism of replication in *E. coli* (Morowitz, 1969). The size of the
chromosome is approximately 1000×10^6 daltons allowing for coding of
well over a thousand cistrons.

Numerous ribosomes measure about 14 nm in diameter. Sedimentation

FIG. 2.11. The entire circle of DNA from *Mycoplasma* sp., Donetta; 350 nm circum-
ference. Courtesy of H. J. Morowitz and S. Klein.

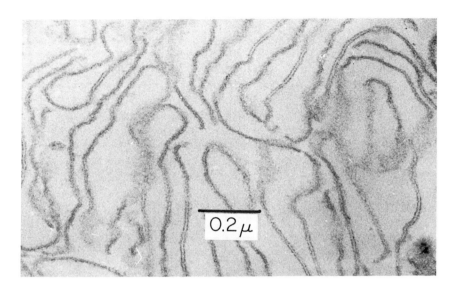

FIG. 2.12. Section of the cytoplasmic membrane of *M. laidlawii* showing typical trilaminar structure with occasional cross striations. Courtesy of S. Razin. Copyright by Academic Press, Inc. Figure 1b, Rottem *et al.* (1968).

analyses show a single component with a sedimentation coefficient of 72 S which on dilution with water yields three fractions with S values of 70, 49, and 32, similar to bacterial ribosomes (Maniloff *et al.*, 1965b). These investigators consider the loose arrangement of single ribosomes to be typical and the other arrays, cuboidal, cylindrical, and rouleau, to be artifacts of preparation.

Structured dense regions occur at one end of the cell in the protrusion or bilaterally if protrusions are seen at both ends of the cell (Maniloff *et al.*, 1965b; Domermuth *et al.*, 1964b; Morowitz and Maniloff, 1966). These are termed blebs, lack nucleic acid, and are considered to be protein, possibly interspersed with lipid. The ultrastructure of the bleb consists of a dense elliptical outer plate adjacent to the cytoplasmic membrane, a flat plate, and fine threads connecting the flat plate to the elliptical plate. Between the threads lie regions which do not stain and could be considered microtubules. Behind the bleb lies an infrableb region which does not stain with indium and is considered to be protein. Ribosomes are noticeably absent in this area, yet these blebs are seen only in actively dividing cells.

The limiting membranes of other species are identical to that of *M. gallisepticum* except the thickness is less, i.e., 7.5 to 10 nm (Domermuth

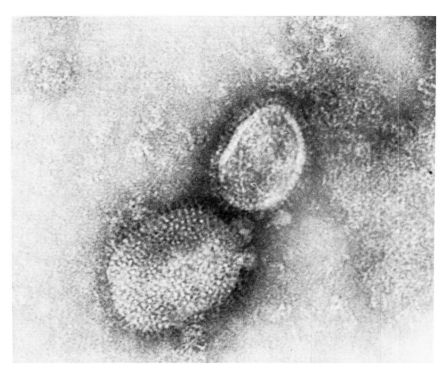

FIG. 2.13. Membrane of *M. pulmonis* showing globular subunits. × 200,000. Courtesy of K. Hummeler. Copyright by American Society for Microbiology. Figure 9, Hummeler *et al.* (1965).

et al., 1964a). Electron micrographs of thin sections of *M. laidlawii* membranes appear to possess some cross striations (Rottem *et al.*, 1968) after negative staining with phosphotungstic acid (Fig. 2.12). The membrane of *M. pulmonis* gives the appearance of being composed of globular subunits (Fig. 2.13) (Hummeler *et al.*, 1965).

No differences occur in the chromosomal and ribosomal structures. The chromosomes of *M. arthritidis*, *M. agalactiae*, and *M. laidlawii* have been shown to be circular (Morowitz, 1969). The size varies from 444×10^6 to 790×10^6 daltons. Forks occur in the chromosomes of all these species.

Dense cytoplasmic bodies have been observed in thin sections of *M. hominis* (Anderson and Barile, 1965), *M. pulmonis* (Hummeler *et al.*, 1965), and a variety of species from several sources (Domermuth *et al.*, 1964a; Edwards and Fogh, 1960) (Fig. 2.14). Most of these investigators speculate that these dense regions may be elementary bodies which can

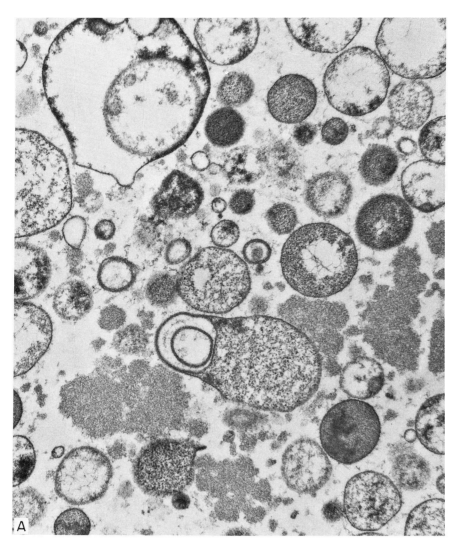

FIG. 2.14. Electron micrographs of thin sections of *M. hominis* showing internal vesicular structures (A, × 60,000) and dense cytoplasmic bodies (B, × 110,000) surrounded by trilaminar membranes. Courtesy of D. L. Anderson and M. F. Barile. Copyright by American Society for Microbiology. Figures 11 and 13, Anderson and Barile (1965).

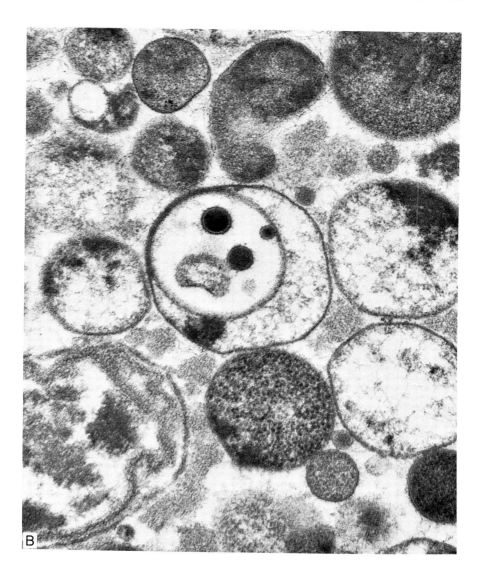

be extruded from the cells. In many cases they bear a marked resemblance
to the bleb regions of *M. gallisepticum* and could be considered sites of
reproduction. Depending upon the angle and the region of the cell sectioned
these dense areas could be located anywhere in the cytoplasm. Another
structure frequently seen in species other than *M. gallisepticum* are empty
vesicles surrounded by a trilaminar membrane (Fig. 2.14). These structures

are more prevalent in aging cells and may represent deterioration (Anderson and Barile, 1965). It is also conceivable that they represent vacuoles from pinocytosis or mesosomes which are common to bacteria.

Motility has been observed in a strain of *M. pulmonis* (Nelson and Lyons, 1965). Motion was characterized by gliding rod-shaped forms and spinning spherical forms but was lost upon repeated subculture. Electron micrographs of intact organisms and thin sections failed to reveal any flagellar structures. Andrewes and Welch (1946) also observed nonflagellar motility in initial isolates from mice.

1. Chemical Composition of Structural Units

a. EXTRACELLULAR POLYSACCHARIDE.

The amorphous extracellular material associated with *M. mycoides* is a galactan (Buttery and Plackett, 1960). Acid hydrolysates contain greater than 90% galactose and a trace of glucose. Its molecular weight has not

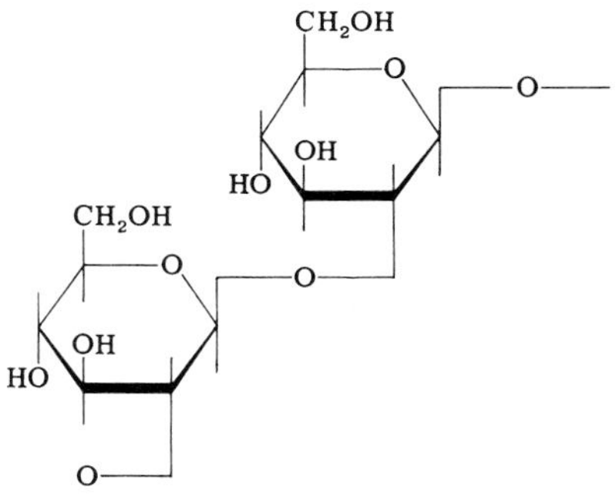

-2- *O*-β-D-Glucopyranosyl-1-

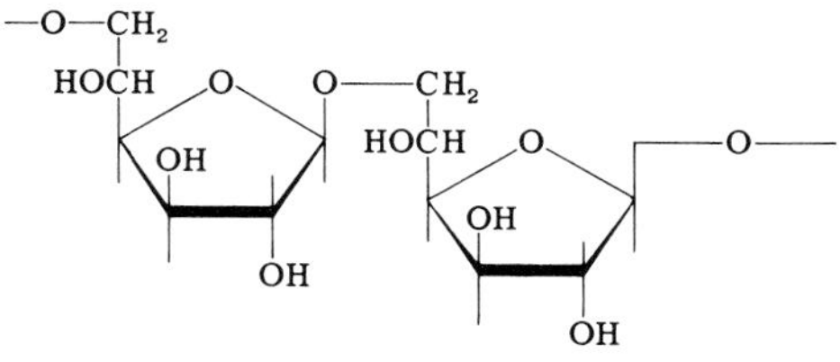

-6- *O*-β-D-Galactofuranosyl-1-

FIG. 2.15. Structures of main repeating units in polysaccharides of *M. mycoides* and related organisms.

been determined. In 0.24% solution the sedimentation boundary is markedly asymmetrical giving a sedimentation coefficient of 19 S. This value decreases in more concentrated solution. The strongly negative optical rotation, $(\alpha)_D$-140 to -150, is indicative of a high proportion of β-linkages. It has been identified as a polysaccharide with the predominant linkage, 6-O-β-D-galactofuranosyl-1- (Plackett and Buttery, 1964) (Fig. 2.15). It possesses serological activity in precipitin and indirect hemagglutination reactions. A small amount of chloroform-extractable material is comprised principally of glycerol and stearic and palmitic acids. Whether this lipoidal material is a contaminant or an integral part of the polysaccharide has not been established.

The bovine arthritis organism contains a polysaccharide with a glucan structure. It is composed entirely of glucose units in the predominant linkage, 2-O-β-D-glucopyranosyl-1- (Plackett et al., 1963) (Fig. 2.15). Its optical rotation is $(\alpha)_D$-9.6. Like the galactan the glucan exhibits serological activity.

b. CYTOPLASMIC MEMBRANE.

The limiting membrane of mycoplasmas is lipoprotein in nature. All membrane analyses suffer from the presence of possible contaminants. Comparisons are only relative as membranes which have been examined were prepared by a variety of methods, e.g., freezing and thawing, sonication, osmotic lysis. Age of the cells introduces another variable. Since mycoplasmas possess the ability to incorporate or adsorb components of the culture medium, variability in culture media has a pronounced effect. The degree of binding or trapping of such cellular components as DNA and RNA must be taken into account. Nevertheless the overall chemical composition of the cytoplasmic membranes of mycoplasmas shows a protein content of 47 to 60% of the dry weight, 35 to 37% lipid, 4 to 7% carbohydrate, 1 to 4% RNA, and 1 to 2% DNA (Razin et al., 1963). Essentially all of the lipid of the cell is associated with the cytoplasmic membrane, based on total lipid, unsaponifiable lipid, and lipid phosphorus analyses (Lynn and Smith, 1960; Smith and Rothblat, 1962; Pollack et al., 1965a).

The nucleic acids associated with the membrane may represent attached or trapped ribosomes and fragments of genome. Whether these components are integral parts of the membrane is unresolved. They will be excluded in this discussion. The carbohydrate reflects primarily the sugars found in glycolipids. A portion of it can be accounted for as hexosamine which occurs in the membrane in variable amount.

Membrane proteins solubilized in phenol–acetic acid–water and electrophoresed on polyacrylamide gels containing 5 M urea and 35% acetic acid exhibit multiple bands, sometimes twenty or more (Rottem and Razin, 1967). Membranes dissolved in sodium dodecyl sulfate yield eleven or more bands (Smith *et al.*, 1969). A large mass of protein remains in the stacking gel, so all of the protein components are not resolved. It is a matter for conjecture as to whether those which do migrate in the gel are native proteins as the treatments for solubilization are rather rigorous. The amino acid composition of the membrane of *M. gallisepticum* is little different from proteins in general. At least sixteen different amino acids are found, with glutamic acid, aspartic acid, leucine, and lysine predominating (Morowitz *et al.*, 1962). Cytochromes, if present, occur in the membrane. Cytochromes of the a and b type were revealed by their difference spectra in *M. arthritidis* (VanDemark and Smith, 1964). A bovine strain exhibits a spectrum suggestive of cytochromes c and o (VanDemark, 1969). Various specific antigens of mycoplasmas are membrane proteins.

A limited number of enzymes have been shown to be associated with the cytoplasmic membrane. These include the glucosidases of *M. laidlawii* and *M. gallinarum* (Henrikson and Smith, 1964), reduced nicotinamide adenine dinucleotide oxidase of *M. laidlawii*, adenosine triphosphatase, ribonuclease, and frequently deoxyribonuclease of several species (Pollack *et al.*, 1965b), cholesterol esterase (Smith, 1959), glucosyl diglyceride synthetases of *M. laidlawii* (Smith, 1969a), phosphatidyl glucose synthetase of *M. laidlawii* (Smith, 1969b), the cholesteryl glucoside synthetase of *M. gallinarum* (P. F. Smith, unpublished), and the quinone and ferricyanide reductases of *M. gallisepticum* (Smith *et al.*, 1963).

The nature of the lipids has been examined in detail for four species and in part for two others. Although the generalization can be made that all mycoplasmas contain sterols or carotenols, glycerophospholipids, and in many cases glycolipids, enough differences are seen to discuss lipids on the basis of species.

i. Mycoplasma laidlawii. Four major carotenoid pigments occur (Rothblat and Smith, 1961; Smith, 1963a). These have been assumed to be carotenoids composed of forty carbon atoms but proof is lacking. They may be C_{50} carotenoids similar to those found recently in *Flavobacterium* (Jensen and Weeks, 1966) and *Sarcina* (Thirkell *et al.*, 1967). Assuming they are C_{40} carotenoids, traces of ζ-carotene, phytoene, and phytofluene also are

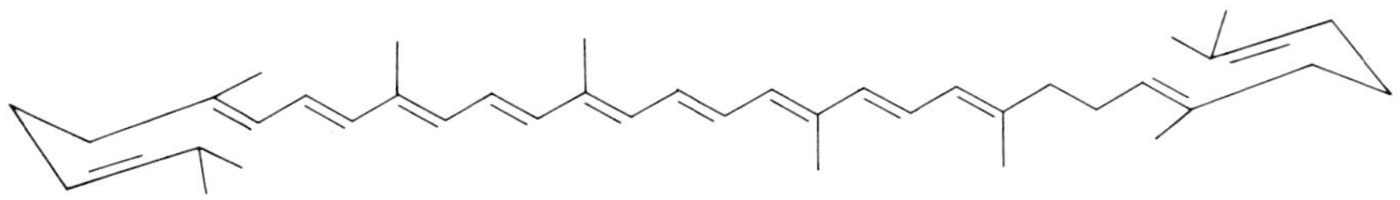

FIG. 2.16. Structure of neurosporene.

present. Of the major pigments the most polar has the characteristics of neurosporene (Fig. 2.16). Spectral and chromatographic properties are identical to the all-trans compound found in tomatoes. The other three pigments are a dihydroxycarotenol and its ester and glucoside derivatives. Based on spectral shifts occurring upon iodine catalysis, the dihydroxy-carotenol has the trans configuration. It is not a hydroxylated neurosporene since the spectral properties of the two compounds do not coincide. Orderly spectral shifts occur with the sequential addition of double bonds in carotenoids (Karrer and Jucker, 1950). The absorption maxima of the *M. laidlawii* carotenol lie intermediate to the neurosporene series (nine conjugated double bonds) and the ζ-carotene series (seven conjugated double bonds) suggesting the presence of eight conjugated double bonds. The location of the two hydroxyl groups has not been established but indirect evidence indicates the 3 and 3′ positions. The fatty acids of the esterified form are primarily acetic with a trace of longer chain acids. Presumably it can occur as both the mono- and diester. The sugar of the glycoside consists entirely of D-glucose. In some strains the linkage is β, in others α. The absence of reducing activity in the intact lipid indicates linkage through the one position of glucose. Removal of the fatty acids from the ester by mild saponification and of the glucose by glucosidase liberates a dihydroxycarotenol identical to the free carotenol (Table II.1). The relative proportions of the

TABLE II.1

Characteristics of Carotenoid Pigments of *Mycoplasma laidlawii*, strain B[a]

	Neurosporene	Carotenol	Carotenyl ester	Carotenyl glucoside
Absorption maxima (nm, *n*-hexane)	414, 438, 468	–, 402, 425, 442	–, 402, 422, 446	408, 430, 454
$E_{1cm}^{1\%}$ at maximum	2968 (438 nm)	348 (425 nm)	97 (422 nm)	112 (430 nm)
Absorption maxima after I_2 catalysis	330, 414, 437, 466	356, 400, 423, 440	–	359, 428, 451
Partition: petroleum ether/ methanol	Epiphasic	Epihypo-phasic	Epiphasic	Hypophasic
Number —OH groups (from acetylation data)	–	2.39±0.20	–	–
Volatile/nonvolatile fatty acids	–	–	2.19±0.08	–
Moles glucose/moles pigment	–	–	–	1.27

[a] Data compiled from Rothblat and Smith (1961) and Smith (1963a).

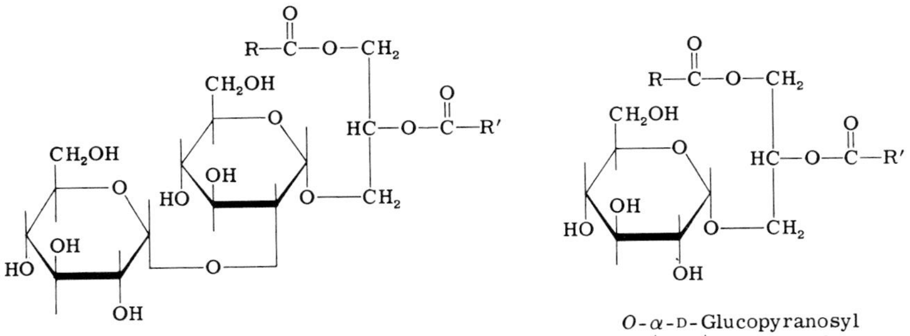

O-α-D-Glucopyranosyl (1→2)-
O-α-D-glucopyranosyl (1→1) diglyceride

O-α-D-Glucopyranosyl
(1→1) diglyceride

R = Palmitic
R′ = Myristic or oleic

FIG. 2.17. Structures of the major glycolipids of *M. laidlawii*, strain B.

carotenol and its derivatives vary with the age and metabolic state of the organisms. At the peak of the logarithmic phase of growth the relative amounts are glucoside > carotenol > ester. Neurosporene remains constant. Carotenyl glucosides also occur in bacteria.

If *M. laidlawii* is grown in a culture medium containing the appropriate sterol, this sterol, its fatty acid esters, and steryl glucoside are found in addition to the carotenol and its derivatives. The sterol found in the organisms is identical to the exogenously supplied sterol. The only change which occurs is esterification with short-chain fatty acids and formation of the glycoside.

No detectable glycerides are found. The remainder of the neutral lipids consist of glucosyl diglycerides (Shaw *et al.*, 1968). These account for about 45% of the total lipids. Synthetic and degradative studies have proven their structures to be O-α-D-glucopyranosyl (1 → 1) diglyceride and O-α-D-glucopyranosyl (1 → 2)-O-α-D-glucopyranosyl (1 → 1) diglyceride (Fig. 2.17). There are trace amounts of a lipid presumed to be a triglucosyl diglyceride. The monoglucosyl compound predominates contrary to the situation found in bacteria. The ratio of mono- to diglucosyl diglyceride varies from unity to almost three during growth, the larger ratios occurring in older cultures. Exogenous cholesterol in the culture medium has no effect on the glycolipid content. No turnover of glycolipid occurs during growth or in pulse labeling with ^{14}C-glucose during metabolism (Smith, 1969c) suggesting a structural role for these lipids. The fatty acids esterified to the glycerol moiety are almost exclusively myristic and palmitic acids. Myristic acid occupies the 2 position of glycerol. If oleic acid is supplied in the culture medium the myristic acid is replaced by oleic acid.

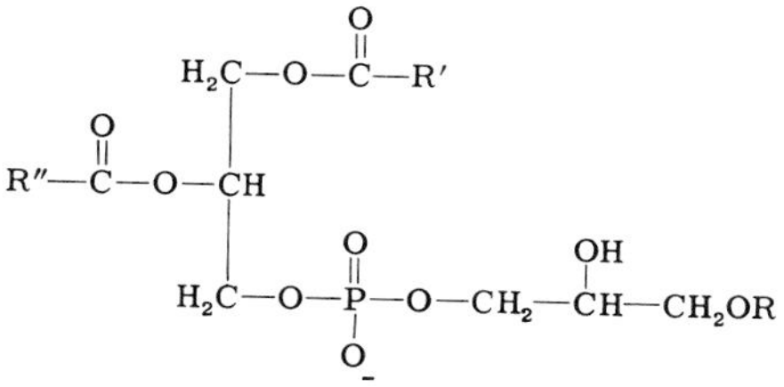

R = H; Phosphatidyl glycerol
R = —C—CH—CH$_3$, Alanyl phosphatidyl glycerol
        ‖   ‖
        O   NH$_2$
R′ = Palmitic
R″ = Myristic or oleic

FIG. 2.18. Structures of phosphatidyl glycerol and its amino acyl esters.

The phospholipids of *M. laidlawii* consist of phosphatidyl glycerol, amino acyl esters of phosphatidyl glycerol (Fig. 2.18), "phosphatidyl glucose," and a trace of diphosphatidyl glycerol (Smith and Henrikson, 1965; Smith *et al.*, 1965; Shaw *et al.*, 1968). The fatty acid composition of all these lipids is identical to the glycolipids. The exact structure of "phos-

TABLE II.2

Properties of "Phosphatidyl Glucose"

Ratios of components	
Intact lipid	Fatty acid:P:glycerol:glucose, 2.2:1.0:1.0:1.0[a]; 2.0:1.0:1.9:2.0[b]
Deacylation product	P:glycerol:glucose, 1.0:0.8:0.9[a]
Reducing activity, intact and deacylated lipids	Negative
Periodate–Schiff reaction, intact lipid	Rapid, purple
Periodate consumption (moles/mole P):	
Intact lipid	4.0[b]
Deacylated lipid	5.0[b]
Formaldehyde produced by periodate oxidation (moles/mole P)	
Intact lipid	1.0[b]
Deacylated lipid	2.0[b]
Alkaline hydrolysis products	Glycerophosphates, fatty acids, O-α-D-glucopyranosyl-(1 → 2)-O-α-D-glucopyranosyl-(1 → 1)-D-glycerol[b]
Acid hydrolysis products	Glycerol, glucose, Pi, fatty acids
Action of phospholipases A, C and D	No action
Action of phosphomonoesterase	No Pi liberation

[a] Most probable structure: glycerophosphoryl-(3 → 6)-O-α-D-glucopyranosyl-(1 → 1)-2,3-diglyceride
[b] Most probable structure: glycerophosphoryl-(3 → 6)-O-α-D-glucopyranosyl-(1 → 2)-O-α-D-glucopyranosyl-(1 → 1)-2,3-diglyceride

TABLE II.3

Percent Total Fatty Acid Composition of *M. laidlawii*, strain B[a]

Fatty acid	Whole cells	Membrane	Cytoplasm
8:0	0.20	0.15	0.04
10:0	8.31	11.93	11.34
13:sat.	1.20	0.40	0.18
13:0	0.97	0.75	0.38
14:sat.	0.82	0.29	0.12
14:0	39.27	57.28	51.70
14:$\Delta^{9,10}$	Trace	Trace	Trace
14:unsat.	1.60	0.85	0.43
15:0	1.29	0.84	0.48
16:0	37.61	22.37	32.80
16:$\Delta^{7,8}$	Trace	Trace	Trace
16:$\Delta^{9,10}$	Trace	Trace	Trace
16:unsat.	Trace	0.08	0.03
16:unsat.	0.83	0.43	0.19
17:0	Trace	0.11	0.06
18:0	1.48	0.86	0.47
18:$\Delta^{8,10}$	3.13	2.03	0.95
18:$\Delta^{11,12}$	1.53	0.81	0.40
18:$\Delta^{9,10}$, $\Delta^{11,12}$	1.76	0.83	0.41

[a] Data compiled from Henrikson and Panos (1969).

phatidyl glucose" has not been established although it appears to be a glycerophosphoryl diglucosyl diglyceride. Probably the monoglucosyl compound also exists (N. Shaw, B. Verheij, and P. F. Smith, unpublished). Table II.2 lists the known properties of this lipid. It accounts for about half of the total phospholipid but its concentration varies with age and metabolic state of the organism. Greatest amounts are found in old cells. Properly it should be called a phosphoglycolipid.

Phosphatidyl glycerol and its amino acyl esters account for the remaining half of the phospholipids. In acidic environment the amino acyl esters predominate at the expense of phosphatidyl glycerol. The amino acids esterified include alanine, glutamic acid, glycine, leucine/isoleucine, lysine and tyrosine (Koostra and Smith, 1969). Alanine predominates and is found as a nonracemic mixture of about 2:1, D:L. D-Alanyl phosphatidyl glycerol also occurs in at least one bacterium, *Leuconostoc mesenteroides* (Ikawa, 1963).

Essentially no free fatty acids occur in *M. laidlawii*. When grown in a medium devoid of fatty acids, strain B contains a tenfold greater amount

TABLE II.4

Characteristics of Sterols Isolated from *M. arthritidis*, strain 07, Grown with Exogenously Supplied Sterol[a]

Property	Cholesterol		Cholestanol		Ergosterol	
	Exogenous	Cellular	Exogenous	Cellular	Exogenous	Cellular
Melting point (°C)						
Free	149	149	142	142	160	160
Acetate	117	117	110	110	181	178
Dibromide	123	123	–	–	–	–
Dibromide formation	Positive	Positive	Negative	Negative	–	–
Digitonin precipitability	Positive	Positive	Positive	Positive	–	–
Absorption maxima (nm)	–	–	–	–	264, 274, 285, 297	264, 274, 285, 297
$[\alpha]_D^{25}$	−39°	−39°	–	–	–	–
Iodine number	63.5	63.5	–	–	–	–

[a] Data compiled from Rothblat and Smith (1961) and Smith (1962).

of saturated than unsaturated acids. A typical analysis of the total fatty acids of strains A and B is shown in Tables II.3 and II.6.

ii. Mycoplasma gallinarum, strain J. The total lipids of this species consist of approximately 50% phospholipid and 50% neutral lipid of which about half is glycolipid (Smith and Mayberry, 1968). These organisms require sterol or some other polyterpenol of appropriate structure for growth. The sterol found in the organisms is identical to the exogenously supplied sterol, similar to the case of *M. arthritidis* (Table II.4). It occurs in the form of free sterol, its ester, and its glycoside (Figs. 2.19 and 3.7). The fatty acids esterified to the sterol are predominantly acetic with smaller amounts of longer-chain fatty acids. The ratio of volatile to nonvolatile fatty acids is 2:1 (Rothblat and Smith, 1961; Smith, 1962; Smith and

FIG. 2.19. Structure of cholesteryl-β-D-glucopyranose.

TABLE II.5

Properties of Cholesteryl-β-D-Glucoside from *M. gallinarum*, strain J[a]

Property	Intact steroid	Free sterol after acid hydrolysis
Liebermann-Buchard reaction	Positive (slow)	Positive (slow)
Digitonin precipitability	Negative	Positive
Melting point (°C)		
Free	283	149
Tetraacetate	161	–
Acetate	–	117
Moles glucose/moles cholesterol	1.00	–

[a] Data compiled from Rothblat and Smith (1961).

Rothblat, 1960b). The existence of esterified sterol as a natural component of mycoplasmas is disputed (Argaman and Razin, 1964; Lynn and Smith, 1960; Rodwell, 1963). Rodwell working with *M. mycoides* found no reduction in the specific activity of ¹⁴C-labeled cholesterol upon its isolation from the organisms leading him to conclude that all of the sterol existed in the form of free cholesterol. The finding of short-chain fatty acids, which do not occur naturally in animals but constitute a major portion of the steryl esters of mycoplasmas, and the fluctuations in ester content with age and metabolic state of the organisms argue for the validity of their natural existence in mycoplasmas. The glycoside of cholesterol in this species has been identified as cholesteryl-β-D-glucopyranose. The configuration of the glucose radical was determined by the lability of the lipid to β-glucosidase. The properties of this lipid are seen in Table II.5. Steryl glucosides have been reported to exist in plants only. The relative amounts of these steroidal lipids is similar to the carotenoids of *M. laidlawii*, i.e., glucoside > carotenol > ester, and is dependant upon age and metabolic state.

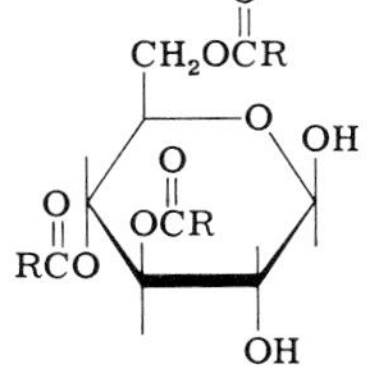

FIG. 2.20. Structure of 3,4,6-triacyl-β-D-glucopyranose.

Mycoplasma gallinarum, strain J, contains one glycolipid other than the steryl glucoside. Its structure has been determined as 3,4,6-triacyl-β-D-glucopyranose (Smith and Mayberry, 1968) (Fig. 2.20). Precedent for such a lipid occurs in *Streptococcus faecalis* which contains a tetraacyl glucose (Welsh *et al.*, 1968). This lipid constitutes 80% of the glycolipids, the remainder being attributable to the steryl glucoside. Over 80% of the fatty acids are unsaturated with oleic acid predominating. Mass-spectral analysis indicates random distribution of the fatty acids on the three positions (N. Shaw, personal communication). In contrast to the cholesteryl glucoside the acylated glucose does not change in concentration during growth of the organisms.

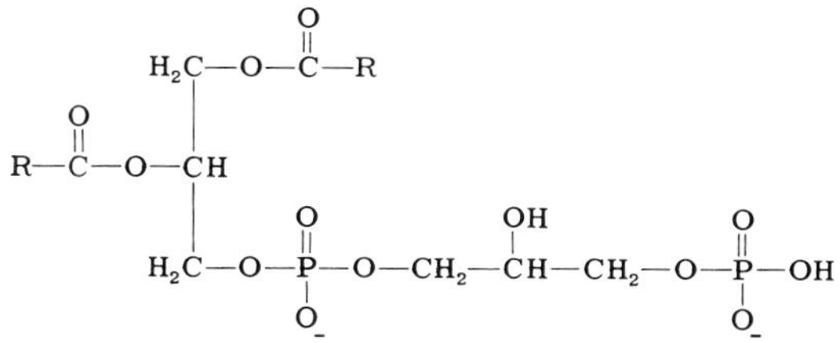

Phosphatidyl glycerophosphate

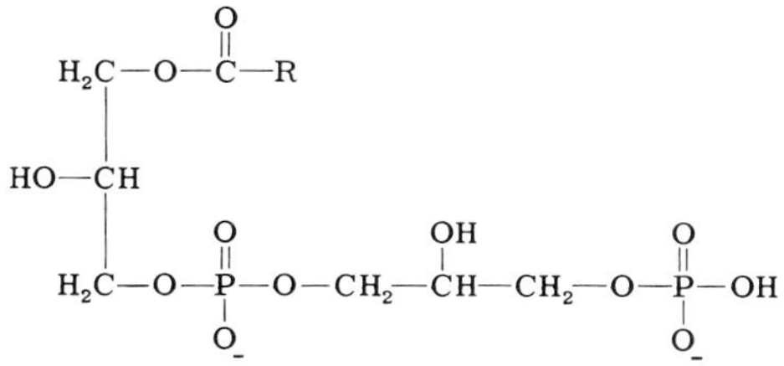

Monoacyl glycerophosphoryl glycerophosphate

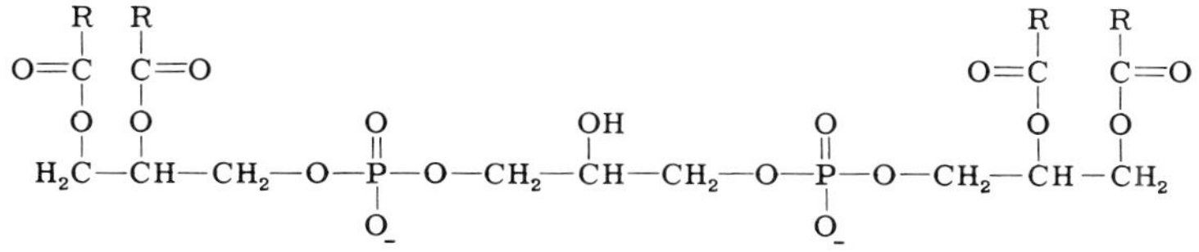

Diphosphatidyl glycerol

FIG. 2.21. Structures of the major phospholipids from *M. gallinarum*.

TABLE II.6

Percent Total Fatty Acid Composition of Mycoplasmas

Fatty acid	M. gallinarum, strain J[a,b]	M. arthritidis, strain 07[a,b]	M. laidlawii, strain A[b,c]
8:0 + 9:0	1	1.2	0.1
10:0	–	0.2	7.2
11:0	1	–	–
12:0	–	0.4	–
13:0	–	–	1.4
13:Br.	–	–	0.5
14:0	15	2.0	33.9
14:Br.	–	–	0.3
15:0	1	3.0	1.6
16:0	23	21.6	18.7
16:1	6	5.3	–
Unknown	–	1.0	–
17:0	1	1.2	0.2
17:1	–	1.4	–
Unknown	2	–	–
18:0	8	7.2	1.3
18:cis$\Delta^{9,10}$ + 18:cis$\Delta^{11,12}$	40	45.5	2.3
			31.6
Unknown	3	7.1	–
18:$\Delta^{9,10}$, $\Delta^{11,12}$	–	–	1.1
19:0	–	2.9	–

[a] Smith and Koostra (1967).

[b] Fatty acids of chain length 6 or less are not included.

[c] Grown with 18:cis$\Delta^{11,12}$ (Panos and Rottem, 1970).

Phosphatidyl glycerophosphate, a monoacyl phosphatidyl glycerophos-phate, and diphosphatidyl glycerol (Fig. 2.21) comprise the phospholipids of M. gallinarum (Smith and Koostra, 1967). No phosphatidyl glycerol or amino acyl esters of this lipid have been detected. The monoacyl phos-phatidyl glycerophosphate differs from the phosphatidyl glycerophosphate by the absence of oleic acid, presumably from the 2 position of glycerol. This lipid does not appear to be an artifact since no phospholipase activity is noted under conditions used for its isolation. The proportion of this lipid decreases with age of the organisms while there is an increase in the concentration of diphosphatidyl glycerol (Smith, 1967b).

The fatty acids of this organism are found only in the complex lipids. No significant free fatty acids exist. Palmitic and oleic acids predominate although a whole spectrum of fatty acids are seen (Table II.6). The oleic acid is derived from the culture medium as it is a growth requirement.

iii. Mycoplasma arthritidis, strain 07. The total lipids of this organism are equally divided between neutral and phospholipids. The neutral lipids are comprised of the sterol which is supplied in the growth medium (Table II.4) and its esterified form (Smith and Rothblat, 1960b; Lynn and Smith, 1960; Rothblat and Smith, 1961; Smith, 1962). The fatty acids esterified to the sterol are primarily volatile (volatile:nonvolatile, 50:1). The volatile fatty acids are comprised principally of butyric with smaller amounts of acetic and propionic acids. The ratios of free to esterified sterol varies with age and metabolic state. No steryl glycoside is found. The existence of steryl glycoside in mycoplasmas correlates with their capacity to utilize glucose and the presence of glucosidases. Glucose nonfermenting mycoplasmas contain neither the steryl glucoside nor the glucosidase (Smith, 1963b). Furthermore, no other glycolipids have been found although a very limited number of nonfermentative organisms have been examined (Smith and Koostra, 1967). There is evidence for quinones in this species but the identity is unknown (VanDemark and Smith, 1965).

The phospholipids of *M. arthritidis* are phosphatidyl glycerol, its *O*-aminoacyl esters and a trace of diphosphatidyl glycerol (Smith and Koostra, 1967). The amino acids found in the *O*-aminoacyl esters include alanine, aspartic acid, glycine, lysine, glutamic acid, methionine, and leucine/isoleucine. The quantity and configuration of these amino acids has not been determined. Production of these esters requires an acidic environment which these organisms can neither produce nor tolerate. Their formation is induced by dropping the pH with mineral acid a few hours prior to their normally attained peak of exponential growth.

As with *M. gallinarum*, the principal fatty acids are palmitic and oleic acids although a variety of others are found in small quantity (Table II.6). Free fatty acids, if they occur, are found in trace amounts.

iv. Bovine arthritis strain V5. Cholesterol or cholestanol, whichever is supplied in the growth medium, is found unchanged and comprises about 20% of the total lipids of this strain and a goat strain (GY) both of which are antigenically related to *M. mycoides* (Rodwell, 1963). No evidence for sterol esters or any sterol transformations has been obtained. Aside from the sterol, neutral lipid fractions contain glycolipids. Upon ^{14}C labeling from exogenous glycerol supplied as a growth requirement, Plackett (1967) identified the main glycolipid as *O*-β-D-galactofuranosyl-(1 → 1)-diglyceride (Fig. 2.22). Unidentified fractions probably contain small amounts of glycosyl diglycerides with more than one sugar residue. The monoglycosyl lipid predominates as in *M. laidlawii*. Little or no turnover of sterol and glycolipid occurs during growth.

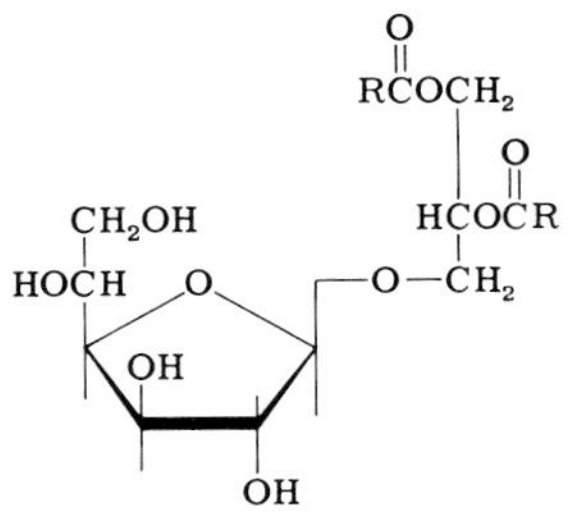

O-β-D-Galactofuranosyl diglyceride

FIG. 2.22. Structure of galactosyl diglyceride of *M. mycoides*.

The major phospholipids are phosphatidyl glycerol and diphosphatidyl glycerol. Since the organisms were grown in a culture medium containing a variety of ill-defined lipids, the natural lipids of the organisms were considered to be those possessing ^{14}C derived from exogenously supplied glycerol and fatty acids. Although sphingomyelin and phosphatidyl choline were found they were not radiolabeled. Incorporation of glycerol occurs primarily into phosphatidyl glycerol. As the organisms age there is a reduction in phosphatidyl glycerol with a concomitant increase in diphosphatidyl glycerol.

The fatty acids found in the phospholipids and glycolipids mimic those found in the culture medium with a preponderance of palmitic, stearic and oleic acids (Placektt, 1967). Strain Y, which cannot synthesize either saturated or unsaturated fatty acids, is capable of growth when elaidic acid (trans 18:1) is the only available fatty acid (Rodwell, 1968). Over 97% of the fatty acids in the lipids were shown to be elaidic.

v. Mycoplasma pneumoniae. Study of the lipid composition of this species has been limited to the identification of serologically active haptens. The necessity for a complex lipid-containing culture medium casts suspicion on the significance of any lipids found in the organisms other than those containing radioactivity derived from labeled precursors. Plackett *et al.* (1969) have found at least four glycolipids which become labeled when the organisms are grown in radioactive glycerol, glucose, or palmitic acid. These were identified as a di- and a trigalactosyl diglyceride, a diglycosyl diglyceride containing both glucose and galactose, and a trihexosyl diglyceride. The exact structures have not been elucidated. Since *M. pneumoniae*, *M. mycoides*, and *Streptococcus* MG exhibit cross serological activities (Lemcke *et al.*, 1965; Marmion *et al.*, 1967; Lind, 1968), it is likely all possess some glycolipids of similar structure. Beckman and Kenny (1968) found a lipid fraction active in complement-fixation reactions. This lipid contained glycerol and phosphate in equimolar amounts together with glucose and galactose. These investigators consider the serologically active lipid to be a glycophospholipid. It is most probable that the glyco-lipids found by Plackett *et al* are the actual haptens and that the phos-phorus found in other preparations represent contaminants. Two radio-labeled phospholipids are found in *M. pneumoniae* (Plackett *et al.*, 1969), namely phosphatidyl glycerol and a phosphatidyl monoglyceride. Prescott *et al.* (1969) have found phosphatidyl glycerol which they consider to be a serologically active lipid. Although they did not use labeled precursors this lipid undoubtedly is natural to *M. pneumoniae*.

vi. Mycoplasma sp., sterol nonrequiring, nonpigmented. Tully and Razin (1969) isolated this species from tissue cultures. Although only preliminary studies have been preformed (P. Plackett and P. F. Smith, unpublished) on the nature of its lipids, this organism differs dramatically from other mycoplasmas. About half of the total lipids is comprised of free fatty acids and free sphingosine base. The neutral lipid fraction yields cholesterol and fatty acids upon methanolysis. Seventy percent of the phospholipids are alkali labile being composed of a monoacyl phosphatidyl glycerol, phos-phatidyl glycerol, and diphosphatidyl glycerol. The alkali stable phospho-lipids are a ceramide phosphatidyl glycerol with the N-acyl group being a hydroxy acid and this lipid with an additional saturated acid esterified to the hydroxyl group either of the long-chain base or the hydroxy acid. The long-chain bases are synthesized by the organism from fatty acids, e.g., palmitic acid gives rise primarily to dihydrosphingosine (P. Plackett, P. F. Smith, and W. R. Mayberry, unpublished). The only other bacterial species known to contain sphingolipids is *Bacterioides*.

c. NUCLEAR MATERIAL.

The DNA of mycoplasmas contains the usual bases—adenine, guanine, cytosine, and thymine—but no hydroxymethyl cytosine (Lynn and Smith, 1957; Morowitz *et al.*, 1962). Adenine-to-thymine and guanine-to-cytosine ratios approximate 1.0 in agreement with the Watson-Crick model. The more recent analyses of base composition have employed buoyant density in cesium chloride gradients and thermal denaturation rather than chemical analysis. The base composition of *M. mycoides* and *M. laidlawii* have been verified by chemical analysis (Chelton *et al.*, 1968). Table II.7 is a compila-tion of the percent G + C of representative species. The existence of deoxy-ribose has been confirmed by chemical analysis.

Ryan and Morowitz (1969) have made use of the low melting point of the bulk DNA from *Mycoplasma* sp., strain Kid (79.5°C; 24.9% G + C) to isolate the native regions coding for rRNA and tRNA. This latter region melts at 88°C. This DNA has saturation hybridization values of 15.9%

TABLE II.7

DNA Base Ratios of Mycoplasmas

Species	% G + C	Reference[a]	Origin
M. neurolyticum	22.8–26.2	2, 3, 4, 8	Rodent
Mycoplasma sp. (calf)	23.6–26.5	2	Bovine
Mycoplasma sp. (avian)	24.1–25.5	7	Avian
Serotype E	24.0	7	Avian
Serotypes K, I	24.5	7	Avian
Serotype M	25.0	7	Avian
Serotype J	25.5	7	Avian
Serotype F	26.5	7	Avian
Mycoplasma sp. (goat)	24.1–25.5	2, 4	Caprine
M. bovirhinis	24.5–25.4	7, 8	Bovine
M. felis	25.2	8	Feline
M. mycoides	26.1–27.0	1, 2, 3	Bovine
M. orale, type 2	25.0–27.8	3, 6, 8	Human
M. orale, type 1	26.0–26.6	3, 6, 8	Human
M. maculosum	26.7–29.6	3, 7	Canine
M. gallinarum	26.5–28.1	3, 4, 7, 8	Avian
M. pharyngis	23.9–27.0	3, 8	Human
M. salivarium	27.0–27.3	3, 6	Human
M. hyorhinis	27.3–27.8	3	Porcine
M. bovigenitalium	28.1–32.0	3, 6, 7	Bovine
M. meleagridis	28.1–28.6	7	Avian
M. pulmonis	27.5–28.3	3, 8	Rodent
M. fermentans	27.0–28.7	2, 3, 6, 8	Human
M. gateae	28.5	8	Avian
M. canis	28.4–29.1	3, 7	Canine
M. spumans	28.4–29.1	3, 7, 8	Canine
M. iners	29.1–29.6	8	Avian
M. histotropicum	29.2	8	Rodent
M. hominis	27.3–29.2	3, 7, 8	Human
M. granularum	30.4–32.1	3, 7	Porcine
M. arthritidis	30.0–33.7	3, 4, 7	Human, rodent
M. synoviae	34.2	7	Avian
M. laidlawii	31.7–34.4	2–8	Compost, sewage
M. gallisepticum	31.8–35.7	3, 4, 6, 7, 8	Avian
M. agalactiae	33.6–34.2	2	Caprine
M. pneumoniae	38.6–40.8	2, 3, 6, 8	Human

[a] 1. Neimark and Pene (1965). 2. Neimark (1967). 3. McGee et al. (1967). 4. Bode (1966). 5. Chelton et al. (1968). 6. Somerson et al. (1967). 7. Kelton and Mandel (1969). 8. Williams et al. (1969).

with rRNA plus tRNA from this species while bulk DNA has values of 0.26% and 0.16% respectively. Based on an estimated genome size of 6.84×10^8 daltons, this strain possesses only enough ribosomal DNA to code for one set of 23 S + 16 S rRNA and only enough DNA complementary to tRNA to code for forty-four different tRNA molecules. Although the genome is only one-fourth the size of the genome of *Escherichia coli* it contains 40% as much genetic material for the production of rRNA. They conclude that only one species of each type of rRNA is required for functioning of this mycoplasma.

d. Ribosomes

No chemical analyses on purified ribosomes of mycoplasmas have been reported. The base composition of total RNA has been performed on *M. arthritidis* and *M. gallisepticum*. The molar proportions of adenine:guanine:cytosine:uracil in *M. arthritidis* are 10.0:17.5:16.8:11.2 with a purine/pyrimidine ratio of 0.98 (Lynn and Smith, 1967). The base ratios for *M. gallisepticum* are 26.0 (adenine)/30.1 (guanine)/18.8 (cytosine)/25.1 (uracil), with a purine/pyrimidine ratio of 1.3. No obvious relationship between the base ratios of DNA and RNA is seen. The RNA of mycoplasma strain 880 was separated into two fractions and analyzed (Hall *et al.*, 1967). The pH 6.0 fraction contains the bulk of RNA and corresponds to the soluble and ribosomal fractions. The mole percent nucleotide composition of this fraction is 22 (adenosine)/25 (cytidine)/25.6 (guanosine)/27.3 (uridine). The corresponding mole percentages in the phenol fraction are 21, 20, 42, 17. They observed less than a 0.1 mole% of methylated bases in this organism.

The transfer RNA of three species, *M. laidlawii*, *M. gallisepticum* and *Mycoplasma* sp., strain Kid, sediment with *E. coli* tRNA. The base composition in mole% of tRNA from the Kid strain is 22.0 (adenine)/29.2 (guanine)/24.6 (cytosine)/24.3 uracil + minor nucleotide bases) (Hayashi *et al.*, 1969). Although the minor nucleotide content of tRNA of mycoplasmas is lower than other microorganisms they do occur (Table II.8). All three contain N-formylmethionyl tRNA.

e. Bleb and Infrableb Region

These ultrastructures have not been isolated for chemical analysis. Histochemical techniques suggest they may be protein possibly interspersed with lipid. There is a notable absence of nucleic acid (Maniloff *et al.*, 1965a). In *M. gallisepticum* ATPase activity appears to be localized in the bleb and infrableb regions exclusively. Acid phosphatase is localized in the

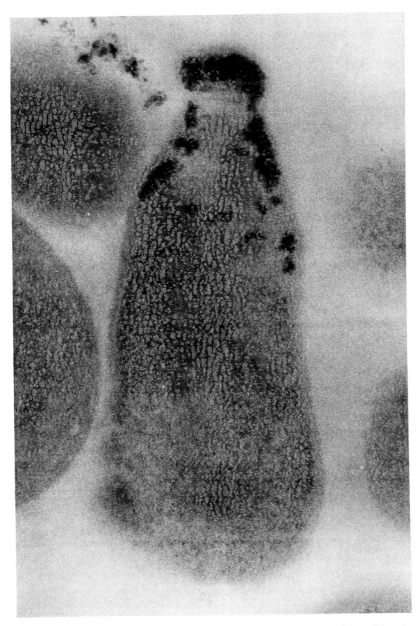

FIG. 2.23. Localization of phosphatases in the bleb region of *M. gallisepticum.*
× 215,000. Courtesy of M. Munkres. Copyright by American Society for Microbiology.
Figure 3, Munkres and Wachtel (1967).

TABLE II.8

Minor Nucleotides of Mycoplasmal tRNA[a]

Mycoplasma sp., strain Kid	Mycoplasma laidlawii, strain B
Ribothymidine	Ribothymidine
Pseudouridine	Pseudouridine
4-Thiouridine	4-Thiouridine
N^1-Methyladenosine	N^2-Methylguanosine
N^6-Methyl adenosine	5-Methyl cytidine or O^2-methyl cytidine
N^7-Methyl guanosine	
N^2-Methyl guanosine	N^6-Methyl adenosine
	N^1-Methyl adenosine
	N^7-Methyl guanosine
	N^6-Isopentenyl adenosine

[a] Data compiled from Hayashi et al. (1969) and Smith and Smith (1970).

infrableb region and does not appear to be membrane associated (Munkres and Wachtel, 1967) (Fig. 2.23).

The nature of the dense particulate elements seen in species other than M. gallisepticum is not known. Similar particles from the Proteus L form have been isolated and shown to be rich in lipid but poor in RNA, DNA, and protein. Their respiratory activity is equivalent to whole organisms but their biosynthetic capability is weak (Weibull and Beckman, 1961). It is impossible to say whether the particles of the two organisms are related.

2. Physical Nature of the Structural Units

a. CYTOPLASMIC MEMBRANE

The mycoplasmal membrane possesses the morphological and compositional features generally found in most biological membranes. The frequency dependence of the dielectric constant and conductivity of intact cells of the one species examined M. gallisepticum is consistent with the existence of such a membrane (Schwan and Morowitz, 1962). Mycoplasmas have one additional feature, the presence of only one membranous structure, which has generated interest in using membranes for models to study the structure of membranes in general. One species M. laidlawii, has been singled out because of the ease in obtaining pure membrane preparations. This organism, when grown in the absence of cholesterol, lyses readily in medium of low ionic strength. The resultant membranes when thoroughly

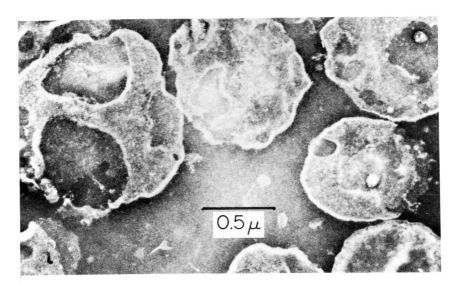

FIG. 2.24. Membranes of osmotically lysed *M. laidlawii* showing holes where cyto-plasmic constituents leaked out. Courtesy of S. Razin. Copyright by Academic Press, Inc. Figure 1a, Rottem *et al.* (1968).

washed and treated with RNase and DNase appear as collapsed empty sacs made of lipoprotein. The cellular contents appear to have leaked from large holes in the membrane (Rottem *et al.*, 1968), (Fig. 2.24). These puri-fied membranes are useful starting material for studies of their molecular structure.

Considerable information on membrane structure has been obtained by examining the effects of enzymes, chemical agents, and nutritional de-ficiencies. Growth of *M. mycoides* in a medium deficient in glycerol, choles-terol or oleic acid, all of which are nutritional requirements, results in death accompanied by lysis. Electron micrographs show bizarre, swollen and rounded organisms compatible with the picture of weakened membranes (Rodwell and Abbot, 1961) (Fig. 2.25). Growth of *M. laidlawii* B in the presence of an unsaturated fatty acid, such as oleic, which is not an absolute nutritional requirement (Smith and Henrikson, 1965; Henrikson and Panos, 1969) induces filamentous growth and increases osmotic stability (Razin *et al.*, 1966). An increase in osmotic lability of *M. laidlawii* B when grown with oleic acid has been the experience of myself and some other investi-gators. Sterol containing mycoplasmas are susceptible to lysis by digitonin (Smith and Rothblat, 1960b; Razin and Argaman, 1963) and by the sterol dependent streptolysin O (Bernheimer and Davidson, 1965) indicative

FIG. 2.25. Swollen cells of *M. mycoides* produced by unbalanced growth. Courtesy of A. W. Rodwell. Copyright by J. Gen. Microbiol. Figure 13, Rodwell and Abbot (1961).

for a structural role of sterol in the cytoplasmic membrane. *Mycoplasma laidlawii*, a sterol nonrequiring species, is not affected by these two agents. However, when grown in the presence of sterol, it incorporates this lipid into its membrane and becomes susceptible to digitonin and polyene antibiotics. In general, sterol-containing mycoplasmas are more stable osmotically than sterol-free mycoplasmas (Razin, 1963; Smith and Sasaki, 1958).

Washing of intact mycoplasmas in hypertonic or hypotonic solutions results in leakage of ultraviolet-absorbing intracellular components, even though morphology is maintained in the hypertonic environment (Rodwell, 1965). Chelating agents, such as ethylenediaminetetraacetic acid, increases leakage. This leakage is prevented by Ca^{2+}, Mg^{2+}, spermidine or spermine. Uranyl ions prevent sterol incorporation into mycoplasmas (Smith and Boughton, 1960) and protect against lysis by detergents (Razin and Argaman 1963). Pancreatic lipase induces lysis of intact mycoplasmas (Razin and Argaman 1963). Phospholipase A causes lysis of cells and solubilizes purified membranes (Smith *et al.* 1969). The inactivity of phospholipases C and D is attributed to the lack of proper substrate presentation to these enzymes. These findings suggest a role for phospholipids and glycolipids in maintenance of the structural integrity of the cytoplasmic membrane. Destruction of the lipids would disrupt lipid–protein interactions. Cation effects reflect their role in binding to or bridging phospholipid molecules.

A structural role for protein is affirmed by the lytic activity of proteolytic enzymes on intact cells and purified membranes. Trypsin and chymotrypsin are active against *M. laidlawii* (Smith *et al.* 1969) and presumably *M. gallisepticum* (Morowitz *et al.* 1962). Papain is without effect and in some instances heat denaturation is a necessary prerequisite for trypsin digestion of intact cells (Razin and Argaman 1963).

Mycoplasmas are extremely sensitive to surface-active agents. Crude lecithin, bile salts long-chain fatty acids soaps alcohols, and anionic, cationic, and nonionic detergents readily cause lysis (Keller *et al.*, 1952; Razin and Argaman, 1963; Rodwell, 1956; Smith and Boughton, 1960; Smith and Sasaki, 1958). Purified membranes are disaggregated by detergents. Both cationic and anionic detergents exhibit equal effectiveness with membranes of *M. laidlawii* containing a mixture of positively and negatively charged lipids derived in part from the culture medium (Rottem *et al.*, 1968). However, only anionic detergents disaggregate *M. laidlawii* membranes containing only their naturally synthesized acidic lipids (Smith *et al.*, 1969).

All of these effects of enzymes, chemicals, and nutritional deficiencies confirm the necessity for lipids, proteins, and cations and their interaction in the physical structure of the mycoplasmal membrane. Determination of the molecular structure is under attack by attempts to solubilize, fractionate, and reform the membrane. Essentially all of these studies have been restricted to *M. laidlawii*, which will be described as the prototype membrane.

Dissolution of membranes from *M. laidlawii* grown in lipid-containing culture medium with sodium dodecyl sulfate yields a preparation with a single symmetrical sedimentation boundary in the ultracentrifuge (Razin *et al.*, 1965) with an S value of 3.3. A lower S value, 2.5, is obtained with membranes of organisms grown in lipid-free culture medium (Smith *et al.*, 1969). The apparent homogeneity originally considered evidence for lipoprotein subunits is artifactual. Density gradient centrifugation revealed separate banding of protein and lipid as their detergent complexes (Engleman *et al.*, 1967). Although Rodwell *et al.* (1967) found the use of deoxycholate necessary to separate lipid from protein in detergent-solubilized

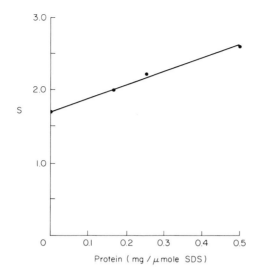

FIG. 2.26. Dependence of S value of solubilized membranes of *M. laidlawii* on concentration of detergent (SDS, sodium dodecyl sulfate).

membrane preparations, fractionation of lipid and protein was confirmed by this group (Rottem *et al.*, 1968). Protein and lipid separation as well as inhomogeneity of detergent solubilized membrane was further proven by polyacrylamide electrophoresis in which multiple protein banding occurs (Rodwell *et al.*, 1967) with a lipid being retained in the stacking gel (Smith *et al.*, 1969). Even the S values are suspect as they are affected by the concentration of detergent and reflect the S value of the detergent micelle (Fig. 2.26).

Any study of the particles arising from detergent disaggregation must consider the introduction into the solubilized preparation of the detergent itself. Dialysis does not remove all of the sodium dodecyl sulfate. The detergent is bound primarily to the lipid since dialysis results in its complete removal from lipid depleted membrane particles. Further it can be shown by equilibrium dialysis that detergent is bound only by lipid-containing membrane. Detergent binding also is a function of the chain of sulfated alcohol. Those with chain lengths of C_{14} and C_{16} are more tightly bound than dodecyl sulfate (Smith *et al.*, 1969). The extent of removal of detergent is affected by Mg^{2+}, its presence retarding the disappearance from the membrane. Use of excessive detergent likewise impedes its removal. Passage of the material through Sephadex G-25 is most effective for ridding the solubilized membrane of detergent (Rottem *et al.*, 1968).

The disaggregated membrane probably is a stable suspension of micelles composed of protein, lipid, and detergent. Any assessment of their size is difficult as different sizes of membrane fragments conceivably could lie in detergent micelles with identical size and density, thereby appearing homogeneous.

Fractionation of the solubilized membrane has met with mixed failure and success. Polyacrylamide electrophoresis in the presence of excess detergent results in smearing throughout the gel. In minimal detergent multiple bands appear as with phenol–acetic acid solubilized membranes electrophoresed in the presence of 6 M urea (Rodwell $et\ al.$, 1967). Attempts to obtain separation on preparative gel electrophoretic columns have yielded a maximum of four components, all of which are heterogeneous on analytic gels and with respect to enzymic activity. Most of the protein and lipid remain in the stacking gel. (Smith $et\ al.$, 1969). Ammonium sulfate fractionation of detergent-poor membrane particles has been unsuccessful. Rodwell $et\ al.$ (1967) found no ATPase or $NADH_2$ oxidase activity in ammonium sulfate precipitated protein. $NADH_2$ oxidase remains in the lipid-rich supernatant fluid at 12% saturation. Glucosidase activity is retained by the solubilized preparation but can be demonstrated only after extensive dialysis. ATPase activity is markedly reduced. These enzymic activities are not fractionated by ammonium sulfate.

The lipids in the solubilized membrane can be partially removed with aqueous acetone or completely with chloroform–methanol. The resultant protein is extremely hydrophobic (Rodwell $et\ al.$, 1967) but the acetone powder still retains $NADH_2$ oxidase activity. The hydrophobic protein can be resolubilized with sodium dodecyl sulfate, by increasing the pH to 11–12 (Rodwell $et\ al.$, 1967) and by a variety of acidic but not positively charged lipids. Among the acidic lipids capable of solubilization of the protein are phosphatidyl glycerol, "phosphatidyl glucose," glucosyl diglycerides, and diphosphatidyl glycerol. The latter is as effective as anionic detergent. It is probable that the protein becomes oriented in a lipid micelle with resultant "solubilization" (Smith $et\ al.$, 1969).

Methods other than detergent lysis have been tried for solubilization of mycoplasmal membranes. A heterogeneous mixture of particles, the major component having an S value of 6.2, is produced by sonication (Razin, 1967). Succinylation of most of the free amino groups (which amount to 0.5 μmoles/mg protein) solubilizes the membrane but gives rise to inhomogeneity, separation of protein from lipid, and destruction of all enzymic activity except for glucosidase. Ethylenediaminetetraacetic acid is without effect even in the presence of high Na^+ which is effective for erythrocyte membranes. Likewise, varying pH and ionic strength result in no solubilization (Smith $et\ al.$, 1969).

Detergent-solubilized membranes are capable of reaggregation in the presence of cation (Razin *et al.*, 1965). This phenomenon has been studied in some detail by Engelman and Morowitz (1968a,b) and Razin *et al.*, (1969). Dialysis against buffer in the absence of divalent cation gives rise to small lipoprotein aggregates with the same protein to lipid ratio as the original membrane. Rottem *et al.* (1968) consider these aggregates formed at low concentration of divalent cation to be bimolecular leaflets of lipid upon which protein eventually becomes bound. These small aggregates have not been seen by electron microscopy. Protein is bound to lipid, since protein and lipid migrate as one band in sucrose density gradient. They exhibit one symmetrical peak in the ultracentrifuge. Dialysis of these small aggregates against buffer containing Mg^{2+} results in further aggregation yielding structures with the trilaminar membranous appearance together with a smaller number of protein species with higher lipid to protein ratios than the original membrane. As Mg^{2+} concentration is increased lighter bands in density gradients are transformed to heavier bands. Protein to lipid ratio is similar to the original membrane as is the buoyant density of 1.18 g/cm^3. The Mg^{2+} to protein ratio of these large aggregates is identical to the original membrane in contrast to the small aggregates which are Mg^{2+} poor. As dialysis time or Mg^{2+} concentration is increased, there occurs an increase in $NADH_2$ oxidase, RNase, and DNase activities. This could be explained as reaggregation or removal of inhibitory detergent. Aggregates formed by removal of most of the detergent prior to exposure to Mg^{2+} appear as vesicles of unit membrane while those formed by exposure to Mg^{2+} concomitant with detergent removal appear as open segments of unit membrane. A scheme showing these phenomena has been devised by Engelman and Morowitz and is shown in Fig. 2.27. Once formed the membranous aggregates retain this form. Resolubilization requires addition of detergent. Chelating agents have no effect.

Cations are essential to the formation of the membranous aggregates. Divalent cations, Ca^{2+}, Mn^{2+}, Zn^{2+}, Cu^{2+}, Fe^{2+}, Mg^{2+}, are equally effective

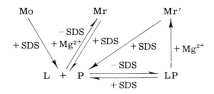

FIG. 2.27. Scheme of Engelman and Morowitz for reaggregation of detergent solubilized membranes of *M. laidlawii*. Mo = original membrane; Mr = reaggregated membrane; Mr' = reaggregated membrane prime; L = lipid; P = protein; LP = lipoprotein aggregate; SDS = sodium dodecyl sulfate.

at 0.02 M concentration (Rottem *et al.*, 1968); lower concentrations of trivalent cations, Al^{3+}, Fe^{3+}, are effective (Smith *et al.*, 1969); monovalent cations are ineffective. The presence of cation impedes removal of detergent by dialysis. The pH has an effect on the amount of divalent cation required, being lower at lower pH. At pH 3.5, 60% of the protein is aggregated at a Mg concentration of 2×10^{-3} M. The mechanism of cation function in reaggregation is not understood. It is speculated that it functions not only by neutralization of the negative charge on the protein and lipid thereby allowing hydrophobic interaction but also by bridging molecules of protein, lipid, and lipid–protein. The fact that high monovalent cation can cause some aggregation which is dispersed upon suspension in water points to charge neutralization. Likewise the decreasing concentration required for aggregation with increased valency of cation supports this explanation. But the necessity for polyvalent cations to form nondissociable aggregates and the inability of chelating agents to solubilize the membrane or reaggregates argue for a bridging mechanism. Probably both are involved. The effect of residual detergent must also be considered. It is possible that reaggregation is due in part or solely to bridging of micellar particles together through the sulfate groups in residual detergent. By use of radionucleides—$^{59}Fe^{2+}$, and $^{45}Ca^{2+}$—it has been shown that about 0.85 μmole cation is bound per milligram membrane protein after removal of detergent by dialysis. EDTA washing removes about half of this cation without change in the aggregate. EDTA does not become bound to the aggregate. Thus a considerable portion of the cation is unavailable to the EDTA and probably is buried within the aggregate. Increase in ionic strength does not make it available. Whether this represents the situation in the natural membrane is debatable. The reformed membrane is similar to the natural membrane morphologically and on the basis of gross chemical composition. Undoubtedly it also contains some contaminating detergent. Some other parameter is needed which will denote similarity to the original membrane, such as loss of enzymic activity upon disaggregation and its recovery upon reaggregation. Until such a parameter is discovered there is no assurance of the naturalness of the reassembled membrane.

All of these studies on membrane properties fail to confirm a lamellar or a corpuscular structure. Conceivably, the reaggregation of disaggregated membranes could be interpreted as (*1*) formation of small lipoprotein units which coalesce into larger aggregates or (*2*) the initial formation of a lipid bilayer into or onto which protein becomes bound. In one study of the synthesis of membranes (Kahane and Razin, 1969), protein and lipid synthesis are not synchronized. Membranes of cells in which protein synthesis was impaired by the presence of chloramphenicol were of lower

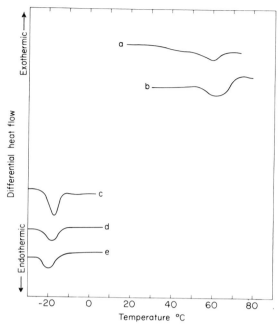

FIG. 2.28. Calorimetric scans of *M. laidlawii* lipids, membranes, and whole cells indicative of melting of hydrocarbon chains in lipid bilayers. (a) Lipids and (b) membranes from cells grown with added stearate; (c) lipids, (d) membranes, and (e) whole cells from medium supplemented with oleate. Courtesy of J. M. Steim. Copyright by National Academy of Sciences. Adapted from Figure 1, Steim *et al.* (1969).

density (1.158 g/cm³) compared to normal membranes (1.170 g/cm³) indicating the presence of increased lipid. Membrane protein turns over faster (half-life, 3 hr) than total lipid (several hours measured as turnover of ³H-oleic acid). Even these results can be interpreted favorably for either proposed structure.

The best evidence in support of a predominantly lamellar structure are the results of thermal phase transition (Steim *et al.*, 1969) and of x-ray diffraction at these phase transitions (Engelman, 1970). If lipids exist in a bilayer held together by hydrophobic interaction of the hydrocarbon chains, melting of the interior would result in a reversible thermotropic gel–liquid crystal phase transition without a molecular rearrangement. Such a transition can be measured by differential scanning calorimetry. The melting point varies with degree of unsaturation and chain length of fatty acids in the phospholipids. The more alike the chains are to one another, the sharper the melting point appears. Calorimetric scans of the membranes and membrane lipids from *M. laidlawii* are seen in Fig. 2.28. The lipid transitions are reversible as with simple lipid bilayers. The transition temperatures are dependant upon the nature of the fatty acids. Although the melting temperature of membranes and intact cells exhibit a broader spread than pure lipid bilayers, there is a significant sharpness of transition. The smaller sceondary transition seen at higher temperatures is considered to result from protein denaturation. It could also be accounted for as lipid–protein interaction. However at least 75% of the lipid can be accounted as participating in the sharper transitions. Therefore it is probable that this much lipid exists in a bimolecular leaflet in resting cells. The remaining 25% could occur in hydrophobic interaction with protein.

X-ray diffraction patterns of membranes from *M. laidlawii* grown with palmitic or erucic (*cis*-13-docosenoic) acids show a gradual shift from a broad strong ring near 0.46 nm to a sharp ring near 0.42 nm as the temperature is lowered. This sharp diffraction is indicative of close hexagonal packing of fatty acid chains at temperatures below transition. A center to center spacing of 0.482 nm similar to the hexagonal phase of long-chain

TABLE II.9

Physical Properties of DNA from Mycoplasmas[a]

Species	Size (daltons)	Density	Number of genes
M. agalactiae bovis	685×10^6		730
M. arthritidis	444×10^6	1.692	600
M. arthritidis, strain 39	510×10^6	1.691	640
M. arthritidis, PG 6	440×10^6		
M. fermentans, PG 18	480×10^6		
M. gallisepticum	1200×10^6	1.693	1500
M. gallisepticum, PG 31	490×10^6		
M. granularum, Friend	950×10^6		
M. hominis, PG 21	450×10^6		
M. laidlawii, strain A	790×10^6		1100
M. laidlawii, strain A	1100×10^6		
M. laidlawii, strain B	760×10^6		1000
M. laidlawii, strain B	1000×10^6		
M. orale 1, Patt	470×10^6		
M. pneumoniae, Mac	480×10^6		
M. salivarium, PG 20	470×10^6		
T strain 27	470×10^6		
T strain 58	440×10^6		

[a] Data compiled from Morowitz (1969), Morowitz *et al.* (1967), and Bak *et al.* (1969).

paraffins is seen. At low temperature (10°C) the structure of the lipids in the membrane is best described as a mono- or bilayer as other arrangements would not allow close hexagonal packing. Above the transition temperature the chains are more fluid, indicating loss of long-range order.

b. THE CHROMOSOME

The chromosomes of a select group of species are circles of typical double-stranded DNA (Morowitz et al., 1967) as judged from direct electron microscopy of spread films and the radioautographic method using tritiated thymidine to label the DNA. Some species, notably M. arthritidis, also show a number of small circles which may be artifacts of breakage or episomes (Morowitz, 1969). These small circles of DNA may represent the satellite DNA found in CsCl density gradients of this organism (Haller and Lynn, 1969). All species examined exhibit double Y's or forks confirming a typical replicative mechanism. The physical properties of selected species is shown in Table II.9. Included are the genome size of several species determined by a novel method which measures genome size from its renaturation rate relative to rate of a known genome. Second-order kinetics are observed (Bak et al., 1969). No base sequencing has been attempted.

c. RIBOSOMES AND MESSENGER RNA

Only M. gallisepticum has been studied with respect to the physical characteristics of RNA. The ribosomal fraction contains a single component with an uncorrected sedimentation coefficient of 72.2 ± 6.5 S. On dilution with water, three peaks are found at 70.2 ± 7.0 S, 49.6 ± 3.4 S and 33.3 ± 3.4 S. After refrigeration for 24 hours followed by dilution in water five peaks are found at 68.3 ± 5.0 S, 48.9 ± 5.1 S, 43.6 ± 4.2 S, 31.5 ± 4.3 S and 20.1 ± 3.2 S. These are equivalent to the 77 S, 56 S, and 38 S values for bacterial ribosomes. The smaller fragments represent subunits of the larger particles. (Morowitz et al., 1962; Maniloff et al., 1965b). Ribosomes have a diameter of about 14 nm and are loosely arranged in young cells. As the cells age they assume a cylindrical packing arrangement. In either form they appear to concentrate near the cytoplasmic membrane. About 5% of the total RNA is messenger RNA which has a half-life of about 2 minutes.

3. Models of Structural Units

An examination of possible models which accommodate the present facts known about the cytoplasmic membranes is useful. Little can be gained by construction of models of the other ultrastructural units because either too little is known or they do not differ from or add to models of these structures in other organisms.

Two different basic models for membrane structure have been advanced. One is the lamellar model first proposed by Danielli and Davson (1935) and modified as the unit membrane by Robertson (1958). The other is the corpuscular model proposed by Green and Perdue (1966), Green and Fleischer (1963), Green et al., (1967), and Benson (1964, 1966). Various modifications of the subunit or corpuscular model have been presented by several investigators including Lenard and Singer (1966) and Wallach and Zahler (1966). A complete description with supporting evidence for these models can be found in the various publications of these and other authors. Only a short description of these models is intended in order to examine the fit of data concerning mycoplasmal membranes.

The unit membrane model is visualized as a bimolecular leaflet of phospholipid held together by hydrophobic interactions of the hydrocarbon chains and sandwiched between two layers of protein. The lipid and the protein layers are considered separate but continuous phases. The proteins are considered to be globular. Robertson considers the two protein layers to be asymmetric, the outer layer being mucopolysaccharide or mucoprotein and the inner layer to be unconjugated protein. The protein layers are held to the inner lipid leaflet by electrostatic forces between polar groups on lipid and protein. The protein layers are visualized as extended polypeptide chains about 2 nm thick and the middle lipid layer 3.5 to 4 nm thick. Much of the evidence supporting this model is biophysical and includes the ubiquitous presence of lipids in all membranes, the electron transparency of the middle layer, the electron density of the outer layers and the dimensions of these layers, the results of x-ray diffraction, polarization microscopy, and differential scanning calorimetry, the frequent inability to see any subunit structure, and the inability to demonstrate unequivocably fragmentation into lipoprotein subunits. Proponents of the corpuscular model counteract this evidence by pointing to the facts that most of the work has been performed on the specialized enzymically inactive myelin membrane, the membranes are in an inactive state when examined, and techniques for electron microscopy preclude visualization of a subunit structure.

The corpuscular or subunit model is defined as a sheet of lipoprotein units, one unit thick, held together by hydrophobic interactions. The protein is found partially in the α-helical form and partially as random coils. The hydrophilic peptide segments are located at the hydrated membrane surfaces and interact with other polar peptide chains and the polar head groups of lipids. Thus the external surfaces of the subunits are polar in character containing the polar peptide chains and polar lipid groups. Within the subunits are hydrophobic peptide chains packed amid the hydrocarbon lipid chains. To account for the permability functions of the membrane, segments exist with a cross section of α-helical and random coil protein (Lenard and Singer, 1966) or in the form of microtubules which could have a polar interior (Wallach and Zahler, 1966). To account for the respiratory and metabolic functions, other units which are detachable without destruction of the basic structure are suggested (Green and Perdue, 1966). However this may be a specialized situation for mitochondria as there is no reason that such enzymically active proteins could not be an integral part of different subunits. Disaggregation by amphipathic agents would lead to formation of individual subunits which must be of similar size and shape (Green et al., 1967). In Green's model the subunits are held together by protein–protein hydrophobic interaction. These are visualized as cubes with two opposite faces occupied by lipid, allowing only the four protein faces to interact to give a sheetlike membrane. Removal of lipid from the intact membrane does not disturb the original structure. However removal of lipid from disaggregated subunits results in reaggregation as three dimensionally packed bulk aggregates. Lipid–protein or lipid–lipid interactions as the mechanism for holding subunits together cannot be discounted as there is doubt that all of the lipid is removed by aqueous acetone extraction of the membranes. Even the 5% residual lipid (Green and Fleisher, 1963) would allow for such interaction and therefore maintenance of the original structure seen in electron micrographs.

There is much evidence favoring the subunit model. In general, it allows for easy accommodation of the permeability and enzymic functions found in the membrane. There is no impassable lipid barrier. It allows for both the random coil and α-helical proteins seen in optical rotatory dispersion and circular dichroism studies (Lenard and Singer, 1966). The disaggregation seen upon treatment with detergents and the reformation of membranous structures upon its removal fit best this model. The fact that protein and lipid become separated in part with such treatment can be explained as disruption of the hydrophobic lipid–protein bonding with the resultant hydrophobic association of lipid and protein with detergent. It is not incompatible with the biophysical and morphological evidence used in support of the lamellar model.

A specialized model of the mycoplasmal cytoplasmic membrane based upon the corpuscular model has been devised to account for the present data on the structural and permeability properties of these membranes (Smith, 1968). The recent biophysical evidence favoring a lamellar structure necessitates some modification of this model. The membrane can be envisioned as a mosaic of regions structured as lamellae and regions con-

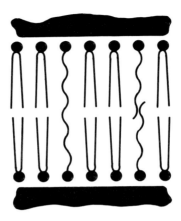

FIG. 2.29. Lamellar model of membrane showing hydrocarbon chains centrally located and in hydrophobic interaction. Polar head groups of lipids are directed outward interacting with charged surface proteins.

taining corpuscular subunits. The finding of discrete holes in membranes of osmotically lysed *M. laidlawii* (Fig. 2.24) suggests areas of different lability and structure. This mosaic can be considered as dynamic with different regions acquiring different physical character dependant upon the age and metabolic state of the cell. Metabolically inactive and impermeable regions would be lamellar in form while the metabolically active and permeable regions would be corpuscular. Allosteric changes in the protein from an inactive to an active state could underlie a transition from one physical form to the other. One test of this hypothesis could be an examination of the proportion of lipids in a lamellar form, as assessed from differential scanning calorimetry, during synchronous division and in different metabolic states.

The lamellar structure in Fig. 2.29 is typical. The primary lipid–lipid interaction is hydrophobic, while protein interacts with lipid principally through ionic bonds. The corpuscular region is pictured in Fig. 2.30. The ovoid structures represent protein subunits in which the hydrophobic peptide chains are coiled within the interior and the hydrophilic peptide chains are lying near and on the surface. Contained within them and bound to the hydrophobic peptide chains are schematically represented dihydroxycarotenol and a dimer of planar sterol with overlapping side chains. The polar hydroxy groups are oriented toward the exterior of the protein subunit. Other lipids, apolar or polar, can occupy similar sites to account for the presence of hydrocarbon carotenes and some phospholipids. Bridging the subunits are molecules of diphosphatidyl glycerol, the apolar

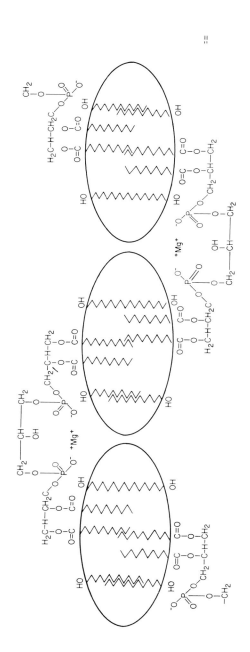

FIG. 2.30. Model of corpuscular segment of mycoplasmal membrane. Details are found in the text. Copyright by Academic Press, Inc. From Smith (1968).

fatty acid chains being bound to the hydrophobic peptide chains. Divalent cation is bound by the two negative charges on the oxygens attached to the phosphorus atoms in the phospholipid. This binding of cation tends to condense the entire structure similar to the effect of cations on monolayers of diphosphatidyl glycerol (Shah and Schulman, 1965).

The following facts known about the mycoplasmal membrane are compatible with this model:

a. Electron micrographs of the membrane give the appearance of a trilaminar structure 7.5 to 11 nm thick with the two electron dense outer layers, 2 to 3 nm thick, sandwiching an inner electron transparent layer 3 to 3.5 nm thick. The length of an all *trans*-C_{40}-carotenoid, exclusive of the terminal hydroxyl groups, is 3.1 nm and a dimer of cholestanol formed by overlapping side chains is 3.0 nm. Hence these molecules could fit across the membrane and together with the many other apolar lipid chains and the apolar peptide chains account for the dimension and electron transparency of the inner layer whether it be in a lamellar or corpuscular configuration. The presence of some polar groups around the pores between subunits account for the striations and subunit structure seen sometimes in electron micrographs. The mixed random coil and α-helical states of the protein as judged by optical rotatory dispersion (Lenard and Singer, 1966) in *M. laidlawii* fit the arrangement given to protein in this model. It is assumed that additional protein of polar character lies together with the polar segments of lipid at the exterior surfaces. These are not drawn in the model.

b. Mixed lamellar and corpuscular regions could account for the phase transitions seen during melting of membranes. That portion of the total lipid not involved could be a corpuscular state. Similarly the x-ray diffraction picture during phase transitions could fit such a model. If the reaggregation phenomenon truly gives rise to a natural membrane, initial formation of a lipid bilayer followed by insertion of protein would be compatible with both physical states of the membrane. Change from one state to another is permissible.

c. The interconvertability of sterol and carotenol and the necessity for these molecules to be planar is explained. (This aspect is discussed fully in Chapter III.) The sterol dimer becomes a molecular structure with the dimensions and conformation of the 3,3'-dihydroxycarotene. The hydroxyl groups are free and available for enzymic reactions.

d. The glycerophospholipids, in particular diphosphatidyl glycerol, are used primarily for bridging subunits explaining not only their ubiquity among mycoplasmas but also their lack of turnover. The glycolipids, which occur in many but not all mycoplasmas, would aid in the maintenance of the structure of individual subunits or lamellar regions rather than binding subunits together. They could be arrayed along the pores between subunits with the polar groups of the sugars lining the pores as suggested by Brundish et al., (1966). Glycerophospholipid bridges between subunits are compatible with the disruptive effects of phospholipases. Cleavage of ester or phosphate bonds would destroy the link with resultant membrane lysis. Proteolytic enzymes also break down the membrane. These could act on the protein surface of the subunits or lamellar regions. The action of phosphomoesterase in solubilizing the M. laidlawii membrane can be accounted for by the hydrolysis of phosphoprotein which has been detected in these membranes (P. F. Smith, unpublished).

e. The susceptibility of the membrane to disruption or solubilization by the action of detergents and other amphipaths can be explained as a disruption of the hydrophobic lipid–protein and lipid–lipid interactions not only holding subunits together but also in maintaining the structural integrity of individual subunits and lamellar areas. Separation of much of the lipid from protein as seen in density gradient analysis of detergent solubilized membrane would reflect the removal of lipid from protein. Lipid is bound to detergent and its substitution in the protein subunits with detergent would produce the proper molecular configuration to allow bridging of subunits. Total removal of detergent requires total lipid extraction also supporting such interactions. Total lipid removal would cause a conformational change in the protein with the resultant exposure of the internal hydrophobic peptide chains. Such treated protein is very hydrophobic but can be resolubilized by acidic lipids. In this phenomenon the apolar groups of the acidic lipids would interact with the apolar peptide chains and result in a charged micelle with the polar lipid groups being on the surface. It is unlikely but possible that after such treatment the protein would recoil in its original state. The model also accounts for the disruptive effects of digitonin on sterol-containing membranes. Removal of sterol would disrupt hydrophobic interactions within subunits and lamellae destroying their stability.

f. The role of cations and the necessity for the multivalency of these cations for reaggregation is explained as the need for neutralization of at least two negative charges to allow for condensation of the membrane. The inability of chelating agents to disaggregate the membrane confirms the primary role of hydrophobic forces in holding the membrane together. Incomplete removal of cation by chelating agents in the case of reaggregated membrane may reflect three dimensional clumping of the subunits barring entry of the chelating agent. Removal of cation would cause expansion of the membrane as a result of allowing the subunits to spread apart from one another. The increase in size of pores all along the membrane would cause leakage of internal cytoplasmic components. Such leakage is exactly the effect of chelating agents on mycoplasmas (Rodwell, 1965). Insertion of divalent cation results in recovery of the viability of the cells and would be expected if the membrane were recondensed by the cations thereby closing the pores. Controlled alternate removal and replacement of cations would have the effect of opening and closing selected pores to allow entry and exit of substrates and end products. The enzymic and structural composition of the areas of subunits lining each pore are considered to vary to account for various functions in different pores. Thus the membrane is visualized as a mosaic of different pores each carrying out a different function or functions. Theoretically different subunits should be separable from one another not on the basis of mass or configuration but rather on the basis of enzymic activity. Such fractionation has not yet been achieved due primarily to the difficulties in maintenance of enzymic activities during the drastic procedures required for membrane solubilization. Specificity of transport phenomena can be accommodated by the model. Further there is no necessity for making transported components lipid soluble. Cations are required for some transport functions. The model could supply these because in order for the pore to open removal of cation is necessary.

g. The phenomena associated with sterol incorporation (described in Chapter III) fit this model. Total lipid removal would destroy the lipid binding sites for the sterol. Uranyl ions would bind to the phosphate groups posing a barrier for entry of sterol into the membrane.

Undoubtedly this model is an oversimplification of what the membrane may be in reality. Although it does account for most of the properties thus far defined there are some discrepancies. There has been no undisputed demonstration of the subunit structure. Although diphosphatidyl glycerol appears to occur in all mycoplasmas it is not always a major lipid component. If other lipids, such as phosphatidyl glycerol or glycolipids, are involved in bridging subunits some other arrangement or ionic interactions must be assumed to hold subunits together. The model as constructed requires a lipid with bilateral apolarity. Phospholipases C and D should disrupt the membrane but do not. This inaction has been explained as unavailability of the phospholipid within the membrane in the form required for hydrolysis by these enzymes. Nevertheless, the intent of this model as all other models is to serve as a basis for further experimentation.

REFERENCES

Anderson, D. R., and Barile, M. F. (1965). *J. Bacteriol.* **90,** 180.
Anderson, D. R., Pollock, M. E., and Brower, L. F. (1965). *J. Bacteriol.* **90,** 1768.
Andrewes, C. H., and Welch, F. V. (1946). *J. Pathol. Bacteriol.* **58,** 578.

Argaman, M., and Razin, S. (1964). *J. Gen. Microbiol.* **38,** 153.
Bak, A. L., Black, F. T., Christiansen, C., and Freundt, E. A. (1969). *Nature (London)* **224,** 1209.
Beckman, B. L., and Kenny, G. E. (1968). *J. Bacteriol.* **96,** 1171.
Benson, A. A. (1964). *Annu. Rev. Plant Physiol.* **15,** 1.
Benson, A. A. (1966). *J. Amer. Oil Chem. Soc.* **43,** 265.
Bernheimer, A. W., and Davidson, M. (1965). *Science* **148,** 1229.
Bode, P. M. (1966). DNA base composition of several mycoplasma and its implication in their taxonomy. M. S. Thesis, Univ. of Connecticut, Storrs, Connecticut.
Bonifas, V. H. (1963). *Pathol. Microbiol.* **26,** 696.
Bridre, J., and Donatien, A. (1925). *Ann. Inst. Pasteur Paris* **39,** 925.
Brown, T. McP., Swift, H. F., and Watson, R. F. (1940). *J. Bacteriol.* **40,** 857.
Brundish, D. E., Shaw, N., and Baddiley, J. (1966). *Biochem. J.* **99,** 546.
Buttery, S. H., and Plackett, P. (1960). *J. Gen. Microbiol.* **23,** 357.
Chelton, E. T. J., Jones, A. S., and Walker, R. T. (1968). *J. Gen. Microbiol.* **50,** 305.
Crawford, Y. E., and Kraybill, W. H. (1967). *Ann. N. Y. Acad. Sci.* **143,** 411.
Cuckow, F. W., and Klieneberger-Nobel, E. (1955). *J. Gen. Microbiol.* **13,** 149.
Danielli, J. F., and Davson, H. A. (1935). *J. Cell. Comp. Physiol.* **5,** 495.
Dienes, L. (1945). *J. Bacteriol.* **50,** 441.
Dienes, L. (1960). *Ann. N. Y. Acad. Sci.* **79,** 356.
Domermuth, C. H., Nielsen, M. H., Freundt, E. A., and Birch-Andersen, A., (1964a). *J. Bacteriol.* **88,** 727.
Domermuth, C. H., Nielsen, M. H., Freundt, E. A., and Birch-Andersen, A. (1964b). *J. Bacteriol.* **88,** 1428.
Edward, D. G. ff. (1954). *J. Gen. Microbiol.* **10,** 27.
Edwards, G. A., and Fogh, J. (1960). *J. Bacteriol.* **79,** 267.
Engelman, D. M. (1970). *J. Mol. Biol.* **47,** 115.
Engelman, D. M., and Morowitz, H. J. (1968a). *Biochim. Biophys. Acta* **150,** 376.
Engelman, D. M., and Morowitz, H. J. (1968b). *Biochim. Biophys. Acta* **150,** 385.
Engelman, D. M., Terry, T. M., and Morowitz, H. J. (1967). *Biochim. Biophys. Acta* **135,** 381.
Fogh, J., and Fogh, H. (1964). *Proc. Soc. Exp. Biol. Med.* **117,** 899.
Fowler, R. C., Coble, D. W., Kramer, N. C., and Brown, T. McP. (1963). *J. Bacteriol.* **86,** 1145.
Fowler, R. C., Coble, D. W., Kramer, N. C., Pai, R. R., Serrano, B. A., and Brown, T. McP. (1967). *Ann. N. Y. Acad. Sci.* **143,** 641.
Freundt, E. A. (1952a). *Acta Pathol. Microbiol. Scand.* **31,** 508.
Freundt, E. A. (1952b). *Acta Pathol. Microbiol. Scand.* **31,** 561.
Freundt, E. A. (1958). "The Mycoplasmataceae," 147 pp. Munksgaard, Copenhagen.
Freundt, E. A. (1960). *Ann. N. Y. Acad. Sci.* **79,** 312.
Gourlay, R. N., and Thrower, K. J. (1968). *J. Gen. Microbiol.* **54,** 155.
Green, D. E., and Fleischer, S. (1963). *Biochim. Biophys. Acta* **70,** 554.
Green, D. E., and Perdue, J. F. (1966). *Proc. Nat. Acad. Sci. U.S.* **55,** 1295.
Green, D. E., Allmann, D. W., Bachmann, E., Baum, H., Kopaczyk, K., Korman, E. F., Lipton, S., MacLennan, D. H., McConnell, D. G., Perdue, J. F., Rieske, J. S., and Tzagoloff, A. (1967). *Arch. Biochem. Biophys.* **119,** 312.
Hall, R. H., Mittelman, A. Horoszewicz, J., and Grace, J. T., Jr. (1967). *Ann. N. Y. Acad. Sci.* **143,** 799.
Haller, G. J., and Lynn, R. J. (1969). *Bacteriol. Proc.* p. 33.
Hayashi, H., Fisher, H., and Söll, D. (1969). *Biochemistry* **8,** 3680.

Henrikson, C. V., and Panos, C. (1969). *Biochemistry* **8**, 646.
Henrikson, C. V., and Smith, P. F. (1964). *J. Gen. Microbiol.* **37**, 73.
Hummeler, K., Tomassini, N., and Hayflick, L. (1965). *J. Bacteriol.* **90**, 517.
Ikawa, M. (1963). *J. Bacteriol.* **85**, 772.
Jensen, S. L., and Weeks, O. B. (1966). *Nor. J. Chem. Mining Met.* **26**, 130.
Kahane, I., and Razin, S. (1969). *Biochim. Biophys. Acta* **183**, 79.
Kandler, O., and Kandler, G. (1954). *Arch. Mikrobiol.* **21**, 178.
Kandler, O., and Zehender, C. (1957). *Z. Naturforsch. B* **12**, 725.
Kandler, O., Zehender, C., and Müller, J. (1956a). *Arch. Mikrobiol.* **24**, 209.
Kandler, O., Zehender, C., and Müller, J. (1956b). *Arch. Mikrobiol.* **24**, 219.
Karrer, P., and Jucker, E. (1950). "Carotenoids." Elsevier, Amsterdam.
Keller, R., Smith, P. F., and Morton, H. E. (1952). *J. Gen. Microbiol.* **7**, 313.
Kelton, W. H., and Mandel, M. (1969). *J. Gen. Microbiol.* **56**, 131.
Klieneberger, E. (1934). *J. Pathol. Bacteriol.* **39**, 409.
Klieneberger-Nobel, E. (1962). "Pleuropneumonia-Like Organisms (PPLO) Myco-plasmataceae." 157 pp. Academic Press, New York.
Koostra, W. L., and Smith, P. F. (1969). *Biochemistry* **8**, 4794.
Langenfeld, M. G., and Smith, P. F. (1963). *J. Bacteriol.* **86**, 1216.
Lemcke, R. M., Shaw, E. J., and Marmion, B. P. (1965). *Aust. J. Exp. Biol. Med. Sci.* **43**, 761.
Lenard, J., and Singer, S. J. (1966). *Proc. Nat. Acad. Sci. U.S.* **56**, 1828.
Lind, K. (1968). *Acta Pathol. Microbiol. Scand.* **73**, 237.
Lynn, R. J., and Smith, P. F. (1957). *J. Bacteriol.* **74**, 811.
Lynn, R. J., and Smith, P. F. (1960). *Ann. N. Y. Acad. Sci.* **79**, 493.
McGee, Z. A., Rogul, M., and Wittler, R. G. (1967). *Ann. N. Y. Acad. Sci.* **143**, 21.
Manchee, R. J., and Taylor-Robinson, D. (1969). *J. Bacteriol.* **100**, 78.
Maniloff, J. (1969). *J. Bacteriol.* **100**, 1402.
Maniloff, J., Morowitz, H. J., and Barrnett, R. J. (1965a). *J. Cell. Biol.* **25**, 139.
Maniloff, J., Morowitz, J. H., and Barrnett, R. J. (1965b). *J. Bacteriol.* **90**, 193.
Marmion, B. P., Plackett, P. and Lemcke, R. M. (1967). *Aust. J. Exp. Biol. Med. Sci.* **45**, 163.
Morowitz, H. J. (1969). *In* "The Mycoplasmatales and the L-Phase of Bacteria" (L. Hayflick, ed.), pp. 405–412. Appleton, New York.
Morowitz, H. J., and Maniloff, J. (1966). *J. Bacteriol.* **91**, 1638.
Morowitz, H. J., Tourtellotte, M. E., Guild, W. R., Castro, E., and Woese, C. (1962). *J. Mol. Biol.* **4**, 93.
Morowitz, H. J., Tourtellotte, M. E., and Pollack, M. E. (1963). *J. Bacteriol.* **85**, 134.
Morowitz, H. J., Bode, H. R., and Kirk, R. G. (1967). *Ann. N. Y. Acad. Sci.* **143**, 110.
Morton, H. E., Lecce, J. G., Oskay, J. J., and Coy, N. H. (1954). *J. Bacteriol.* **68**, 697.
Munkres, M., and Wachtel, A. (1967). *J. Bacteriol.* **93**, 1096.
Naide, Y. (1963). *Jap. J. Microbiol.* **7**, 135.
Neimark, H. C. (1967). *Ann. N. Y. Acad. Sci.* **143**, 31.
Neimark, H. C., and Pene, J. J. (1965). *Proc. Soc. Exp. Biol. Med.* **118**, 517.
Nelson, J. B. (1950). *J. Exp. Med.* **91**, 309.
Nelson, J. B., and Lyons, M. J. (1965). *J. Bacteriol.* **90**, 1750.
Nocard, E., Roux, E. R., Borrel, M. M., Salimbeniet, and Dujardin-Beaumetz (1898). *Ann. Inst. Pasteur Paris* **12**, 240.
Panos, C., and Rottem, S. (1970). *Biochemistry* **9**, 407.
Partridge, S. M., and Klieneberger, E. (1941). *J. Pathol. Bacteriol.* **52**, 219.
Plackett, P. (1957). *Biochim. Biophys. Acta* **26**, 664.
Plackett, P. (1959). *Biochim. Biophys. Acta* **35**, 260.

Plackett, P. (1967). *Biochemistry* **6**, 2746.

Plackett, P., and Buttery, S. H. (1964). *Biochem. J.* **90**, 201.

Plackett, P., Buttery, S. H., and Cottew, G. S. (1963). *In* "Recent Progress in Microbiology," (N. E. Gibbons, ed.), pp. 535–547. Univ. of Toronto Press, Toronto.

Plackett, P., Marmion, B. P., Shaw, E. J., and Lemcke, R. M. (1969). *Aust. J. Exp. Biol. Med. Sci.* **47**, 171.

Pollack, J. D., Razin, S., Pollack, M. E., and Cleverdon, R. C. (1965a). *Life Sci.* **4**, 973.

Pollack, J. D., Razin, S., and Cleverdon, R. C. (1965b). *J. Bacteriol.* **90**, 617.

Prescott, B., Chernick, S. S., James, W., Caldes, G., and Chanock, R. M. (1969). *Bacteriol. Proc.* p. 94.

Razin, S. (1963). *J. Gen. Microbiol.* **33**, 471.

Razin, S. (1964). *J. Gen. Microbiol.* **36**, 451.

Razin, S. (1967). *Ann. N. Y. Acad. Sci.* **143**, 115.

Razin, S. (1968). *J. Bacteriol.* **96**, 687.

Razin, S., and Argaman, M. (1963). *J. Gen. Microbiol.* **30**, 155.

Razin, S., and Oliver, O. (1961). *J. Gen. Microbiol.* **24**, 225.

Razin, S., Argaman, M., and Avigan, J. (1963). *J. Gen. Microbiol.* **33**, 477.

Razin, S., Morowitz, H. J., and Terry, T. M. (1965). *Proc. Nat. Acad. Sci. U.S.* **54**, 219.

Razin, S., Cosenza, B. J., and Tourtellotte, M. E. (1966). *J. Gen. Microbiol.* **42**, 139.

Razin, S., Ne'eman, Z., and Ohad, I. (1969). *Biochim. Biophys. Acta* **193**, 277.

Robertson, J. D. (1958). *J. Biophys. Biochem. Cytol.* **4**, 349.

Rodwell, A. W. (1956). *Aust. J. Biol. Sci.* **9**, 105.

Rodwell, A. W. (1963). *J. Gen. Microbiol.* **32**, 91.

Rodwell, A. W. (1965). *J. Gen. Microbiol.* **40**, 227.

Rodwell, A. W. (1968). *Science* **160**, 1350.

Rodwell, A. W., and Abbot, A. (1961). *J. Gen. Microbiol.* **25**, 201.

Rodwell, A. W., Razin, S., Rottem, S., and Argaman, M. (1967). *Biochim. Biophys. Acta* **122**, 621.

Rothblat, G. H., and Smith, P. F. (1961). *J. Bacteriol.* **82**, 479.

Rottem, S., and Razin, S. (1967). *J. Bacteriol.* **94**, 359.

Rottem, S., Stein, O., and Razin, S. (1968). *Arch. Biochem. Biophys.* **125**, 46.

Ryan, J. L., and Morowitz, H. J. (1969). *Proc. Nat. Acad. Sci. U.S.* **63**, 1282.

Schwan, H. P., and Morowitz, H. J. (1962). *Biophys. J.* **2**, 395.

Shah, D. O., and Schulman, J. H. (1965). *J. Lipid Res.* **6**, 341.

Sharp, J. T. (1963). *J. Bacteriol.* **86**, 692.

Shaw, N., Smith, P. F., and Koostra, W. L. (1968). *Biochem. J.* **107**, 329.

Shepard, M. C. (1958). *J. Bacteriol.* **75**, 351.

Shepard, M. C. (1960). *Ann. N. Y. Acad. Sci.* **79**, 397.

Shifrine, M., Pangborn, J., and Adler, H. E. (1962). *J. Bacteriol.* **83**, 187.

Smith, P. F. (1956). *Appl. Microbiol.* **4**, 254.

Smith, P. F. (1959). *J. Bacteriol.* **77**, 682.

Smith, P. F. (1962). *J. Bacteriol.* **84**, 534.

Smith, P. F. (1963a). *J. Gen. Microbiol.* **32**, 307.

Smith, P. F. (1963b). *In* "Recent Progress in Microbiology" (N. E. Gibbons, ed.), pp. 518–525. Univ. of Toronto Press, Toronto.

Smith, P. F. (1967a). *In* "A Microbial Enigma" (C. Panos, ed.), pp. 71–163. World Publ., Cleveland, Ohio.

Smith, P. F. (1967b). *Ann. N. Y. Acad. Sci.* **143**, 139.

Smith, P. F. (1968). *Adv. Lipid Res.* **6**, 69.

Smith, P. F. (1969a). *J. Bacteriol.* **99**, 480.

Smith, P. F. (1969b). *Bacteriol. Proc.* p. 121.

Smith, P. F. (1969c). *Lipids* **4,** 331.

Smith, P. F., and Boughton, J. E. (1960). *J. Bacteriol.* **80,** 851.

Smith, P. F., and Henrikson, C. V. (1965). *J. Lipid Res.* **6,** 106.

Smith, P. F., and Koostra, W. L. (1967). *J. Bacteriol.* **93,** 1853.

Smith, P. F., and Mayberry, W. R. (1968). *Biochemistry* **7,** 2706.

Smith, P. F., and Rothblat, G. H. (1960a). *Ann. N. Y. Acad. Sci.* **79,** 461.

Smith, P. F., and Rothblat, G. H. (1960b). *J. Bacteriol.* **80,** 842.

Smith, P. F., and Rothblat, G. H. (1962). *J. Bacteriol.* **83,** 500.

Smith, P. F., and Sasaki, S. (1958). *Appl. Microbiol.* **6,** 184.

Smith, P. F., and Smith, M. R. (1970). *J. Bacteriol.* **103,** 27.

Smith, P. F., Koostra, W. L., and Henrikson, C. V. (1965). *J. Bacteriol.* **90,** 282.

Smith, P. F., Koostra, W. L., and Mayberry, W. R. (1969). *J. Bacteriol.* **100,** 1166.

Smith, S. L., VanDemark, P. J., and Fabricant, J. (1963). *J. Bacteriol.* **86,** 893.

Somerson, N. L., James, W. D., Walls, B. E., and Chanock, R. M. (1967). *Ann. N. Y. Acad. Sci.* **143,** 384.

Somerson, N. L., Reich, P. R., Chanock, R. M., and Weissman, S. M. (1967). *Ann. N. Y. Acad. Sci.* **143,** 9.

Steim, J. M., Tourtellotte, M. E., Reinert, J. C., McElhaney, R. N., and Rader, R. L. (1969). *Proc. Nat. Acad. Sci. U.S.* **63,** 104.

Swift, H. F., and Brown, T. McP. (1939). *Proc. Third Int. Congr. Microbiol.* p. 183.

Taylor-Robinson, D., and Manchee, R. J. (1967). *Nature (London)* **215,** 404.

Thirkell, D., Strang, R. H. C., Chapman, J. R. (1967). *J. Gen. Microbiol.* **49,** 157.

Tully, J. G., and Razin, S. (1969). *J. Bacteriol.* **98,** 970.

VanDemark, P. J. (1969). *In* "The Mycoplasmatales and the L-Phase of Bacteria" (L. Hayflick, ed.), pp. 491–502. Appleton, New York.

VanDemark, P. J., and Smith, P. F. (1964). *J. Bacteriol.* **88,** 122.

VanDemark, P. J., and Smith, P. F. (1965). *J. Bacteriol.* **89,** 373.

Wallach, D. F. H., and Zahler, P. H. (1966). *Proc. Nat. Acad. Sci. U.S.* **56,** 1552.

Weibull, C., and Beckman, H. (1961). *J. Gen. Microbiol.* **24,** 379.

Weibull, C., and Lundin, B. M. (1962). *J. Bacteriol.* **84,** 513.

Weibull, C., and Lundin, B. M. (1963). *J. Bacteriol.* **85,** 440.

Welsh, K., Shaw, N., and Baddiley, J. (1968). *Biochem. J.* **107,** 313.

Williams, C. O., Wittler, R. G., and Burris, C. (1969). *J. Bacteriol.* **99,** 341.

Dynamics of Reproduction and Growth

A. ENERGY PRODUCTION

The mycoplasmas can be separated into two general classes, fermentative and nonfermentative, with respect to energy production. The fermentative class derives its carbon and energy by the dissimilation of hexoses. The nonfermentative class comprises a group capable of fatty acid oxidation, metabolism of short-chain carbon compounds, or amino acid degradation. This division is a broad generalization derived from the study of a limited number of species. No doubt wide variations exist within each class.

1. Carbohydrate Metabolism

Fermentative species usually produce acid from glucose, fructose, mannose, maltose, glycogen, and starch. Some species of avian origin are capable of fermentation of galactose and sucrose. No fermentation of lactose, pentoses, or polyols has been detected (P. F. Smith, 1964a). Utilization of maltose, glycogen, and starch implies the existence of hydrolytic or transglycosidation activities. Glucosidases have been demonstrated in *M. laidlawii* and *M. gallinarum* (fermentative species) but not in *M. arthritidis*, a nonfermentative species (Henrikson and Smith, 1964). The enzymes of *M. laidlawii*, strain B, and *M. gallinarum* are specific for β-glucosides while that of *M. laidlawii*, strain A appears specific for α-glucosides. The characteristics of the enzyme have been defined for *M. laidlawii*, strain B, and include a pH optimum of 6.8, a temperature optimum of 30°C (the optimum temperature for growth), a specificity for β-glucosides, preference for an aryl group as the aglycon, and absolute specificity for carbon atoms 4 and 5 of the glycon. Amygdalin inhibits competitively and the enzyme does not catalyze transglycosidation reactions. The glucosidases of all species examined are found exclusively in the cytoplasmic membrane.

The dissimilation of glucose has been examined in some detail for three species, *M. mycoides* (Rodwell, 1960, 1967; Rodwell and Rodwell, 1953, 1954a,b,c), *M. gallisepticum* (Tourtellotte, 1960), and *M. laidlawii* (Castrejon-Diez *et al.*, 1963). Glycolysis has been demonstrated in *M. mycoides*. Glucose enters the pathway by phosphorylation with hexokinase, and mannose and fructose by their phosphorylated intermediates. Glucose 6-phosphate, fructose 6-phosphate, and fructose 1,6-diphosphate are oxidized but 6-phosphogluconate is not. Aldolase was demonstrated directly. Glycerol is not attacked anaerobically and catalase is required to maintain its oxidation aerobically. It probably is phosphorylated to *sn*-glycerol 3-phosphate and then oxidized by a flavoprotein to triose phosphate. No nicotinamide adenine dinucleotide (NAD) dependant glycerolphosphate dehydrogenase can be demonstrated. The absence of a reversible reaction for the oxidation of glycerol phosphate is used to explain the nutritional requirement for glycerol which is necessary for synthesis of phospholipids and glycolipids. Iodoacetate inhibits glucose fermentation suggesting the necessity for sulfhydryl-containing enzymes, possibly an NAD-dependant triosephosphate dehydrogenase. The inhibitory effect of fluoride indicates the presence of enolase. Pyruvate is reduced to lactate by an NAD-requiring dehydrogenase. Anaerobically pyruvate undergoes dismutation to lactate and acetate. Aerobically it is oxidized by the pyruvate oxidase system which requires inorganic phosphate, coenzyme A, α-lipoic acid, NAD, and cocarboxylase.

Glucose is not attacked anaerobically by intact cells of *M. mycoides* even though an NAD-linked lactic dehydrogenase is present. Rodwell postulated that pyruvate is removed preferentially by the pyruvate oxidase system and that the organism possesses no other anaerobic mechanism for the reoxidation of $NADH_2$ formed by the oxidation of triose phosphate. Therefore $NADH_2$ accumulates upon depletion of pyruvate. Evidence favoring this hypothesis includes (*1*) rapid fermentation of glucose in the presence of arsenite, an inhibitor of the pyruvate oxidase system, (*2*) production of a synergistic effect on glucose fermentation by exogenous pyruvate, and (*3*) ready attack of glucose by broken cells when coupled with a system for NAD regeneration, such as yeast alcohol dehydrogenase plus acetaldehyde. Low concentrations of certain amino acids, e.g., serine, threonine, or cystine, have the same effect as higher concentrations of pyruvate and are presumed to provide an additional source of α-ketoacid for NAD regeneration. Lower concentrations are effective since amino acids are metabolized much slower than glucose. A high salt concentration (0.1 M) is necessary. The function of the monovalent salt is not defined but cations might be required to exchange with H^+ to maintain intracellular pH.

The aerobic phosphogluconate pathway is absent as judged by the inability of $M.$ $mycoides$ to oxidize 6-phosphogluconate and the nondetectability of transaldolase and transketolase. Neither intact nor broken cells are capable of oxidation of di- and tricarboxylic acids, indicating the absence of a di- or tricarboxylic acid cycle. $Mycoplasma$ $pneumoniae$ appears to carry out glucose fermentation similar to $M.$ $mycoides$ (Low and Eaton, 1965).

Broken cells of $M.$ $gallisepticum$ reduce triphenyltetrazolium in the presence of the following substrates: glucose, pyruvate, lactate, hexose diphosphate, glucose 1-phosphate, glucose 6-phosphate, fructose 6-phosphate, ribose 5-phosphate, phosphoglyceric acid, glycerol, fructose, mannose, mannose 6-phosphate, and ribose. The soluble fraction of the organisms contains kinases for the phosphorylation of fructose, glucose 1-phosphate, glucose 6-phosphate, and fructose 6-phosphate. The particulate fraction phosphorylates glucose, mannose, and ribose. Specific demonstration has been made of phosphofructokinase, aldolase, and nicotinamide adenine dinucleotide phosphate (NADP) linked glucose-6-phosphate dehydrogenase, a pyridine nucletoide-linked glyceraldehydephosphate dehydrogenase, and an NADP linked glycerolphosphate dehydrogenase. As in $M.$ $mycoides$ pyruvate is dismutated anaerobically and oxidized to acetate and carbon dioxide aerobically with the requirements for coenzyme. A, α-lipoic acid, and cocarboxylase. Small amounts of acetylmethylcarbinol also are formed by the active aldehyde pathway found in yeast but not by the bacterial pathway involving α-acetolactate. Inhibitor studies confirmed the existence of the glycolytic pathway in this species. (Tourtellotte, 1960).

$Mycoplasma$ $gallinarum$, strain J does not produce acid from glucose although it utilizes this hexose for carbon and energy. Detailed studies on glucose dissimilation have not been performed. This organism contains a phosphoglucomutase, glucose-6-phosphate dehydrogenase, hexokinase, phosphohexose isomerase, and pyruvate decarboxylase (P. F. Smith, unpublished). Glycerolphosphate dehydrogenase is absent. The nature of the end products have not been established other than the considerable amounts of $^{14}CO_2$ evolved from ^{14}C-glucose.

$Mycoplasma$ $laidlawii$, strains A and B convert ^{14}C-glucose to CO_2, acetate, pyruvate, and lactate in both resting and growing states. Low recovery of CO_2 suggest its fixation (Castrejon-Diez et $al.$, 1963). Low specific activities of the end products relative to the glucose substrate are indicative of pooling or equilibration with endogenous pools. Kinases were demonstrated for glucose, to a lesser degree for galactose, but not for mannose or fructose. Glucosamine inhibits hexokinase but acetylglucosamine is neither an inhibitor nor a substrate. In addition to the kinases, triosephosphate dehydrogenase, aldolase and lactic dehydrogenase were demonstrated directly. Strain B yields CO_2 of higher specific activity from glucose-1-^{14}C than from glucose-6-^{14}C suggesting the presence of the hexose monophosphate pathway. Confirmation of this pathway was obtained by demonstration of the presence in the B strain but not in the A strain of an NADP-specific glucose-6-phosphate dehydrogenase, transketolase, and ribose-5-phosphate isomerase. Accumulation of heptose and fructose occurs when cell-free extracts are incubated with ribose 5-phosphate and ribulose 5-phosphate. The presence of ^{14}C in the acetate following fermentation of glucose indicates the existence of a dismutase or pyruvate decarboxylase.

Cursory examination of other fermentative species suggest the existence of the glycolytic pathway (Tourtellotte and Jacobs, 1960). The end products of glucose metabolism in growing cultures of a variety of species are predominantly lactate together with small amounts of pyruvate, acetate, and acetylmethylcarbinol. Resting cells oxidize glucose quantitatively to acetate and CO_2. Lactate is oxidized rapidly but acetate, α-ketoglutarate, succinate, malate, and oxalacetate only slowly. Citrate, acetaldehyde, and ethanol are not oxidized. Similar results were obtained by Neimark and Pickett (1960) and Gill (1962). These results indicate the presence of the Embden-Meyerhof pathway and the absence of the tricarboxylic acid cycle.

Nonfermentative species, in particular *M. arthritidis*, are capable of oxidizing various intermediates of the glycolytic and pentose phosphate pathways (Gewirtz and VanDemark, 1966). Cell free extracts were shown to possess fructose diphosphatase, phosphofructokinase, aldolase, pentose epimerase, pentose isomerase, transketolase, transaldolase, and NAD-linked glyceraldehyde-3-phosphate and lactate dehydrogenase activities. No hexokinase, glucose-6-phosphate or 6-phosphogluconate dehydrogenases were demonstrable. Carbohydrate metabolism in these organisms probably reflects synthetic rather than catabolic functions.

Acetokinase has been demonstrated by the hydroxamate reaction and by the transfer of phosphate from acetyl phosphate to ADP. Mg^{2+} or Mn^{2+} are required for activation. The enzyme is specific for acetate in *M. spumans*, *M. agalactiae*, *M. laidlawii*, and *M. gallisepticum* (Castrejon-Diez et al., 1962), but *M. gallinarum* can phosphorylate several short-chain fatty acids. Although Rodwell and Rodwell (1954b) were unable to demonstrate acetyl coenzyme A and acetyl phosphate as intermediates of pyruvate decarboxylation in *M. mycoides*, Rottem and Razin (1967) found acetokinase activity associated with the soluble fraction of this organism. *Mycoplasma laidlawii* and *M. gallinarum* also contain phosphotransacetylase (P. F. Smith and Henrikson, 1965a). Acetyl CoA synthetase occurs in *M. arthritidis* and *M. gallinarum* (VanDemark and Smith, 1965). In fermentative species these reactions presumably catalyze substrate level phosphorylation during pyruvate oxidation and activate acetate for synthesis. In the nonfermentative species these reactions probably are involved in activation of acetate for entry into the tricarboxylic acid cycle or for activation of fatty acids for β-oxidation.

The existence of the tricarboxylic acid and the glyoxylate cycles have been shown in *M. arthritidis*. Oxygen uptake occurs with isocitrate, α-ketoglutarate, succinate, fumarate, malate, acetate, and pyruvate (VanDemark and Smith, 1964b). Lack of oxygen uptake in the presence of citrate and glyoxylate is presumed to be due to either inhibition in the case of glyoxylate and impermeability or chelation of essential cations in the case of citrate. With the exception of malate synthetase and citrate-condensing enzyme, cell extracts were shown to contain all of the enzymes of the tricarboxylic acid and glyoxylate cycles, i.e., NADP-specific isocitric dehydrogenase, isocitratase, NAD-specific α-ketoglutaric dehydrogenase, succinic dehydrogenase, fumarase, NAD-specific malic dehydrogenase, acetyl CoA synthetase, and citratase. Isotope labeling indicate the probable existence of the malate synthetase and the citrate condensing enzyme. Incubation of acetate-2-^{14}C alone or in the presence of unlabeled glyoxylate, oxalacetate, or citrate resulted in appearance of radioactivity in these pools. The highest degree of labeling occurs in the dicarboxylic acids, malate, succinate, and fumarate, regardless of the presence or absence of an unlabeled pool. Thus the possibility exists that some other pathway, e.g., a dicarboxylic acid cycle, occurs in this organism.

2. Nitrogen Metabolism

Proteolysis as measured by liquefaction of inspissated serum or gelatin has been reported for *M. mycoides* (Freundt, 1958; Rodwell, 1960), *M. laidlawii* (Freundt, 1958), and certain strains from goats (Edward, 1950). Slight ammonia production is characteristic of many species (Freundt, 1958) and presumably arises from deamination of amino acids (P. F. Smith, 1955a, 1960a). Indole formation and nitrate reduction never have been found. Large amounts of ammonia are produced by the T strains as a result of the hydrolysis of urea (Shepard and Lunceford, 1967). Some species (*M. mycoides*, var. *capri* and *M. laidlawii*) produce small amounts of hydrogen sulfide.

Freeze–thaw preparations of *M. mycoides* depolymerize RNA with the liberation of adenosine 5′-phosphate indicative of a phosphodiesterase (Plackett, 1957). A ribonuclease also occurs in *M. laidlawii* that can degrade native or heat-denatured RNA, requires Mg^{2+} or Mn^{2+}, and has an alkaline pH optimum. The greatest nuclease activity occurs during the early logarithmic phase of growth (Razin *et al.*, 1964). Greater nuclease activity is found in broken than in intact cells, although both soluble and membrane fractions exhibit activity (Pollack *et al.*, 1965).

Deoxyribonuclease activity is widespread among mycoplasmas (Neimark, 1964; Razin *et al.*, 1964). However the activity with intact cells does not seem sufficient to interfere seriously with transformation experiments. The deoxyribonuclease of *M. laidlawii*, strain A can be found in the culture supernatant fluid, possesses a pH optimum between 7 and 8, is inhibited by RNA and requires Mg^{2+} or Mn^{2+} for activation. It appears similar to the endonucleases of *Streptococcus* and *E. coli*. The deoxyribonuclease is found in the soluble fraction of some species but not in others (Pollack *et al.*, 1965).

Adenosine triphosphatase is present in all species examined. It is membrane-associated, Mg^{2+}-dependant but not activated by Na^+ or K^+, and is insensitive to ouabain (Rottem and Razin, 1966).

The T strains of mycoplasmas possess a very active urease (Shepard and Lunceford, 1967). Its pH optimum is 6.0, the optimal pH for growth of these organisms. Hydroxyurea, allylurea, thiourea, arginine, ornithine, citrulline, proline, and glutamine do not serve as substrates. The function of the urease is unknown but the absolute requirement of urea for growth suggests that it must serve as a nitrogen source. It could not serve as a source of energy. Exposure to excess urea results in the production of enough ammonia to cause a lethal rise in pH which cannot be neutralized by the CO_2 released. The existence of urease in these strains may reflect an adaptation to the environment in which they normally occur, namely the genitourinary tract. Further studies of the metabolic character of these organisms would be enlightening.

Mycoplasma arthritidis utilizes a variety of amino acids including arginine, glutamine, glutamic acid, aspartic acid, histidine, leucine, and threonine under aerobic conditions and tyrosine and tryptophan under anaerobic conditions (P. F. Smith, 1955a; 1960a). This utilization was determined by measurement of disappearance of amino acids and of ammonia production. Only two of these appear related to the generation of energy, glutamine and arginine (Fig. 3.1). Glutamine at alkaline pH undergoes hydrolytic deamination but at acid pH it undergoes phosphorolysis with the formation of ATP, glutamic acid, and ammonia. The phosphorolysis reaction is reversible with the equilibrium favoring ATP formation (equilibrium

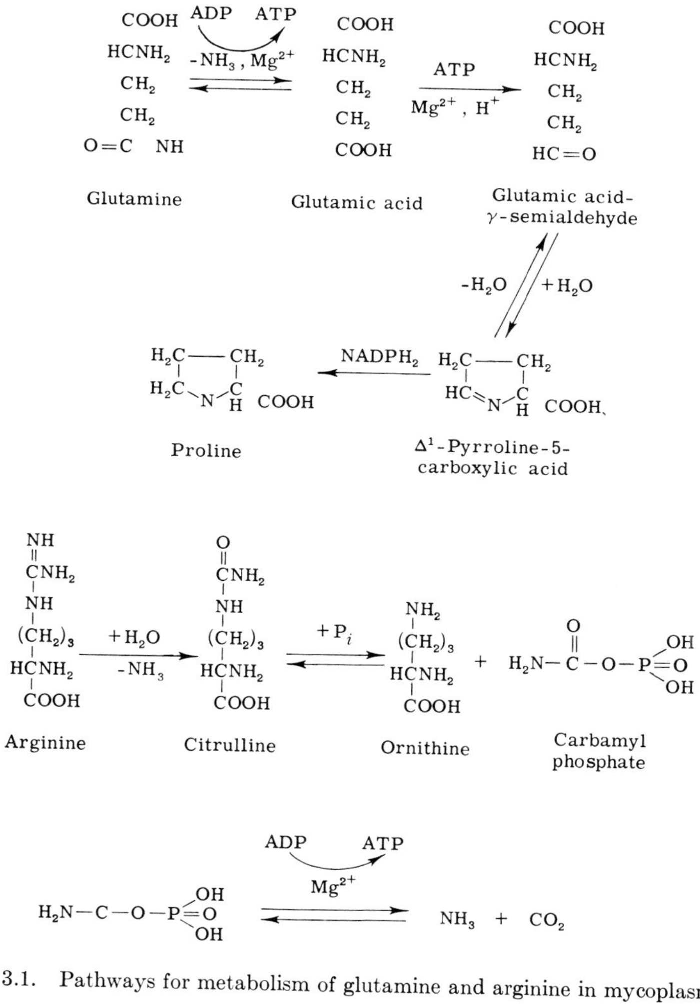

FIG. 3.1. Pathways for metabolism of glutamine and arginine in mycoplasmas.

constants: ATP formation, 4.0; glutamine synthesis, 0.02). Thus glutamine phosphorolysis could be a source of energy (P. F. Smith, 1957a). Further reactions involving glutamic acid appear concerned with synthesis. Arginine undergoes quantitative hydrolytic desimidation to citrulline (P. F. Smith, 1955a, 1957c, 1960a; Schimke and Barile, 1963; Barile *et al.*, 1966) mediated by arginine desimidase. Citrulline undergoes phosphorolysis by ornithine transcarbamylase to yield ornithine and carbamyl phosphate. Carbamyl

TABLE III.1

Properties of Arginine Desiminase, Ornithine Transcarbamylase and Carbamyl Kinase
from *M. arthritidis*[a]

Arginine desiminase
   Nine- to tenfold purification
   1600 units per mg protein[b]
   pH optimum, 6.5–6.7
   Km arginine, 1–4 × 10⁻⁴ *M*
   Reaction irreversible
   MW 78,300

Ornithine transcarbamylase
   25-fold purification
   6300 units per mg protein
   pH optimum, carbamyl phosphate formation, 7.3
   pH optimum, citrulline formation, 8.4
   Km citrulline, pH 7.3, 4–7 × 10⁻⁴ *M*
   Km ornithine, pH 8.4, 3.6 × 10⁻³ *M*
   MW 360,000

Carbamyl kinase
   25-fold purification
   73 units per mg protein
   pH optimum, both directions, 8.3–8.5
   Km ATP formation, pH 8.3, 1.4 × 10⁻³ *M*
   Km ADP formation, pH 8.3, 2.0 × 10⁻⁴ *M*
   Km carbamyl phosphate formation, pH 8.3, 2 × 10⁻⁵ *M*
   MW 61,000

---

[a] Data compiled from Schimke *et al.* (1966).
[b] One unit is amount of enzyme catalyzing formation of 1 μmole product per minute.

phosphate is cleaved by carbamate kinase in the presence of ADP with the formation of ammonia, CO_2, and ATP. Both the ornithine transcarbamylase and the carbamate kinase reactions are reversible. P. F. Smith (1957c) found the equilibrium constants of the combined reactions to favor citrulline synthesis (ATP formation, 0.5; citrulline synthesis, 500). Furthermore ornithine formation was dependant upon removal of ornithine, as a level of 12 μmoles almost completely inhibited the overall reaction. In *M. arthritidis* ornithine removal appeared too slow to obviate inhibition. Schimke (1966) arrived at the opposite conclusion. The amount of growth was dependant upon the concentration of exogenous arginine. Arginine desiminase and ornithine transcarbamylase constitute about 10% and 4%, respectively, of the total soluble protein of the organism. The three enzymes involved have been purified and their properties studied

(Table III.1). The differences in conclusions can be resolved by the apparent differences in the course of the reaction in growing versus resting cells. In growing cells there is a constant formation of ADP from ATP allowing for continuous utilization of carbamyl phosphate. Ornithine accumulation in growing cultures does not have the same inhibitory effect seen in resting cells. Km's for ornithine transcarbamylase and carbamyl kinase favor ATP synthesis. The properties of the three enzymes are similar to those found for streptococci.

Among species examined (Barile *et al.*, 1966) most of the nonfermentative organisms contain arginine desiminase activity while only one among the fermentative species (*M. fermentans*) contains it. *Mycoplasma canis* and *M. hyorhinis* among the nonfermentative species lack the activity.

Mycoplasma mycoides is capable of degrading serine and threonine by dehydrases with the formation of the corresponding α-ketoacids which are oxidized by the pyruvate oxidase system (Rodwell, 1960). However the rate of utilization is too low to be of consequence as an energy yielding mechanism in this glucose fermenting species.

3. Lipid Metabolism

No phospholipase activity has been demonstrated in mycoplasmas (P. F. Smith and Koostra, 1967). The phosphoglycerides do not turn over during growth or during metabolism of glucose (P. F. Smith, 1969a). The glucose and the phosphate of "phosphatidyl glucose" in *M. laidlawii* turn over during metabolism of glucose. This phospholipid labeled with ^{32}P during resting cell metabolism loses its radioactivity upon ensuing growth in complete culture medium. The nature of this breakdown has not been explored. If enzymic the enzyme is distinct from the usual phospholipase C.

A nonspecific lipase capable of hydrolysis of triglycerides, natural fats, and simple fatty acid esters is found in mycoplasmas (P. F. Smith, 1959). It is distinct from the sterol esterase based upon its cellular location, its heat lability, and its lability to pretreatment at acid and alkaline pH. It is found in the soluble portion of the cell, has no requirement for inorganic ions, and has an alkaline pH optimum (Rottem and Razin, 1964).

Transacylation also appears to be nonexistent in mycoplasmas. A very active lysophospholipase has been found associated with the membranes of *M. laidlawii*, strain B. Its specificity for the position of fatty acid is not yet established. However lysophosphatidyl glycerol is hydrolyzed almost ten times the rate of lysophosphatidyl choline. The function of this enzyme probably is protective as mycoplasmal membranes are very sensitive to lytic agents (R. N. McElhaney, personal communication).

TABLE III.2

Effect of Sterol Structure on Esterase Activity of *M. arthritidis*[a]

Acetate of	μmoles Free sterol formed/mg N/6 hr
Δ^5-Cholesten-3β-ol	0.91
Δ^5-Cholesten-3α-ol	0.04
Cholestan-3β-ol	0.64
Cholestan-3α-ol	0.44
Coprostan-3β-ol	0.53
Coprostan-3α-ol	0
β-Sitosterol	0.35
Stigmasterol	0.18

[a] Data compiled from P. F. Smith (1959, 1964b).

A membrane-associated sterol esterase is found in all species examined (P. F. Smith, 1959). This enzyme has been studied in some detail in *M. arthritidis*. It is capable of hydrolytic or thiolytic cleavage of steryl esters and carotenyl esters. The product of thiolytic cleavage appears to be an acyl coenzyme A based on the formation of hydroxylamine reactive products. The enzyme requires the micellar form of the ester formed in combination with some amphipathic lipid. It possesses little specificity toward different fatty acids but does have a specificity toward the sterol. (Table III.2). Esters of the cholestanols are more easily hydrolyzed than are those of the Δ^5-cholestenols, indicating that unsaturation in the B ring impedes the esterase (Smith, 1964b). With sterols containing cis-fused A/B rings, i.e., coprostanols, esters of the axial 3-hydroxyl group are more readily hydrolyzed than are those of the equatorial 3-hydroxyl group. No difference is noted in sterols with a trans-fused A/B ring, i.e., cholestanols. Increase in length of the side chain over that found in the cholestane and coprostane series retards esterase activity, e.g., sitosterols and stigmasterol. All trans, i.e., planar, carotenol esters are easily hydrolyzable by the esterase (P. F. Smith, unpublished). Argaman and Razin (1964) observed little incorporation of ^{14}C-cholesteryl oleate into the free cholesterol fraction of several species causing them to conclude that the esterase is absent. Detection of the ester is dependant upon age and metabolic state of the organisms since the fatty acid moiety turns over rapidly during active metabolism with little or no accumulation of ester (P. F. Smith, 1969a).

Nonfermentative species, in particular *M. arthritidis*, are able to oxidize short-chain fatty acids and derive a major portion of their energy by this mechanism. Fatty acids of chain length two through ten are oxidized, the rate decreasing with increase in chain length (Lynn, 1960). The mechanism

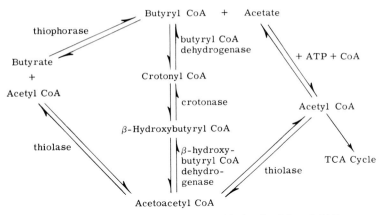

FIG. 3.2. Pathway for fatty acid oxidation by *M. arthritidis*.

of fatty acid oxidation follows the typical β-oxidative pathway. *Myco-plasma arthritidis* contains an acetyl coenzyme A synthetase which also exhibits some activity toward propionate (VanDemark and Smith, 1964b, 1965) but none with formate or other longer-chain fatty acids. Activation of fatty acids other than acetate or propionate occurs through the media-tion of a propionate coenzyme A transferase. Although the specificity of this enzyme is not known, the inability of the organism to oxidize fatty acids of chain length greater than ten suggests limited specificity. The other enzymes of the pathway have been demonstrated using butyrate as the initial substrate. These are an acyl coenzyme A dehydrogenase, croto-nase, an $NADH_2$ requiring β-hydroxyacyl coenzyme A dehydrogenase stimulated markedly by Mg^{2+} and β-ketothiolase. (Fig. 3.2). The acetyl coenzyme A is metabolized further via the tricarboxylic acid cycle.

B. BIOSYNTHESIS

1. Nucleic Acids and Their Precursors

All mycoplasmas require preformed nucleotides or purines and pyrimi-dines. These can be made available by the action of nucleases on RNA and DNA supplied in the culture medium. A few interconversions among the purines and pyrimidines have been shown to occur in *M. arthritidis*. Adenine is converted to hypoxanthine and cytidine to uridine (N. L. Somerson, unpublished). A nucleoside phosphorylase catalyzes the phos-phorolytic cleavage or arsenolysis of thymidine, deoxyinosine, deoxyadenosine, and deoxyguanosine but not of deoxycytidine with the liberation of the free base and phosphorylated deoxypentose. This enzyme can carry out the transfer of the deoxypentose moiety from thymidine to hypoxanthine and xanthine but not to adenine to form the corresponding purine deoxyribosides. Thymine cannot act as a deoxypentose acceptor with purine deoxyribosides as deoxypentose donors (Lynn, 1956). The biosynthetic pathway to pyrimidines is lacking in *M. arthritidis* and *M. orale* as judged by the inability of these organisms to incorporate ureido-^{14}C-citrulline into orotic acid (Woodson *et al.*, 1965). These findings are consistent with the nutritional requirements. The pyrimidine nucleosides are required but purine nucleosides are not. Interconversions occur unidirectionally from pyrimidine to purine nucleosides.

Nutritional studies with *M. laidlawii*, strain B (D. W. Smith and Hanawalt, 1968) suggest the existence of pathways for nucleoside synthesis similar to *E. coli*. In the presence of uridine neither cytosine nor deoxycytosine are required. As in *E. coli* deoxycytosine can serve as a precursor for uridine monophosphate (UMP) which is a direct precursor of all four pyrimidine triphosphates. Uracil is incorporated directly into RNA suggesting its direct conversion to UMP without the intermediate formation of the nucleoside. The requirement for one of the three nucleosides, uridine, cytosine, or deoxycytosine is indicative of the absence of the orotic acid pathway. *Mycoplasma laidlawii* probably can synthesize dUMP from these three nuclosides. Thymidine is not a precursor of UMP nor can thymine be converted to deoxythymidine monophosphate (dTMP). Therefore thymidylate synthetase probably is lacking. Purine synthesis apparently occurs although adenosine cannot be converted to guanosine monophosphate (GMP). Thymidine deprivation results in increase of cell mass but loss of viability. Inhibition of protein synthesis with chloramphenicol permits thymineless death to a survival level of less than 0.5% while inhibition of RNA synthesis results in 10% survival. Thus *M. laidlawii* undergoes thymineless death similar to *E. coli* and this phenomenon is coupled to RNA synthesis.

Analysis of DNA fragment by cesium chloride equilibrium sedimentation following density labeling for varying time periods by substituting 5-bromodeoxyuridine for thymidine gives results consistent with semiconservative replication (D. W. Smith, 1969). Replication proceeds unidirectionally from a limited number of growing points. The finding that some DNA is replicated twice before all of the DNA has replicated once is explained as being due to 5-bromouracil induced initiation of another round of replication. The 5-bromouracil would arise from the 5-bromodeoxyuridine supplied in the growth medium to produce hybrid (density labeled) DNA. The buoyant density distribution of intact chromosomes is more intermediate than in mildly sheared DNA and may be due to trapping of sheared DNA. Replication apparently occurs throughout the generation time as suggested by thymineless death and the appearance of whole chromosomes. The replication rate must be considerably slower than in bacteria because of the long generation time (4.5 to 5 hours) and the small size of the chromosome (about 800×10^6 daltons). In general it would appear that DNA replication in mycoplasmas has no real distinction from that found in other organisms.

Nothing is known about the biosynthesis of transfer RNA in myco-plasmas. Transfer RNA has been isolated from three species, *M. laidlawii*, strain B, *M. gallisepticum*, strain A5969, and *Mycoplasma* sp., strain Kid. The sedimentation coefficients approximate 5 S (Hayashi *et al.*, 1969) al-though Kirk (1966) found tRNA in *M. gallisepticum* of 2.5 S. Minor nu-cleosides occur but in much smaller quantity than in bacteria. For example, the Kid strain has less than one molecule of ribothymidine per 80 nucleotide residues. The hydrolysates of tRNA from *M. gallisepticum* and *M. laidlawii* possess cytokinin activity suggesting the presence of isopentenyl adenosine or its methylthio derivative. Isopentenyl adenosine has been shown to occur in *M. laidlawii* and to be derived from mevalonic acid (Smith and Smith, 1970). All three species examined contain *N*-formylmethionyl tRNA which is formed with formyltetrahydrofolate as formyl donor and with homologous formylating enzymes. The *N*-formylmethionyl tRNA and methionyl tRNA of *M. laidlawii* have been purified. Mycoplasmal tRNA's function in the cell-free synthesis of proteins with homologous or heter-ologous enzymes when directed by homologous messenger RNA (Tourtel-lott *et al.*, 1967), polyuridylic acid or f2 RNA (Hayashi *et al.*, 1969). *Mycoplasma laidlawii* tRNA also mediates the transfer of L-alanine to phos-phatidyl glycerol to form L-alanyl phosphatidyl glycerol (Koostra and Smith, 1969).

Formation of ribosomes also has not been studied. Their existence is known from electron micrographic examination and the appearance of large particulate RNA in sedimentation analyses. In *M. gallisepticum* ribosomes constitute about 80% of the total RNA (Kirk, 1966). Ribo-somes are required for cell-free protein synthesis. The fact that protein synthesis is sensitive to macrolide antibiotics which bind to 70 S ribosomes but not to cycloheximide which binds to 80 S ribosomes indicates the ex-istence of 70 S ribosomes in *M. laidlawii*. Ribosomes of *M. laidlawii* are similar to those of bacteria and blue-green algae but differ from those of yeasts, protozoans, plants, and animals (Tourtellotte *et al.*, 1967; Tourtel-lotte, 1969).

The existence of messenger RNA to the extent of about 5% of the total RNA is based primarily on the instability of this fraction (Kirk, 1966).

RNA synthesis inhibited by actinomycin D results in eventual cessation of protein synthesis consistent with turnover of mRNA (Tourtellotte, 1969). The half life of mRNA is approximately 4 minutes. The delayed inhibition of protein synthesis and the immediate cessation of incorporation of ^{14}C-uridine into RNA seen in several species is evidence for the existence of a DNA-dependant RNA polymerase responsible for transcription of the code from DNA.

2. Amino Acids and Proteins

Mycoplasmas as a group vary in their ability to synthesize amino acids. Most studies have been performed with *M. arthritidis* and *M. laidlawii*. *M. arthritidis* possesses weak transaminase activity principally forming alanine from pyruvate and glutamine (Smith, 1960a). *Mycoplasma gallisepticum* contains a glutamic–aspartic transaminase system favoring the formation of aspartic acid (Gill, 1962). No transamination has been detected in *M. mycoides* (Rodwell, 1960) or *M. laidlawii* (Razin and Cohen, 1963). Failure to demonstrate significant transaminase activities may reflect technical difficulties rather than absence of enzymes as many mycoplasmas exhibit a fair degree of competence for amino acid synthesis. No significant alanine racemase activity occurs in *M. laidlawii* and a murine strain (Plapp, 1963). The source of D-alanine for aminoacyl phosphatidyglycerol in *M. laidlawii*, strain B synthesis probably occurs by transamination of pyruvate with glutamic acid (Koostra and Smith, 1969). Aspartic acid is deaminated by *M. arthritidis* and serves as a precursor of homoserine and threonine (P. F. Smith, 1960a). Asparagine can be deaminated to give rise to aspartic acid and glutamine to glutamic acid. Lysine is formed by the decarboxylation of meso-α,ϵ-diaminopimelic acid. Synthesis of lysine in mycoplasmas does not involve the intermediate, α-aminoadipic acid. Glutamic acid is converted to proline via the intermediate formation of glutamic-γ-semialdehyde and Δ^1-pyrroline-5-carboxylic acid. Ornithine and citrulline are derived from the degradation of arginine. Glutamic acid does not serve as a precursor for ornithine (P. F. Smith, 1957a,b,c, 1960a, 1966).

Protein synthesis by mycoplasmas occurs by the classical mechanism. Amino acid activation is carried out by amino acid–specific tRNA synthetases in the presence of amino acid and ATP to form AMP–amino acid–tRNA synthetase complex and pyrophosphate. The amino acid then is transferred to amino acid–specific tRNA with the formation of aminoacyl tRNA and the liberation of AMP and free enzyme. Aminoacyl tRNA's have been demonstrated for valine, leucine, isoleucine, and phenylalanine in *M. laidlawii*, strain B, *M. gallisepticum*, and *M. hominis* (Tourtellotte *et al.*, 1967; Tourtellotte, 1969); for valine, methionine, and *N*-formyl-methionine in *M. laidlawii*, strain B, *M. gallisepticum*, and *Mycoplasma* sp., strain Kid (Hayashi *et al.*, 1969); for L-alanine in *M. laidlawii*, strain B (Koostra and Smith, 1969). Turnover of leucine in the presence of complete protein synthesizing system and saturation of its specific tRNA was demonstrated in *M. laidlawii* (Tourtellotte, 1969). The synthetases of mycoplasmas charge tRNA to a lesser extent than those of *E. coli* but can be stimulated to complete charging upon the addition of ammonium chloride. Potassium can substitute for ammonium ion. This stimulation is similar to the effect on yeast tRNA synthetases (Hayashi *et al.*, 1969).

Cell-free protein synthesis in *M. laidlawii* requires amino acid, ATP, an ATP generating system such as phosphoenolpyruvate and its kinase, ribosomes, and supernatant enzymes. Addition of the membrane fraction stimulated incorporation of ^{14}C-phenylalanine by 20-fold (Tourtellotte *et al.*, 1967). Cell-free protein synthesis is susceptible to ribonuclease and antibiotics which bind 70 S ribosomes, namely puromycin, chloramphenicol, and erythromycin. The inhibitory effects of these antibiotics occur on both total protein and membrane protein synthesis by intact cells. Ribonuclease has no effect on the intact cell system suggesting impermeability of cells to this enzyme. tRNA charged with phenylalanine is active in the formation of polyphenylalanine directed by polyuridine in the presence of the complete system (Hayashi *et al.*, 1969). ^{14}C-Phenylalanine is incorporated into membranes *in vitro* to the same extent as into cellular protein in intact cells. Overall protein synthesis requires activation of amino acids, formation of aminoacyl tRNA, synthesis of DNA-dependent messenger RNA, messenger RNA-directed amino acid incorporation and the presence of ribosomes.

3. Carbohydrates

Nutritional studies suggest that preformed ribose and deoxyribose are required by *M. arthritidis* and *M. laidlawii*. However these species possess the hexose monophosphate pathway and probably are capable of deriving pentoses from glucose. Glucose carbon is incorporated into the galactan of *M. mycoides* and into the glucan of the bovine arthritis strain as well as into the pentoses of the nucleic acids (Plackett, 1967b). Although the presence of similar linkages in the galactan and the glycolipid of *M. mycoides* suggested that the glycolipid might function as a membrane transport intermediate for extracellular synthesis of galactan, pulse labeling studies proved this not to be the case. Galactan synthesis proceeds under conditions in which very little turnover of galactolipid occurs. The possible roles of UDP hexoses and the C_{55} isoprenol which are involved in lipopolysaccharide and peptidoglycan synthesis by bacteria have not been examined.

4. Lipids

a. FATTY ACIDS

There exist two known types of mycoplasmas with respect to ability for fatty acid biosynthesis. One group is capable of the biosynthesis of only saturated fatty acids and is represented by *M. laidlawii*. This species can be differentiated further into that strain which requires an unsaturated fatty acid (strain A) and strain B, which is satisfied with saturated acids alone. Growth of strain B in the virtual absence of fatty acids results in the appearance of essentially no unsaturated acids. Myristic and palmitic acids (P. F. Smith and Henrikson, 1965b) or these two fatty acids together with lauric acid (Henrikson and Panos, 1969) comprise 90% of total fatty acids. ^{14}C-Acetate is incorporated only into the saturated fatty acids of both strains A and B (Pollack and Tourtellotte, 1967; Rottem and Razin, 1967). A second group of mycoplasmas is incapable of the biosynthesis of either saturated or unsaturated acids and includes *M. mycoides* and probably *M. arthritidis, M. gallinarum,* and *M. gallisepticum.*

A detailed study of saturated fatty acid biosynthesis and interconversions of unsaturated fatty acids has been performed by Panos and co-workers (Panos and Henrikson, 1969; Rottem and Panos, 1970; Panos and Rottem, 1970) using *M. laidlawii,* strains A and B. The malonyl CoA pathway occurs in *M. laidlawii,* strain A. A soluble fatty acid synthetase system incorporates ^{14}C-acetate into saturated fatty acids in the presence of malonyl CoA, $NADPH_2$, and Mg^{2+}. The products are mainly stearic, palmitic, and myristic acids although a trace of C_{20} acid is formed. Only palmitic and myristic acids are formed by intact cells. Omission of malonyl CoA results in almost complete cessation of synthesis. The inability to detect malonyl CoA synthesis has not been explained but is thought to be due to low acetyl CoA carboxylase activity. Acyl carrier protein and the fatty acid synthetase complex occur in largest amount in cells of the stationary phase. The synthetase system is inhibited by acyl carrier protein from *E. coli* and by free coenzyme A.

The octadecenoic acid requirement of *M. laidlawii,* strain A, is satisfied by oleic, *cis*-vaccenic, elaidic, *trans*-vaccenic or lactobacillic acids. The trans isomers are more effective in promoting growth. *cis*-Vaccenic is incorporated preferentially to lactobacillic acid. No isomerization is carried out by the organism as the incorporated fatty acid can be found unchanged in the membranes. When the organisms are supplied with β-hydroxydecanoic acid (the normal precursor at the biosynthetic step where branching of the pathway for formation of unsaturated fatty acids occurs in bacteria) together with the β-hydroxythioester dehydrase of *E. coli*, unsaturated fatty acids are synthesized. Therefore the requirement for unsaturated fatty acid in *M. laidlawii*, strain A is due to the absence of β-hydroxythioester dehydrase. *cis*-9-Hexadecenoic acid is the predominant product although a trace of *cis*-11-octadecenoic acid is formed. The shorter-chain monoenoic acids, *cis*-5-tetradecenoic and *cis*-9-hexadecenoic acids cannot replace octadecenoic acids but are incorporated. The former is elongated to *cis*-7-hexadecenoic acid. Efficiency of elongation increases as the position of the double bond is moved farther from the carboxyl group. *trans*-5-Tetradecenoic acid also is incorporated with some isomerization to its cis isomer and some elongation.

Growth of *M. laidlawii*, strain B in the presence of *cis*-5-tetradecenoic or *cis*-9-hexadecenoic acids, known precursors of octadecenoic positional isomers in bacteria, results in elongation. With the former acid a large increase of the *cis*-7-hexadecenoic isomer occurs with a small amount of oleic acid being formed presumably by elongation of the C_{16} isomer. Palmitoleic acid is elongated to an even greater extent to *cis*-vaccenic acid. The organisms preferentially incorporate *cis*-vaccenic when exposed to equimolar amounts of this acid and its positional isomer, oleic acid. Growth in the presence of *cis*-5-tetradecenoic, palmitoleic, or oleic plus *cis*-vaccenic acids depresses the synthesis of saturated fatty acids. 2-Hydroxydecanoic and 2-hydroxydodecanoic acids are incorporated but have no effect on the ratio of saturated to unsaturated acids. The latter compound apparently serves as a precursor of palmitic acid. Palmitelaidic acid is elongated to the homologous *trans*-vaccenic acid but to a much lesser extent than elongation of the opposite isomer, palmitoleic, to its homologous isomer, *cis*-vaccenic. Palmitelaidic also is incorporated intact into both glycolipids and phospholipids, but preferentially into phospholipids. Thus both strains A and B of *M. laidlawii* are capable of elongation but not the synthesis of unsaturated fatty acids. Strain A can elongate trans unsaturated acids to C_{16} unsaturated acids but is limited in the ability to elongate to C_{18} acids. Strain B generally can elongate only cis unsaturated acids (Panos and Henrikson, 1969) although some isolates may not be as specific (McElhaney and Tourtellotte, 1970a, b).

b. GLYCOLIPIDS

The total glycosyl diglycerides of *M. mycoides* (Plackett, 1967a) and of *M. laidlawii* (Shaw *et al.*, 1968) and the triacyl glucose of *M. gallinarum* (P. F. Smith and Mayberry, 1968) vary little with the age of the organisms. The ratio of monoglucosyl to diglucosyl diglyceride in *M. laidlawii* approximates unity during the logarithmic phase of growth, reaching a maximum of about two in the stationary phase (Shaw *et al.*, 1968). Short-term pulse labeling experiments during the metabolism of ^{14}C-glucose by resting cells show synthesis but not turnover of diglucosyl diglyceride (P. F. Smith, 1969a). Glucose serves as precursor of galactosyl diglycerides in *M mycoides*. Pulse labeling studies could not detect any turnover in washed suspensions although the radiolabeled galactan becomes diluted upon chase with unlabeled glucose (Plackett, 1967b). Radioactive glucose, glycerol, and palmitate are incorporated into the glycosyl diglycerides of *M. pneumoniae* (Plackett *et al.*, 1969).

The mechanism of biosynthesis of mono- and diglucosyl diglycerides has been established for *M. laidlawii*, strain B (P. F. Smith, 1969b). The monoglucosyl diglyceride is synthesized by a membrane-associated enzyme from 1,2-diglyceride and uridine 5′-diphosphoglucose. A preference for 1,2-diglyceride from the homologous organism was noted although other mixed 1,2-diglycerides were functional. Homogeneous diglycerides, such as 1,2-dipalmitin, cannot serve as glucose acceptors. 1,3-Diglycerides also are inactive. A medium of high ionic strength and sodium dodecyl sulfate stimulate synthesis. The diglucosyl diglyceride is formed by a membrane associated enzyme from monoglucosyl diglyceride and uridine 5′-diphosphoglucose. Monogalactosyl diglyceride cannot serve as glucose acceptor. Both reactions require Mg^{2+} and proceed optimally at pH 8. Solubilization of the membrane by various methods results in their inactivation. Both are dependant upon substrate concentrations. The rate of biosynthesis of the monoglucosyl diglyceride is tenfold greater than of the diglucosyl diglyceride consistent with the predominance of the former lipid in the organisms.

$$\text{Glucose} + \text{ATP} \xrightleftharpoons{\text{hexokinase}} \text{Glucose 6-phosphate}$$

$$\text{Glucose 6-phosphate} \xrightleftharpoons{\text{phospho-glucomutase}} \text{Glucose 1-phosphate}$$

$$\text{Glucose 1-phosphate} + \text{UTP} \xrightleftharpoons[\text{uridylyl-transferase}]{\text{UTP: }\alpha\text{-glucose 1-phosphate}} \text{UDP-Glucose} + \text{P—P}$$

$$\text{UDP-Glucose} + \text{1,2-Diglyceride} \xrightarrow{\alpha\text{-1-glucosyl transferase}} \text{Monoglucosyl diglyceride}$$

$$\text{UDP-Glucose} + \text{Monoglucosyl diglyceride} \xrightarrow{\alpha\text{-1-glucosyl transferase}} \text{Diglucosyl diglyceride}$$

FIG. 3.3. Pathway for biosynthesis of glucosyl diglycerides by *M. laidlawii*.

Uridine 5'-diphosphoglucose apparently is synthesized in the organisms by the usual pathway (Fig. 3.3) as glucose, ATP, and UTP or glucose 1-phosphate and UTP can substitute for uridine 5'-diphosphoglucose. Both reactions are specific for uridine 5'-diphosphoglucose. Neither uridine 5'-diphosphogalactose nor guanosine 5'-diphosphomannose can substitute for uridine 5'-diphosphoglucose. Nothing is known about the source or the biosynthesis of 1,2-diglycerides in this organism. They exist in negligible quantity.

c. PHOSPHOLIPIDS

Mycoplasmas are competent for the synthesis of all their phospholipids. Radiolabeling studies have shown the incorporation of glycerol and palmitate into the phosphatidyl glycerol and phosphatidyl monoglyceride of *M. pneumoniae* (Plackett *et al.*, 1969), of glycerol, palmitate, and oleate into diphosphatidyl glycerol and phosphatidyl glycerol of *M. mycoides* (Plackett, 1967a), of inorganic ^{32}P and oleic acid into the phosphatidyl glycerol of *M. laidlawii* (P. F. Smith, 1967, 1969a; P. F. Smith *et al.*, 1969), and inorganic ^{32}P, oleic acid, and glucose into "phosphatidyl glucose" of this organism.

Exogenous glycerol is required by the bovine arthritis strain Y for the biosynthesis of glycerolipids. Dihydroxyacetone phosphate is not reduced nor does the labeling pattern using 1-^{14}C-glycerol and 2-^{3}H-glycerol support the formation of an intermediate acyl dihydroxyacetone phosphate. However, glycerol carbon is diluted by glucose carbon. It has been postulated that glycerophosphate oxidase bound dihydroxyacetone phosphate from the triose phosphate pool equilibrates with that formed by glycerol oxidation. In this way the specific activity of the ^{14}C in the lipids becomes diluted with carbon from glucose while the ^{3}H remains constant (Plackett and Rodwell, 1970). A peculiar specificity for fatty acid incorporation occurs in this organism. When grown with a mixture of elaidic and behenic acids, elaidate is incorporated almost exclusively during early stages of growth and behenate at later stages. These results suggest a rapid turnover of diglycerides.

Little or no turnover of glycerophospholipids occurs during growth or metabolism. In *M. mycoides* (Plackett, 1967b) and *M. gallinarum* (P. F. Smith and Koostra, 1967) an increase in diphosphatidyl glycerol occurs during the stationary phase of growth concomitant with a reduction of phosphatidyl glycerol in the former organism and monoacyl glycerophosphoryl glycerophosphate in the latter. However, there is no good evidence to conclude that these lipids serve as precursors for diphosphatidyl glycerol. Turnover of both phosphate and glucose in "phosphatidyl glucose" occurs during growth and metabolism of *M. laidlawii*, strain B (P. F. Smith, 1967, 1969a). Formation of aminoacyl phosphatidyl glycerol occurs at the expense of phosphatidyl glycerol although total phosphatidyl glycerol does not vary (P. F. Smith and Koostra, 1969).

Two possible mechanisms for the biosynthesis of "phosphatidyl glucose" have been examined, i.e., cytidine diphosphodiglyceride + glucose and phosphatidic acid + uridine 5'-diphosphoglucose (P. F. Smith, 1969c). Little or no incorporation of glucose occurs when cytidine diphosphate diglyceride is present as glucose acceptor. The rate of formation of "phosphatidyl glucose" from cytidine diphosphodiglyceride is much slower than the rate with phosphatidic acid. The amount of lipid synthesized is not dependant upon the concentration of cytidine diphosphodiglyceride. Although CMP and CDP inhibit synthesis, CTP stimulates at low but inhibits at high levels. In the presence of phosphatidic acid and uridine 5'-diphosphoglucose, "phosphatidyl glucose" synthesis proceeds at a linear rate for 120 minutes and is dependant upon the concentration of substrates. The reaction requires phosphatidic acid, uridine 5'-diphosphoglucose, and Mg^{2+}. Optimal synthesis occurs at pH 8.5 and is stimulated by sodium dodecyl sulfate. Other nucleotide sugars, uridine 5'-diphosphogalactose and guanosine 5'-diphosphomannose, and nucleotide glucoses, adenosine 5'-diphosphoglucose, guanosine 5'-diphosphoglucose, cytidine 5'-diphosphoglucose, and *d*-thymidine 5'-diphospholgucose cannot serve as glucose donors. The enzymic activity is associated with the membrane. Although the evidence favors the participation of phosphatidic acid and uridine 5'-diphosphoglucose, definition of the specific pathway must await determination of the exact structure of the lipid. If its structure is glycerophosphoryl diglucosyl diglyceride, the effect of CTP may be due to a requirement for CDP glycerol as glycerophosphate donor.

L-Alanyl phosphatidyl glycerol is formed by the transfer of L-alanine from L-alanyl tRNA to phosphatidyl glycerol (Fig. 3.4) (Koostra and Smith, 1969). Synthesis has been demonstrated using L-alanine, ATP or an ATP generating system, tRNA, aminoacyl tRNA synthetase, Mg^{2+}, and phosphatidyl glycerol as well as from L-alanyl tRNA and phosphatidyl glycerol. The enzyme carrying out the terminal reaction is membrane associated while aminoacyl tRNA synthesis requires the whole cell lysate. The reaction is ribonuclease sensitive and occurs at a linear rate for about 50 minutes. Synthesis is stereospecific for the L-alanyl isomer. No competitive effect is seen with D-alanine. The product formed is solely the L isomer.

D-Alanyl phosphatidyl glycerol is formed by the transfer of D-alanine from the AMP–D-alanyl enzyme complex to phosphatidyl glycerol. Although this intermediate was not isolated its existence was proven by the demonstration of ATP-^{32}P exchange activity of sephadex column eluates.

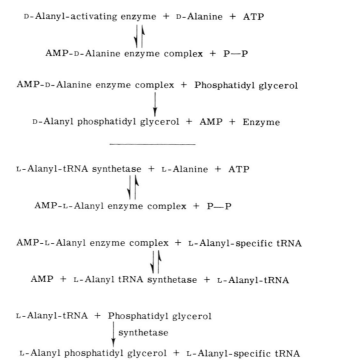

FIG. 3.4.   Pathways for biosynthesis of D- and L-alanyl phosphatidyl glycerols by
M. laidlawii.

Synthesis from D-alanine, ATP, and phosphatidyl glycerol requires whole
cell lysate and is ribonuclease insensitive. Synthesis is stereospecific for the
D-isomer and is independant of the synthesis of L-alanyl phosphatidyl
glycerol. The product maintains the specific isomeric configuration. In
contrast to the L isomer, synthesis of the D isomer continued for 30 minutes
followed by a rapid decline. Within the 30-minutes time period twice as
much D isomer was synthesized relative to the L isomer.

The mechanisms for the biosynthesis of phosphatidyl glycerol and diphosphatidyl glycerol have not been examined in mycoplasmas but are
presumed to be the same as the bacteria. Plackett and Rodwell (1970).
have presented evidence favoring the synthesis of phosphatidyl glycerol
from cytidine diphosphodiglyceride and *sn*-glycerol 3-phosphate. Likewise
no studies have been performed on the biosynthesis of the sphingophos-
pholipids of *Mycoplasma* sp., strain 743. Since the ^{14}C from labeled palmitate or myristate appears in the long-chain base, these appear to be direct

precursors of the dihydrosphingosine. Glycerol and inorganic ^{32}P are in-incorporated into these lipids during growth.

d. POLYTERPENES AND THEIR DERIVATIVES

Nutritional studies have indicated that sterol nonrequiring mycoplasmas are capable of *de novo* biosynthesis of polyterpenes, whereas sterol-requiring mycoplasmas are either totally deficient or possess specific enzymic blocks. The group of sterol nonrequiring mycoplasmas which contain sphingolipids have not been studied in this regard. It is conceivable that the large quantity of free long-chain base serves as a substitute for sterol or carotenoid pigments. Three species have been examined for enzymes in the pathway to polyterpenes, *M. laidlawii* B, *M. arthritidis* and *M. gallinarum. M. laidlawii*, a sterol nonrequiring species can incorporate ^{14}C-acetate and ^{14}C-mevalonic acid into its unsaponifiable lipids while the other two, representative of sterol-requiring species cannot (P. F. Smith and Rothblat, 1962). The pathway for biosynthesis of polyterpenes is shown in Fig. 3.5. A compilation of enzymic activities of the three organisms involved in the formation of γ,γ-dimethylallyl pyrophosphate from acetate is seen in

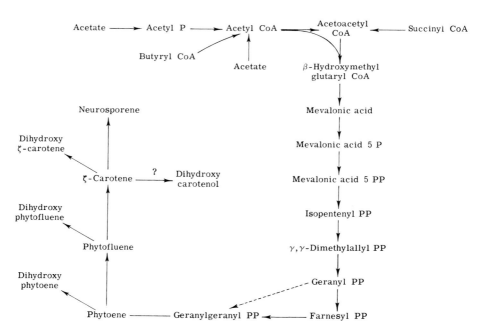

FIG. 3.5.   Pathway for biosynthesis of polyterpenes by mycoplasmas.

TABLE III.3

Enzymes of the Biosynthetic Pathway to Polyprenols in Mycoplasmas[a]

Enzyme	Reaction	M. laidlawii B	M. arthritidis 07	M. gallinarum J
Acetate kinase	Acetate → acetyl P	+	0	+
Phosphoacetyl transferase	Acetyl P → acetyl CoA	+	0	+
Acetyl CoA synthetase	Acetate → acetyl CoA	0	+	+
Propionate CoA transferase	Acetyl CoA → butyryl CoA	0	+	+
3-Ketoacid CoA transferase	Succinyl CoA → AcAcCoA	+	−	+
Acetoacetyl CoA thiolase	Acetyl CoA → AcAcCoA	+	+	+
Hydroxymethylglutaryl CoA synthase	AcCoA + AcAcCoA → HMGCoA	+	0	+
Hydroxymethylglutaryl CoA reductase	HMGCoA → MVA	+	0	+
Mevalonate kinase	MVA → MVAP	+	0	0
Phosphomevalonate kinase	MVAP → MVAPP	+	0	0
Pyrophosphomevalonate decarboxylase	MVAPP → IPP	+	0	0
Isopentenylpyrophosphate isomerase	IPP → DMAPP	+	0	+
	Dimethylallyl pyrophosphate → polyprenols	+	0	+

[a] Data compiled from Henrikson and P. F. Smith (1966a), P. F. Smith and Henrikson (1965a), VanDemark and Smith (1965) and P. F. Smith (1968).

Table III.3. All three organisms are capable of formation of acetyl CoA and acetoacetyl CoA by one or more mechanisms. *Mycoplasma laidlawii* possesses the full complement of enzymes for the synthesis of γ,γ-dimethylallyl pyrophosphate. *Mycoplasma arthritidis* is completely deficient beyond acetoacetyl CoA formation. *Mycoplasma gallinarum* lacks the three enzymes involved in the conversion of mevalonic acid to isopentenyl pyrophosphate. As judged from nutritional studies, *M. arthritidis* probably also is deficient in the enzymic steps from γ,γ-dimethylallyl pyrophosphate to polyterpenes although it may be capable of their hydroxylation. *Mycoplasma gallinarum* is sufficient in enzymes beyond the steps involving synthesis of isopentenyl pyrophosphate since this compound can replace the sterol requirement of this organism. Growth in the presence of isopentenyl pyrophosphate results in its conversion to polyterpenes and their hydroxylated derivatives (P. F. Smith, 1968). These polyterpenes give infrared and ultraviolet absorption spectra similar to colorless carotenoids. Total reduction of the hydrocarbon fraction yields a compound identical to lycopersane in gas–liquid chromatographs. Substitution of the sterol in the growth medium with all-trans carotenes with degrees of unsaturation not exceeding that of neurosporene (twelve double bonds, nine conjugated), e.g., phytoene, phytofluene, ζ-carotene, or neurosporene, leads to hydroxylation of these compounds. The position(s) of hydroxylation are not established but are presumed to be at the 3 and 3′ positions.

Studies on the inhibition of polyterpene biosynthesis in $M.$ $laidlawii$ have been revealing in regard to the possible function of sterols and carotenols in mycoplasmas. All evidence points to analogous functions for sterols and carotenols, the sterol requirement of some reflecting the inability to synthesize the necessary polyterpenes. Cholesterol spares the biosynthesis of carotenoid pigments in $M.$ $laidlawii$ (P. F. Smith, 1963). It has been inferred that no analogy exists and that $M.$ $laidlawii$ can function in the absence of both sterol and carotenol (Rottem and Razin, 1967; Razin and Rottem, 1967). This conclusion was derived from the findings that during growth in the absence of coenzyme A no ^{14}C from labeled acetate appears in neutral or polar lipid fractions and, secondly, growth occurs in the presence of propionate which impairs acetate transport with the resultant lack of incorporation of exogenous acetate into neutral lipids. Furthermore under these conditions no pigmentation was observed. These data are not incompatible with the postulated analogy between sterols and carotenols. In all cases the organisms were grown in the presence of glucose which is dissimilated to acetate. Impairment of transport by propionate or the assimilation of exogenous acetate by reduction of exogenous level of coenzyme A merely shifts the source of acetate for polyterpene biosynthesis from an exogenous supply to that arising from glucose metabolism. The absence of pigmentation probably reflects inhibition of oxidation of polyterpenes. Oxidation results in formation of conjugated double bonds, the basis for coloration. Colorless polyterpenes can be hydroxylated and function as well as the colored compounds. This has been shown with $M.$ $laidlawii$ grown in the presence of diphenylamine which inhibits the stepwise oxidation of C_{40} polyterpenes. In this situation hydroxylated compounds with the chromatographic and spectral characteristics of hydroxyphytoene, hydroxyphytofluene, and hydroxy-ζ-carotene are formed by $M.$ $laidlawii$ (P. F. Smith, unpublished). Although concentrations of diphenylamine which prevent oxidation of polyterpenes do not prevent growth of $M.$ $laidlawii$, inhibitors of reactions in the pathway to polyterpenes prior to the formation of phytoene do inhibit growth (P. F. Smith and Henrikson,

TABLE III.4

Nature of Unsaponifiable Lipids of *M. laidlawii*, strain B, Grown Under Conditions Inhibiting Carotenogenesis[a]

Addition to culture medium	Dry weight culture (μg/ml)	Cholesterol (μg/mg dry wt)	Pigment OD_{438}/mg dry wt
No addition	27.2 ± 0.36	0.003	0.013
Cholesterol (2.8×10^{-5} M)	37.8 ± 0.06	53.3 ± 1.3	0.010
Cholesterol (2.8×10^{-5} M) + phenethylbiguanide (10^{-3} M)	30.4 ± 1.14	70.9 ± 1.7	0.002

[a] Data compiled from P. F. Smith and Henrikson (1966).

1966). Examples of such inhibitors include farnesenic acid which inhibits the phosphorylation of mevalonic acid, β-diethylaminoethyldiphenylpropyl acetate hydrochloride and vanadium trichloride which inhibit the conversion of isopentenyl pyrophosphate to geranyl pyrophosphate and phenethylbiguanide which inhibits the further utilization of farnesyl pyrophosphate. These inhibitions can be overcome by supplying exogenous cholesterol in the culture medium. On the other hand, compounds such as chlorpropamide and tolbutamide, which prevent the cyclization of squalene, have no effect on growth of *M. laidlawii*. This is to be expected because cyclization of squalene is a reaction on the pathway to sterols which diverges from the pathway to carotenoids at the level of farnesyl or geranyl pyrophosphate. The reversal of inhibition by cholesterol is not due to detoxification but rather to the incorporation of sterol in lieu of the biosynthesis of carotenoids. Organisms grown under conditions in which carotenoid biosynthesis is blocked prior to phytoene formation contain cholesterol rather than carotenoid pigments (Table III.4).

The site of cholesterol inhibition of polyterpene biosynthesis has been established as isopentenyl pyrophosphate isomerase (P. F. Smith and Smith, 1970). This inhibition appears to be competitive and may be related to the structural similarity of the apolar termini of isopentenyl pyrophosphate [$-C=C(CH_3)_2$] and cholesterol [$-CH_2-CH(CH_3)_2$]. No accumulation of isopentenyl pyrophosphate or isopentenol occurs in organisms grown with cholesterol. The need of the organisms for isopentenyl adenosine obviates complete blockage of the isomerase.

Mycoplasmas make no changes in the basic structure of the sterol molecule or of the final product in the path to dihydroxy carotenes. The fermentative species are capable of the synthesis of the glucosides of these polyterpenols, and both fermentative and nonfermentative species can esterify fatty acids to the hydroxyl groups. Esterification requires the presence of coenzyme A and ATP and appears to be limited to short-chain fatty acids (P. F. Smith, 1959). This enzymic activity is associated with the membrane fraction. The principal fatty acid esters of the nonfermentative *M. arthritidis* are butyric, propionic, and acetic; of the fermentative *M. gallinarum* and *M. laidlawii* it is acetic acid.

Cholesteryl glucoside biosynthesis has been examined only superficially in *M. gallinarum* (P. F. Smith, unpublished) and in *M. laidlawii* (P. F. Smith, 1969a). The rapid appearance of label from ^{14}C-glucose and its equally rapid disappearance during pulse labeling experiments with *M. laidlawii* are indicative of rapid synthesis and hydrolysis. In *M. gallinarum*, strain J, ^{14}C-glucose from uridine 5'-diphosphoglucose is incorporated into cholesteryl glucoside by the membrane fraction. Uridine 5'-diphosphogalactose allows incorporation of about 10% of the radioactivity seen with uridine 5'-diphosphoglucose while no incorporation of mannose from guanosine 5'-diphosphomannose is seen. Other nucleotide glucoses are inactive. The Km of the reaction using uridine 5'-diphosphoglucose is 3.63×10^{-5} M, suggesting a reaction velocity compatible with glucose metabolism in this organism. Mg^{2+} is required and the pH optimum is 8.0. By dropping the pH to 6.8 during biosynthesis, loss of the formed cholesteryl glucoside can be observed. This loss is due to the degradation of the compound by a membrane-associated β-glucosidase. Only membrane-contained cholesterol functions in these reactions. Biosynthesis is inhibited by deoxycorticosterone and uranyl nitrate but not by N-ethylmaleimide, iodoacetic acid, 2,4-dinitrophenol, and various respiratory inhibitors. Both deoxycorticosterone and uranyl nitrate inhibit glucose transport in this organism.

C. NUTRITION

1. Chemical Requirements for Growth

a. PROTEINS, PEPTIDES, AND AMINO ACIDS

P. F. Smith and Morton (1951) isolated and partially characterized a protein from bovine serum which could replace the serum requirement of certain mycoplasmas. This protein retained its growth-promoting activity upon removal of lipids but was shown later to be inactive in a lipid-free basal medium. Refinement of fractionation procedures resulted in the recovery of an ultracentrifugally and electrophoretically pure protein with properties similar to α_1-lipoprotein of serum (P. F. Smith *et al.*, 1954). It possesses a sedimentation coefficient of 3.76 S, a molecular weight of about 200,000, and an electrophoretic mobility of 7.98 $\times$ 10 μ/sec/V/cm. Qualitative amino acid analysis demonstrated the presence of eight amino acids—tryptophan, leucine, valine, alanine, glutamic acid, glycine, arginine, and lysine—the latter two predominating (P. F. Smith and Morton, 1952). Associated with the protein were esterfied cholesterol and phospholipid. This protein supports optimal growth at a level of 0.5 to 1.0 mg/ml culture medium but can be replaced with larger quantities of fraction V bovine albumin (Edward and Fitzgerald, 1951; P. F. Smith, 1960b; P. F. Smith and Boughton, 1960) or β-lactoglobulin. These two proteins contain contaminating lipoprotein which accounts for their activities. Rodwell (1956) independantly isolated a similar protein from horse serum which satisfies part of the protein requirement of *M. mycoides*. This protein also contains cholesterol and phospholipid. However, *M. mycoides* requires lipid-free fraction V bovine albumin in addition to this protein.

Fraction V bovine albumin is considered to serve as a carrier for essential fatty acids, acting as a detoxifier by permitting restricted release of fatty acids at a rate of utilization by the organisms (Rodwell, 1960; Rodwell

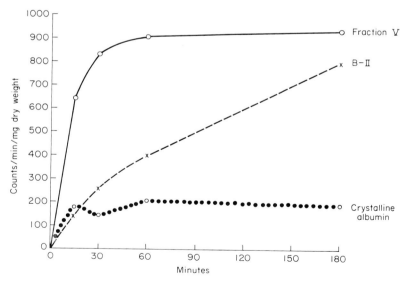

FIG. 3.6.   Effect of various proteins on incorporation of ^{14}C-sterol by *M. arthritidis*. Fraction V bovine serum albumin; lipoprotein factor from bovine serum (B-II); crystalline bovine serum albumin. Copyright by American Society for Microbiology. Figure 3, P. F. Smith and Boughton (1960).

and Abbot, 1961). The concentration of bovine serum albumin required increases with increasing fatty acid concentration. Too low levels of albumin results in cell lysis. Binding of fatty acids and growth promotion by albumin are destroyed by treatment with pronase (Rodwell, 1969c). Smith and Boughton found a correlation between the ability of a protein to support growth and its ability to regulate the incorporation of sterol into the organisms (Fig. 3.6). All proteins capable of supporting growth were also capable of neutralizing the lytic effect of surface-active agents, such as detergents, bile salts, and salts of long-chain fatty acids. Detoxification is not the sole explanation of the protein requirement in sterol-requiring species, since proteins incapable of supporting growth, e.g., crystalline serum albumin, also neutralize the lytic effects of surface-active agents. These proteins do not increase significantly the aqueous solubility of cholesterol. Nor do the organisms incorporate the protein as demonstrable by the absence of 2,4-dinitrobenzene in the cells after growth in the protein growth factor labeled with this compound. Destruction of sulfhydryl and hydroxyl groups on the protein results in diminution or complete loss of ability to support growth and marked diminution of sterol uptake by the organisms. The fraction C required by *M. mycoides* aids in dispersion of cholesterol and is insensitive to pronase. The best conclusion as to the function of this protein alone or combined with fraction V bovine albumin is the regulation of sterol and undoubtedly also fatty acid incorporation into the organisms. In addition it also serves to detoxify the nutritionally required fatty acids.

This requirement for protein by sterol requiring mycoplasmas can be obviated under specified conditions. Lund and Shorb (1966) succeeded in growing *M. gallinarum*, strain J, in medium defined except for peptones (trypticase and hycase) substituting for the serum a mixture of cholesterol and a diacetyl tartaric ester of tallow monoglycerides (TEM-4T). Kurzepa *et al.* (1969) demonstrated growth of several species (*M. arthritidis, M. salivarium, M. pneumoniae,* and unclassified bovine and swine strains) in a lipid-free basal medium to which was added a mixture of cholesterol, lecithin, and cardiolipin. Rodwell (1969a,b) has grown goat strain Y in the absence of protein or protein digests but with cholesterol and TEM-4T or diacetoxysuccinyl esters of monoolein and monopalmitin. Undoubtedly these lipids were presented to the organisms in a physical state absorbable by and nontoxic to the organisms.

Proteins have a stimulatory effect on the growth of sterol nonrequiring mycoplasmas, particularly those with fatty acid requirements and when small inocula are used. Crystalline serum albumin promotes the growth of *M. laidlawii,* strain A, which requires an unsaturated fatty acid (Razin and Knight, 1960). With these organisms the function of the protein simply is detoxification of the lytic action of fatty acids.

Peptides are required by *M. laidlawii*, strain Y from goats, and *M. gallinarum*, strain J (Tourtellotte *et al.*, 1964; Rodwell, 1967; Lund and Shorb, 1966). *M. laidlawii*, strain B, grown in the presence of peptides prepared from ^{14}C-algal protein and ^{14}C-amino acids, selectively incorporates glutamic and aspartic acids from the peptides but very little free glutamic and aspartic acids. (Tourtellotte, 1969). Asparagine and glutamine could replace the peptide requirement. Subsequently asparagine could be replaced with aspartic acid. Strain Y can grow with added protease digest of purified proteins including insulin. The intact B chain of insulin is fully active in growth promoting ability after digestion with chymotrypsin, pepsin, and rennin but not with trypsin (Rodwell, 1967). Based upon the specificity of these enzymes it was suggested that a carboxyl terminal alanine might be the key to the activity of peptides. However, the tetrapeptide, Thr-Pro-Lys-Ala, promoted rapid growth but the tripeptide, Ala-Ala-Ala, only slow growth similar to several other peptides with amino terminal alanine. No dipeptides, even those composed solely of alanine, could promote growth. Even in the presence of growth-promoting peptides, all free amino acids are required except aspartic and glutamic acids and cystine. However these could be derived from asparagine, glutamine, and cysteine, which are required.

Several functions have been postulated to explain the peptide requirements of mycoplasmas. These include (*1*) an assimilible source of required amino acid (Rodwell, 1967; Tourtellotte *et al.*, 1964), (*2*) neutralization of the toxicity of fatty acids, (*3*) the availability of preformed peptides, the amino acids of which cannot be encoded by mycoplasmas, and (*4*) initiation of peptide chain formation (Tourtellotte, 1969). Evidence favors the first two functions. Peptide chain initiation requires formyl methionine. Three mycoplasmal species have been shown capable of formylation of methionyl tRNA (Hayashi *et al.*, 1969). The requirement for all amino acids even in the presence of peptides probably rules out the third mentioned function. Furthermore, no correlation exists between the sequence of amino acids in the peptides and their ability to support growth. Even the function ascribing the need for an assimilible form of amino acid is unlikely, particularly in the case of *M. laidlawii*, since glutamine replaces the peptide requirement. The major function probably is that suggested by Tourtellotte (1969), i.e., neutralization of fatty acid toxicity or the need for a positively charged carrier of required fatty acids. In his series of experiments it was shown that in a defined medium containing glutamine, *M. laidlawii* grew only in the presence of added Tween 80, a source of

TABLE III.5

Defined Culture Media for Various Mycoplasmas

	Content mg/liter				
	M. arthritidis[a]	*Mycoplasma* sp., strain Y[b]	*M. laidlawii* strain A[c]	*M. laidlawii* strain B[d]	*M. gallinarum* strain J[e]
		Amino acids and proteins			
Alanine	–	–	200(DL)	725	200(DL)
Arginine	70	170	200	440	200
Asparagine	–	130	200	–	200
Aspartic acid	60	–	–	90	–
Cysteine	1	160	–	–	–
Cystine	–	–	30	30	30
Glutamine	100	300	100	1110	–
Glutamic acid	75	–	–	75	100
Glycine	–	150	100	240	100
Histidine	–	155	150	310	150
Isoleucine	40(DL)	130	600(DL)	480	600(DL)
Leucine	–	130	800(DL)	1010	800(DL)
Lysine	–	150	–	840	–
Methionine	15	150	200(DL)	325	200(DL)
Phenylalanine	50(DL)	150	400(DL)	–	400(DL)
Proline	–	120	–	1310	–
Serine	–	105	–	725	–
Threonine	–	120	400(DL)	460	400(DL)
Tryptophan	20(DL)	100	–	20	–
Tyrosine	–	90	50	–	50
Valine	–	115	–	725	–
L-Ala-ala-ala	–	50	–	–	–
Tryptic digest of casein	–	–	–	–	5000
Lipoprotein	500	–	–	–	–
Bovine serum albumin	–	–	10,000	–	–
		Nucleic acid derivatives			
Adenine	–	10	–	–	–
Guanine	0.3	10	–	–	–
Uracil	–	10	–	–	–
Thymine	–	5	–	–	–
Hypoxanthine	0.3	–	–	–	–
Adenosine	–	–	100	5	10
Guanosine	–	–	100	5	10
Uridine	–	–	–	5	–
Cytidine	–	–	100	5	10

TABLE III.5 continued

	Content mg/liter				
	M. arthritidis[a]	*Mycoplasma* sp., strain Y[b]	*M. laidlawii* strain A[c]	*M. laidlawii* strain B[d]	*M. gallinarum* strain J[e]
Thymidine	–	–	–	5	10
Deoxyadenosine	–	–	–	5	–
Deoxyguanosine	–	–	–	5	–
Deoxycytidine	–	–	–	5	–
ATP	1	–	–	–	–
RNA	5	–	–	–	–
DNA	5	–	–	–	–
Vitamins and coenzymes					
Biotin	–	–	–	0.01	0.01
Choline	0.5	–	–	–	16
Coenzyme A	–	1	–	1	–
Ca Pantothenate	0.01	–	–	–	–
Folic acid	0.01	–	–	–	–
Folinic acid	–	–	1	–	1
Inositol	–	–	–	–	6
α-Lipoic acid	–	0.2	–	–	0.5
Nicotinic acid	–	1	2.5	0.025	2.5
Pantetheine	–	–	–	–	0.5
Pyridoxal	–	–	2.5	–	2.5
Pyridoxine	0.05	–	2.5	0.025	2.5
Pyridoxamine P	–	–	–	–	0.5
Riboflavin	–	1	2.5	0.01	2.5
Thiamin	0.01	1	2.5	0.01	2.5
Cobalamin	–	–	–	–	0.01
Lipids and precursors					
Cholesterol	–	50	–	–	10
Cholesteryl laurate	10	–	–	–	–
Tween 80[f]	–	–	–	5	–
TEM-4T[g]	–	50	–	–	10
Oleic acid	–	–	5[h]	–	–
Lecithin	5	–	–	–	–
Carbohydrates					
Glucose	–	7200	7500	10,000	–
Maltose	–	–	–	–	5000
Glycerol	–	180	–	–	–
Sodium acetate	1000	–	–	50	–

TABLE III.5 continued

	Content mg/liter				
	M. arthritidis[a]	*Mycoplasma* sp., strain Y[b]	*M. laidlawii* strain A[c]	*M. laidlawii* strain B[d]	*M. gallinarum* strain J[e]
	Inorganic salts				
NaCl	6600	–	6800	8000	6800
Na_2HPO_4	–	18,100	100	120	100
NaH_2PO_4	140	1500	–	–	140
Tris(hydroxymethyl aminomethane)	–	–	6000	1000	6000
KCl	400	750	400	400	400
$MgCl_2 \cdot 7H_2O$	200	250	200	200	200
$Fe(NO_3)_3$	0.5	–	–	–	–
Spermine	–	35	–	–	–
$(NH_4)_2SO_4$	–	–	7000	120	120
Ash of Bacto peptone	from 0.5 g	–	–	–	–
$CaCl_2$	200	–	–	–	–

[a] P. F. Smith (1955b).
[b] Rodwell (1969a,b).
[c] Razin and Cohen (1963).
[d] Tourtellotte, Pollack and Parizek (unpublished).
[e] Lund and Shorb (1966).
[f] Polyoxyethylene sorbitan monoester of oleic acid.
[g] Diacetyl tartaric acid ester of tallow monoglyceride.
[h] Rottem and Panos (1970).

detoxified fatty acids, or in the presence of added free fatty acids plus peptides. No growth occurred in this medium with free fatty acids, peptides, or Tween 80 plus free fatty acids alone. The requirement for glutamine and the more favorable effect of asparagine relative to aspartic acid is considered to reflect and the necessity for the animated form of dicarboxylic amino acids for transport across the cytoplasmic membrane. The role of peptides in transport of amino acids in species other than *M. laidlawii* cannot be discounted.

The amino acid requirements have been defined for a few species (Table III.5). *M. laidlawii*, strain B, grows well in a medium containing 17 amino acids including glutamine (Tourtellotte, 1969). Aspartic acid obviates the requirement for asparagine, cystine the requirement for cysteine. Phenylalanine and tyrosine can replace alanine, but neither is required in the presence of alanine. Demonstration of the incorporation of ^{14}C-shikimic acid into phenylalanine suggests the existence of the shikimic pathway to aromatic amino acids in this organism. Strain Y from goats also requires 17 amino acids (Rodwell, 1969a,b). Glutamine and asparagine supply the requirements for aspartic and glutamic acids. In the presence of cysteine no cystine is required. Alanine is not required as the free amino acid but is supplied as the tripeptide of L-alanine. Neither of these organisms requires protein or protein hydrolysates in synthetic medium although strain Y has a requirement for cholesterol and fatty acids offered in the form of the diacetyl tartaric acid ester of tallow monoglyceride or diacetoxysuccinoyl esters of monoolein and monopalmitin. *Mycoplasma gallinarum*, strain J grows in a medium with thirteen amino acids together with tryptic digest of casein (Lund and Shorb, 1966). *Mycoplasma laidlawii*, strain A requires at least thirteen amino acids (Razin and Cohen, 1963) and *M. arthritidis* nine amino acids (P. F. Smith, 1955b), but in both instances dialyzed protein was added which conceivably could supply some of the amino acid requirements. Antagonisms or sparing activities of amino acids in mycoplasmas have not been studied in any systematic fashion. The D forms do not appear to have any inhibitory effect on the utilization of L-amino acids. Alterations in concentrations of several amino acids relative to others markedly reduces growth of strain Y (Rodwell, 1969a).

b. Nucleic Acids, Purines, and Pyrimidines

A requirement for DNA by several species of mycoplasmas for initial isolation was observed by Edward and Fitzgerald (1952a,b) but was lost upon continued cultivation on artificial culture media. Early attempts to devise defined media showed the requirement for DNA and RNA by *M. arthritidis* (P. F. Smith, 1955b) and *M. mycoides* (Razin and Knight, 1960). The nucleases of the organisms no doubt degrade these large molecules making available the individual nucleosides. In *M. mycoides* an excess of either nucleic acid inhibits growth probably by inhibiting the respective nucleases (Razin and Knight, 1960).

Further definition of the requirements for nucleic acid precursors by *M. arthritidis* (Lynn, 1956) showed that on solid medium growth occurred with the free bases, guanine, uracil, and cytosine, together with ribose and deoxyribose. Growth in a defined liquid medium required deoxyadenosine, deoxyguanosine, deoxycytidine, and thymidine only. However, only deoxycytidine and thymidine of the deoxyribosides were required if adenosine, guanosine, inosine, xanthosine, cytidine, and uridine were supplied. These requirements are compatible with the known biosynthetic activities of this organism. The existence of the pentose phosphate pathway in this organism (Gewirtz and VanDemark, 1966) indicates its ability to supply pentoses from the metabolism of hexoses. The minimal requirements of *M. laidlawii*, strain A (Razin, 1962) and probably *M. gallinarum*, strain J (Lund and Shorb, 1966) are adenosine, guanosine, and cytidine. In the absence of folinic acid thymidine also is required. Apparently adenine or one of the mononucleotide phosphates of adenine (2′, 3′, or 5′) can replace adenosine. The 2′ and 3′ mononucleotides of guanine and cytosine are inactive as are pyrimidine precursors, ureidosuccinic and orotic acids. Guanosine and cytidine can be replaced by their respective 5′ mononucleotides. *Mycoplasma laidlawii* grows continually but suboptimally in the presence of free bases together with ribose and deoxyribose. Optimal growth requires the nucleosides, thymidine, adenosine, cytidine, and guanosine (Tourtellotte *et al.*, 1964). *Mycoplasma mycoides*, strain V5 and goat strain Y have a minimum requirement for the free bases, adenine, guanine, uracil, and thymine. Cytosine and pentoses are not required. Neither guanine nor uracil can be replaced with hypoxanthine or orotic acid (Rodwell, 1967, 1969a).

D. W. Smith and Hanawalt (1968) demonstrated an absolute requirement by *M. laidlawii*, strain B for uridine and thymidine, a partial requirement for guanosine and deoxyguanosine, but no requirement for adenosine, deoxyadenosine, cytosine, and deoxycytosine. The latter two could partially satisfy the uridine requirement. Deprivation of thymidine but not the other growth requirements results in loss of viability, i.e., thymineless death.

Generally mycoplasmas are incapable of the biosynthesis of purines and pyrimidines and in some cases the nucleosides, but all are capable of DNA and RNA synthesis.

c. CARBOHYDRATES

Initially *M. arthritidis* was shown to require preformed pentoses for nucleic acid synthesis (Lynn, 1956). Later studies revealed that this and other nonfermentative species are capable of formation of pentoses from hexoses via portions of the pentose phosphate and glycolytic pathways (Gewirtz and VanDemark, 1966). No other carbohydrate appears essential for nonfermentative species.

Mycoplasma mycoides (Rodwell and Abbot, 1961) and *M. laidlawii*, strain A (Castrejon-Diez *et al.*, 1963) do not require pentoses, the pentose phosphate pathway having been demonstrated in the latter species. Those species requiring nucleosides could derive their pentose requirements from these compounds.

All fermentative mycoplasmas require hexoses as carbon and energy sources. Since energy yield is low as governed by the restrictions of glycolysis and the absence of a complete respiratory chain, large amounts of hexose are consumed. A small proportion is incorporated into glycolipids, polysaccharides, and nucleic acids. Avian species (Gill, 1962), *M. mycoides* (Rodwell and Abbot, 1961), *M. laidlawii* strains A and B (Razin and Cohen, 1963; Tourtellotte *et al.*, 1964) and *M. pneumoniae* (Low and Eaton, 1965) require glucose. Glucose can be replaced by maltose, less effectively by mannose or fructose, but not by galactose for *M. mycoides* (Rodwell, 1960). Likewise maltose can replace glucose for *M. laidlawii*, strain A, but mannose, fructose, galactose, sucrose and lactose are ineffective (Razin and Cohen, 1963). Maltose can replace glucose for *M. gallinarum*, strain J (Lund and Shorb, 1966).

Lactate, particularly the L isomer, in high concentrations stimulates the growth of *M. mycoides* (Rodwell, 1960). More is required under aerobic than microaerophilic conditions. The minimum concentration of the DL mixture giving a maximal effect is 0.03 M. Crude supplements are as effective as lactate in lower concentrations. The function of the lactate is not known. It does not serve as an energy source but may function to maintain the osmotic requirements of the medium, as a precursor for glycerol, or to maintain a satisfactory ratio of lactate to pyruvate or $NADH_2$ to NAD in the cell. Lactate spares the glycerol requirement in aerated cultures. Lactate inhibits growth of *M. laidlawii* for inapparent reasons (Razin and Knight, 1960).

Mycoplasma mycoides and caprine strains possess a requirement for glycerol. The bovine arthritis strain grows poorly without exogenous glycerol with eventual lysis of the cells. Glycerol is oxidized aerobically by this organism and is incorporated into glyco- and phospholipids. The requirement is greater in aerobic cultures (Rodwell, 1969a). Only a small fraction of the metabolized glycerol appears in cellular constituents (Plackett, 1961).

d. LIPIDS

Early studies with mycoplasmas distinguished two nutritional types, those requiring mammalian serum and called parasitic and those having no such requirement and called saprophytic. The necessary component of serum was shown to be the α_1-lipoprotein (P. F. Smith *et al.*, 1954). Although all three components of this lipoprotein—protein, phospholipid, and sterol—are necessary for growth (Edward and Fitzgerald, 1951; P. F. Smith *et al.*, 1954), only cholesterol is incorporated (P. F. Smith and Rothblat, 1960). As previously mentioned, the protein requirement can be dismissed under special circumstances. Edward and Fitzgerald (1951)

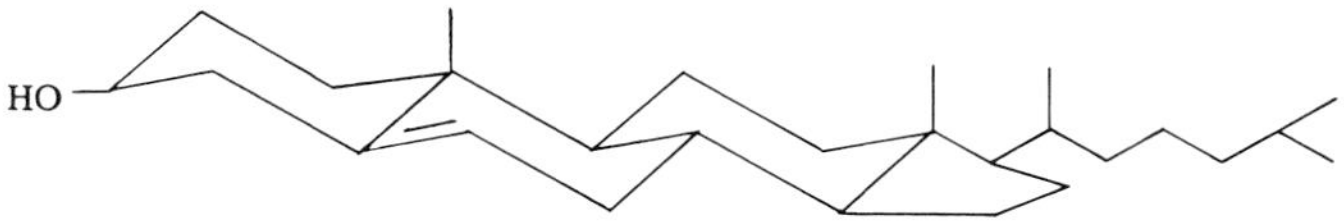

Cholesterol

Cholestanol

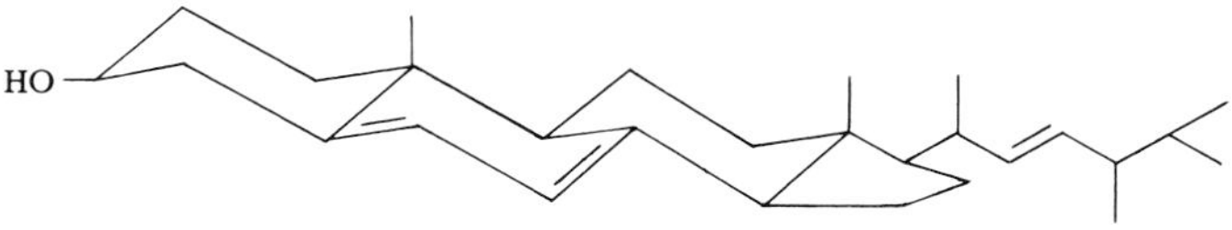

Ergosterol

FIG. 3.7.   Structures of planar sterols (cholesterol, cholestanol, ergosterol) and non-planar sterols (cholestan-3α-ol, coprostan-3β-ol, coprostan-3α-ol).

were able to replace the serum requirement with a lipid extract of egg yolk, partially by cholesterol, and completely by a combination of cholesterol and the acetone-insoluble lipids of egg yolk. The cephalin fraction of egg yolk lipids was as effective as the total acetone-insoluble lipid fraction but purified cephalin, lecithin, and sphingomyelin fractions were not. The cholesterol requirement could be satisfied with cholestanol or stigmasterol but not with ergosterol, coprostanol, cholesteryl esters or cholesteryl hydrogen phthalate. Using *M. arthritidis*, P. F. Smith *et al* (1954) could substitute cholesteryl laurate but not esters of longer-chain fatty acids for cholesterol. The cholesterol esterase in the organisms probably make available a supply of free cholesterol. *Mycoplasma mycoides* possesses a requirement for cholesterol (Rodwell, 1956) which is replaceable with cholestanol or lathosterol (Rodwell, 1963). In addition this species requires other serum lipids which can be replaced with Tween 80 or sodium oleate. Among all these sterol-requiring mycoplasmas there is an interrelationship between the levels of sterol and phospholipid or fatty acid (Edward and

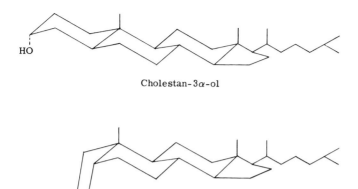

Cholestan-3α-ol

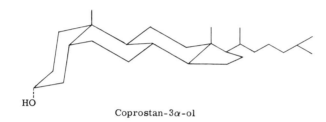

Coprostan-3β-ol

Coprostan-3α-ol

FIG. 3.7B

Freundt, 1956; Rodwell, 1963; P. F. Smith *et al.*, 1954). Usually twice as much sterol as phospholipid or fatty acid is required on a molar basis or growth inhibition occurs (P. F. Smith, 1960b). It is probable that sterol in this proportion is necessary to prevent the lytic action of the surface-active compounds since both protein and cholesterol counteract the lytic and growth inhibitory properties of this class of compounds (Rodwell and Abbot, 1961; P. F. Smith and Boughton, 1960; Rodwell, 1969c).

Studies on the incorporation of sterols by resting and growing cells (P. F. Smith, 1962, 1964b; P. F. Smith and Rothblat, 1960) and on the ability of sterols to support growth (P. F. Smith, 1964a; P. F. Smith and Lynn, 1958) in relation to their molecular configuration and conformation led to the conclusion that only planar sterols possessing an equatorial 3-hydroxyl group and an apolar side chain were satisfactory (Fig. 3.7). The inability of ergosterol to support growth as reported by Edward and Fitzgerald (1951) was probably due to contamination of this sterol with

TABLE III.6

Incorporation of Steroids by Mycoplasmas[a]

Steroid	Counts/min		
	0 min.	30 min.	180 min.
Δ⁵-Cholesten-3β-ol-4¹⁴C	5	17	93
Δ⁵-Cholesten-3α-ol-4¹⁴C	4	42	84
Cholestan-3β-ol-4¹⁴C	3	20	91
Cholestan-3α-ol-4¹⁴C	5	27	95
Coprostan-3β-ol-4¹⁴C	9	33	65
Coprostan-3α-ol-4¹⁴C	5	29	44
Progesterone-4¹⁴C	0	2	3
Testosterone-4¹⁴C	0	0	0

[a] Data compiled from P. F. Smith (1964b) and P. F. Smith and Rothblat (1960).

its oxidation products which are inhibitory. The apolar side is required for irreversible binding of the sterol in the membrane (Table III.6). Thus steroids such as progesterone and testosterone which lack this side chain are not incorporated, while sterols, ketosterols, and hydrocarbons of both cholestane and coprostane series are bound whether or not they support growth. No competition in uptake of any two sterols possessing identical side chains is observed due to lack of saturation of binding sites. Conversely, noncompetitive growth inhibition occurs in the presence of two equally incorporable sterols but with one incapable of supporting growth, e.g., cholesterol and coprostanol. The requirements for planarity and an equatorial 3-hydroxyl group in order for growth to occur (Table III.7) must be explained on some other terms than binding to the membrane. The probable functions of these structural requirements are discussed in Chapter IV, Section A,1.

Mycoplasmas not requiring sterol contain carotenoid pigments with the exception of one species which contains sphingolipids. Free sphingosine base in these organisms may function in lieu of sterol or carotenol. This fact together with the analogy between the biosynthetic pathways to sterols and carotenoids suggest that sterol requiring species might be incapable of polyterpenoid biosynthesis. This has been shown to be the case since precursors of polyterpenes are capable of replacing the sterol requirement (Henrikson and Smith, 1966b). Only carotenoid precursors are effective and then only for one of two species examined (Table III.7). None of the intermediates replace the sterol requirement of *M. arthritidis* while all

TABLE III.7

Compilation of Compounds Tested and Their Ability to Satisfy the Sterol
Growth Requirement

	Response[a]	
	M. arthritidis	*M. gallinarum*
Polyterpene precursors		
Acetate	0	0
Mevalonic acid	0	0
5-Phosphomevalonic acid	0	0
5-Pyrophosphomevalonic acid	0	0
Isopentenyl pyrophosphate	0	+
Geranyl pyrophosphate	0	0
Farnesyl pyrophosphate	0	0
Geranylgeranyl pyrophosphate	0	0
Squalene	0	0
Phytoene	±	+
Phytofluene	0	+
ζ-Carotene	0	+
Neurosporene	±	+
Lycopene	0	0
β-Carotene	0	0
Hydroxylated terpenes		
Geraniol	0	0
Farnesol	0	0
Nerolidol	0	0
Phytol	0	0
Geranylgeraniol	0	0
M. laidlawii carotenol	+	+
Lutein	+	+
Chloroxanthin	0	0
Sarcinaxanthin	+	+
Rubixanthin	0	±
Solanesol	0	±
Dolichol	0	0
Steroids		
Δ^5-Cholesten-3β-ol	+	+
Δ^5-Cholesten-3α-ol	0	ND
Cholestan-3β-ol	+	ND
Cholestan-3α-ol	0	ND
Coprostan-3β-ol	0	ND
Coprostan-3α-ol	0	ND
β-Sitosterol	+	ND
Ergosterol	+	ND

See footnote at end of table.

TABLE III.7 continued

	Response[a]	
	M. arthritidis	M. gallinarum
Stigmasterol	+	ND
Cholesteryl esters (propionate to laurate)	+	ND
Cholesteryl esters (myristate to linoleate)	0	ND
Cholestane	0	ND
Bicholesteryl ether	0	ND
Ketosteroids	0	ND
Bile acids	0	ND

[a] + = Positive growth response; ± = poor growth response; 0 = no growth; ND = not done.

precursors beyond 5-pyrophosphomevalonic acid except geranyl and far-nesyl pyrophosphates replace the sterol for *M. gallinarum*, strain J. The ineffectiveness of the latter two compounds probably is due to the impermeability of the mycoplasma to long-chain phosphorylated compounds.

The sterol requirement of *M. gallinarum* can be replaced by hydrocarbon carotenoids with unsaturation identical to neurosporene or other carotenoids occurring prior to neurosporene in the biosynthetic pathway. Evidence is available to suggest that these compounds can be hydroxylated without further unsaturation. Even *M. arthritidis* gives some response to phytoene and neurosporene suggesting its ability to hydroxylate these carotenoids. All-*trans*-3,3'-dihydroxycarotenes can replace sterol for both *M. arthritidis* and *M. gallinarum* (Table III.7). Other terpenols with only one hydroxyl group or with this group located on some carbon atom other than 3 and 3' are ineffective. Apparently the carotenols are incorporated without change. The carotenol of *M. laidlawii* is taken up by *M. gallinarum* and can be isolated in its original form. Some contamination with the cis isomer of this carotenol is seen but results undoubtedly from exposure to light during its isolation and during incubation of the *M. gallinarum* culture. These nutritional studies are corroborated by biosynthetic studies and suggest that the sterol requirement of some mycoplasmas reflects a deficiency in enzymic capacity to synthesize carotenoid pigments or similar polyterpenols. Thus the sterol requirement is fortuitous.

Incorporation of sterol or carotenol into mycoplasmas is dependant upon other components of the lipoprotein, i.e., protein and phospholipid (amphipathic compound). As already mentioned, the role of the protein moiety

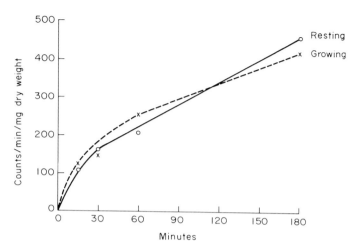

FIG. 3.8.   Uptake of ¹⁴C-cholesterol by resting and growing cells of *M. arthritidis*.
Copyright by American Society for Microbiology. From P. F. Smith and Rothblat
(1960).

is regulation of sterol incorporation. The uptake of sterol is an orderly
process which occurs in both resting and growing cells (Fig. 3.8) (Smith
and Rothblat, 1960). It follows a typical adsorption isotherm (Fig. 3.9).
Increases in time, temperature, and cell concentration result in increased
incorporation. Uptake continues to occur slowly even after 8 hours. The

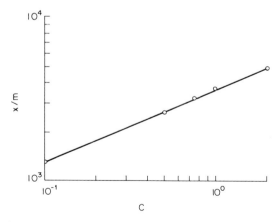

FIG. 3.9.   Adsorption isotherm for incorporation of cholesterol by mycoplasmas.
Copyright by American Society for Microbiology. From P. F. Smith and Rothblat
(1960).

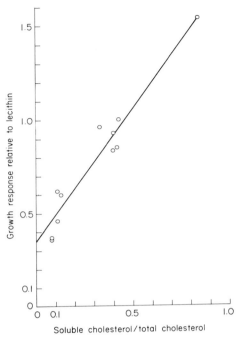

FIG. 3.10. Relation of growth response to amphipaths and their capacity to solubilize cholesterol in an aqueous medium. Copyright by American Society for Microbiology. Figure 6, P. F. Smith and Boughton (1960).

pH has no effect except at the isoelectric point of the organisms at which uptake is reduced. Heating or aging of the organisms, pretreatment of the organisms with protein end group reagents (e.g., 1-fluoro-2,4-dinitrobenzene, p-chloromercuribenzoate, and potassium periodate), respiratory inhibitors, and acetone extraction do not affect sterol incorporation. Extraction with ethanol–ether and growth in excess cholesterol reduce the amount of sterol incorporated, while chloroform–methanol extraction and pretreatment of the organisms with uranyl acetate abolish it. These results suggest that the sterol or carotenol is bound in the membrane by hydrophobic bonding between the apolar portions of the polyterpene and the phospholipid molecules.

The function of the phospholipid component of the lipoprotein is considered to be the aqueous solubilization of sterol or carotenol making it available to the organisms in an assimilible form. This requirement is nonspecific. Any amphipathic compound is functional as long as it is not so lytic as to be toxic to the organisms. Aqueous solubilization of sterol is the only property of these compounds (salts of long-chain fatty acids, bile salts, and positively charged phospholipids) which correlates with their ability to support growth (Fig. 3.10). Neither uptake (unless fatty acids are used as the amphipath) nor degradation of these compounds occur. The absence of incorporation of exogenously supplied phospholipids and the nonspecificity of their requirement is compatible with the conclusion that mycoplasmas synthesize their phospholipids *de novo*.

Growth of sterol nonrequiring mycoplasmas (*M. laidlawii*) has been shown to be stimulated by mammalian sera which is partially replaceable by cholesterol (Butler and Knight, 1960a). This effect probably reflects the protective action of serum for small inocula and the sparing of carotenoid synthesis. That the cholesterol requirement was replaceable with certain 3-ketosteroids reflects the probable detoxification function with this organism. Increasingly unsaturated analogs of these 3-ketosteroids and corticosteroids inhibited growth and exhibited competition with cholesterol. The inhibition of growth by steroids containing a hydrocarbon side chain can be explained by their incorporation into sites required for sterol or carotenol with subsequent interference with the function(s) of these compounds.

Mycoplasmas, to the extent that they have been studied, can be divided into three classes with respect to fatty acid requirements for growth. One class, represented by *M. mycoides*, requires both saturated and unsaturated fatty acids; another, represented by *M. laidlawii*, strain A requires only unsaturated fatty acid; a third, represented by *M. laidlawii*, strain B, requires neither.

Mycoplasma mycoides requirements are met with equimolar amounts of a saturated and an unsaturated fatty acid, e.g., palmitate or stearate and oleate (Rodwell and Abbot, 1961). The requirements of goat strain Y have been examined in detail (Rodwell, 1967, 1969b). As with *M. mycoides*, optimum growth requires the presence of both saturated and unsaturated fatty acids. Growth response was examined with pairs of saturated and unsaturated acids: monoenoic acids of the oleic series varying in chain length from C_{14} to C_{24}; straight-chain saturated acids varying in length from C_{10} to C_{20}. Although no definitive patterns were observed, the trend generally indicated that an increase in chain length of the unsaturated acid resulted in increasing effectiveness of saturated acids of progressively shorter chain length but not with those of longer chain length. A variety of unsaturated acids can fulfill this requirement. A shift in the position of the double bond toward the polar end of the molecule reduces the range of saturated acids permitting growth, while a shift in the other direction increases the range to include even the C_{12} saturated acid. Cis,trans isomerism had little effect as judged by the equal growth response to elaidate and *trans*-vaccenate with saturated acids ranging in chain length from C_{10} to C_{20}. Growth occurs after a lag phase in the presence of specific pairs of saturated acids, i.e., arachidate (C_{20}) and either laurate or myristate but not with any of these alone or with palmitate or stearate paired with shorter chain acids. Growth in the presence of a single fatty acid sometime is initiated but always is followed by lysis. However, good growth occurs with two acids supplied singly, elaidate and octadec-12-enoate. In the case of elaidate the total fatty acids of the organism were comprised of 97% elaidate (Rodwell, 1968). The fact that elaidate can be incorporated into either the 1 or 2 position of glycerol (Lands, 1965) may explain its ability to supply the total fatty acid requirement. Usually the 1 position is occupied by a saturated acid and the 2 position by an unsaturated, cyclopropane, or shorter-chain saturated fatty acid. Trace quantities of palmitate and stearate derived from the bovine albumin used as fatty acid carrier accounted for the remainder. When elaidate is supplied together with saturated acids varying in chain length from C_{10} to C_{20}, equimolar proportions of elaidate and the saturated acid are found in the lipids. Thus an interrelationship exists between unsaturated and saturated fatty acid requirements which is thought to be governed by their fit into the membrane.

The fatty acid requirement of *M. laidlawii*, strain A, can be met with oleic acid offered together with defatted bovine serum albumin or as Tween 80. Saturated acids have no stimulatory effect on growth (Razin and Rottem, 1963). Rottem and Panos (1969, 1970) in a detailed study found trans isomers of monoenoic acids to be more effective in promoting growth than cis isomers. Greater toxicity and poorer growth was noted with cyclopropane acids. Best growth was observed with elaidate (*trans*-9-octadecenoic), then oleic (*cis*-9-octadecenoic) followed by *cis*-vaccenic (*cis*-11-octadecenoic). Poor growth with ensuing lysis occurred with dihydrosterculic (*cis*-9,10-methylene octadecanoic) and lactobacillic acid (*cis*-11,12-methylene octadecanoic). The fatty acid requirement of this species, goat strain Y, and *M. gallinarium*, strain J, can be supplied by diacetyltartaric acid esters of tallow monoglyceride (Lund and Shorb, 1966) or diacetoxysuccinyl esters of monoolein and monopalmitin (Rodwell, 1969b). The fatty acid compostion of the former material consists of palmitic, stearic, oleic, and small amounts of palmitoleic and linoleic acids.

Mycoplasma laidlawii, strain B, when grown in a defined medium, grows optimally in the presence of five fatty acids, myristic, palmitic, oleic, linoleic, and linolenic (Tourtellotte *et al.*, 1964), although these can be replaced with acetate together with Tween 80 as a source of oleic acid. This species can grow in the absence of any fatty acid, save acetate, in a lipid-free but undefined peptone medium (Henrikson and Panos, 1969). The fatty acid composition of the organisms grown under this condition exhibits a fatty acid content of greater than 90% saturated acids comprised primarily of lauric, myristic, and palmitic. The unsaturated fatty acid content is negligible. There is some evidence for small quantities of branched methyl fatty acids. The defatted medium contained less than 0.003% fatty acid and the fatty acid composition of the organisms did not mimic the pattern of this residual fatty acid. Furthermore growth yields, growth rate, and cellular morphology of this strain were unchanged from those in a fatty acid-containing medium.

Fatty acids and other lipids or lipid precursors do have effects on the biological properties of other species. An adequate supply of all lipid precursors promotes growth of *M. mycoides* in the form of long branched filaments (Rodwell and Abbot, 1961). Deficiency of glycerol results in swelling of cells which undergo lysis upon further incubation with the formation of membranous ghosts. Deficiency of fatty acids, either saturated or unsaturated, causes the production of swollen branching or asteroid forms with eventual lysis. Cholesterol deficiency also leads to cell death and lysis but at a slower rate. Inhibition of cytoplasmic synthesis by uracil deprivation or by chloramphenicol prevents cellular death and lysis due to lipid deficiencies. It has been concluded that lipid deficiencies result in unbalanced growth of cytoplasmic and membranous constituents with the resultant loss of stability of the membrane. The goat strain Y (Rodwell, 1969a) and *M. laidlawii*, strain B (Razin *et al.*, 1966a) are affected by the nature of the fatty acids in the culture medium. Oleate appears to induce filamentous growth which is more resistant to osmotic lysis (Razin *et al.*, 1966b). This is in contradistinction to *M. pneumoniae* which is more susceptible to osmotic lysis when grown in the presence of added oleate (Pollack *et al.*, 1969a).

Acetate is required by *M. laidlawii* for biosynthesis of carotenoids (P. F. Smith and Rothblat, 1962; P. F. Smith and Henrikson, 1965a) and for saturated fatty acids (Pollack and Tourtellotte, 1967; Panos and Rottem, 1970). It can be supplied exogenously or be derived from hexose metabolism. Nonfermentative species derive energy from the oxidation of acetate (Lynn, 1960; VanDemark and Smith, 1964a,b).

e. VITAMINS AND COENZYMES

Mycoplasma laidlawii, strain A requires nicotinic acid, riboflavin, folinic acid, pyridoxine, and thiamin (Razin and Knight, 1960; Razin and Cohen, 1963). Nicotinamide, NAD, and NADP are less effective than nicotinic acid, but FAD, thiamin pyrophosphate, and pyridoxal or pyridoxal phosphate effectively substitute for the parent vitamins. There is no requirement for cobalamin, biotin, thioctic acid, or putresine. *Mycoplasma laid-*

lawii, strain B requires thiamin, pyridoxine, pyridoxal, nicotinic acid, nicotinamide, biotin, and coenzyme A (Tourtellotte *et al.*, 1964). The latter cannot be replaced by pantothenate and adenosine phosphates. *Mycoplasma arthritidis* requires biotin, folic acid, pantothenate, pyridoxine, and thiamin but not riboflavin or nicotinic acid (P. F. Smith, 1955b). *Mycoplasma gallinarum*, strain J requires biotin and other B vitamins as well as thioactic acid (Lund and Shorb, 1966, 1967). Pantetheine can substitute for coenzyme A but pantothenate cannot. The goat strain Y requires riboflavin, nicotinamide, and thiamin but not biotin, folinic acid, or cobalamin (Rodwell, 1969c). Pyridoxamine is required if free alanine rather than L-alanyl tripeptide is supplying the alanine requirement or if an alanine source is absent. Coenzyme A is essential and cannot be replaced by pantothenate or pantetheine. Omission of thioctic acid has no effect on growth but cells thus grown are deficient in pyruvate oxidase. This enzymic activity can be restored by addition of thioctic acid and coenzyme A to suspensions of deficient cells. Deficiency of coenzyme A or spermine results in lysis of this organism.

Many species of mycoplasmas appear to exhibit better growth if inositol and choline are present in the medium (P. F. Smith, 1955b; Rodwell and Abbot, 1961; Razin and Cohen, 1963). These probably are not used for lipid synthesis as no lecithins or inositides occur in these mycoplasmas.

f. INORGANIC REQUIREMENTS

No well-controlled studies of inorganic requirements have been performed. Sodium chloride is used to maintain the osmotic tonicity of the medium. Although potassium chloride is required, concentrations greater than 0.04 to 0.06 M are inhibitory (Gill, 1962; Leach, 1962; Razin and Cohen, 1963; Rodwell, 1967). Phosphate, usually as the sodium salt, is necessary but concentrations greater than 0.04 M inhibit *M. laidlawii* (Tourtellotte *et al.*, 1964). In addition to these salts, *M. laidlawii*, strain A gives optimal growth with added magnesium sulfate, manganous, cupric, and molybdenum ions (Razin and Cohen, 1963); *M. laidlawii*, strain B with magnesium sulfate and ammonium sulfate (Tourtellotte *et al.*, 1964); *M. arthritidis* with calcium chloride, magnesium sulfate, ferric nitrate, and ash of peptone (Difco). The latter can be replaced with stannous ions, but cadmium, cobalt, and zinc ions were poor substitutes (P. F. Smith, 1955b). *Mycoplasma gallinarum*, strain J also requires added magnesium sulfate and ammonium sulfate (Lund and Shorb, 1966). Goat strain Y requires magnesium, manganese, and ferrous sulfates (Rodwell and Abbot, 1961). In later studies (Rodwell, 1967) salts of manganese, zinc, cobalt, and ferrous iron were found to be growth inhibitory in concentrations ranging from 1 to 100 $\times$ 10^{-6} M. Spermine is necessary to prevent lysis of goat strain Y, $M.$ $mycoides$, and probably $M.$ $gallinarum.$ No such requirement has been found for $M.$ $laidlawii.$ Ion requirements and the inhibitory activity of some salts may reflect trace metal contamination. Therefore none of the ion requirements can be considered to be well defined.

g. GASEOUS REQUIREMENTS

Gaseous requirements ultimately reflect the respiratory physiology. Those species with a cytochrome-terminated respiratory pathway should grow better aerobically while those with a flavin-terminated pathway should prefer anaerobic or microaerophilic conditions, especially if peroxides are formed. Since studies on gaseous requirements have been performed with crude culture media, accurate assessment is not possible. Constituents of the culture medium have pronounced effects. For example, growth of $M.$ $arthritidis$ in suboptimal media is improved by increasing the level of carbon dioxide (Morton et $al.,$ 1951); glucose is not attacked by $M.$ $mycoides$ and other bovine strains under anaerobic conditions necessitating the presence of other carbon and energy sources (Rodwell, 1960); $M.$ $gallisepticum$ requires both glucose and pyruvate for anaerobic growth. (Gill, 1962). Growth of $M.$ $mycoides$, bovine arthritis strains, and goat strains under strongly aerobic conditions in defined medium requires addition of lactate, increase in concentration of glycerol, and reduction of the concentration of sodium phosphate to maintain the proper tonicity of the medium (Rodwell, 1969a). Most species grow equally well aerobically and under reduced oxygen tension on crude media. Species from rodents sometimes require added carbon dioxide (Warren, 1942). Yields of $M.$ $mycoides$ are increased by vigorous aeration (Newing and MacLeod, 1956; Rodwell and Rodwell, 1954a). $Mycoplasma$ $pneumoniae$ appears to be a strict aerobe (Low and Eaton, 1965). $Mycoplasma$ $salivarium$ requires anaerobic conditions for initial isolation but loses this requirement upon repeated transfer (Shklair et $al.,$ 1962). Added carbon dioxide is required for initial isolation of pathogenic species from avian and human sources (Fabricant, 1959; Ford, 1962) but no stimulation by this gas is seen with established species (Fabricant et $al.,$ 1962). Fixation of $^{14}CO_2$ appears to occur in some undefined way in $M.$ $arthritidis$ (P. F. Smith and Henrikson, 1965a).

2. Physical Requirements for Growth

a. TEMPERATURE

Early workers noted that species isolated from mammals grew best at temperatures near 37°C while $M.$ $laidlawii$ grew at 22°C and 37°C but best at 30°C. These generalizations were confirmed by Edward (1950). *Mycoplasma gallisepticum* reportedly grows better at 38°C and may be explained by its natural occurrence in fowl which have relatively high body temperatures. The T strains from the genitourinary tract of man multiply satisfactorily between 30°C and 36°C but 36°C is optimal (Ford, 1962). Low temperatures, although not permitting growth, are not deleterious.

b. pH Requirements

Most species grow optimally at pH between 7 and 8. However growth will occur over a broader range, i.e., pH 6.8 to 9.2 (Edward, 1950; Shepard and Lunceford, 1965; DaMassa and Adler, 1969). Fermentative species consume large amounts of hexose with the production of much acid necessitating good buffering of the medium. The amount of buffer that can be tolerated is limited because of the osmotic requirements of the organisms (Rodwell, 1969a). Tris (hydroxymethylaminomethane) can be substituted for a portion of the buffering phosphate in media for *M. laidlawii* (Tourtellotte *et al.*, 1964; Razin and Cohen, 1963). Such substitution is not possible with *M. mycoides* (Rodwell, 1969c). Some of the newer buffers have found good use in balancing tonicity against buffering capacity. *N*-Tris(hydroxymethyl)-2-aminoethane sulfonic acid and *N*-2-hydroxyethylpiperazine-*N'*-2-ethane sulfonic acid are most effective for *M. pneumoniae* (Pollack *et al.*, 1969b). Tris(hydroxymethyl)aminomethane, triethanolamine, and 3,6-endomethylene-1,2,3,6-tetrahydrophthalic acid buffers inhibit growth of this species.

An exception among the mycoplasmas are the T strains which require a pH less than 7 for optimal growth (Ford, 1962; Shepard and Lunceford, 1965). Best growth in either liquid or solid medium is at pH 6.0. Since alkaline pH is lethal to these organisms and they possess a very active urease, buffering is of great importance. The incorporation of *N*-2-hydroxyethylpiperazine-*N'*-2-ethanesulfonic acid into the medium permits better growth and survival than any other buffer tested (Manchee and Taylor-Robinson, 1969).

c. Osmotic Requirements

Leach (1962) in the only detailed study of the osmotic requirements for growth found the optimal osmotic pressure for a variety of species to lie between 6.8 and 14.0 atmospheres. Some species, e.g., *M. gallisepticum*, grow only within a narrow range, 6.8 to 14.0 atmospheres, while others, e.g., *M. laidlawii*, grow over a wide range, 2.7 to 27.0 atmospheres. An osmotic pressure of 41 atmospheres greatly retards growth of *M. mycoides*. Rodwell (1960) observed optimal growth of this species at 12 atmospheres. Tonicity of the medium can be maintained with acetate, various inorganic salts, such as sodium chloride and sodium phosphate, and even with sucrose. There is little adaptation by mycoplasmas to hypotonic and hypertonic environments. In general, resistance to hypotonic environment increases as the temperature is lowered and decreases as the temperature is elevated.

D. MODES OF REPRODUCTION

The reproductive mechanism of mycoplasmas is unresolved. Several mechanisms have been proposed which can be reduced to three: (*1*) filament formation followed by beading and disaggregation into coccoidal elements, (*2*) budding from multiple reproductive centers in an individual organism, and (*3*) binary fission. There is reliable evidence favoring all three mechanisms. The actual mechanism probably is a compromise of all three. Controversy stems no doubt from the facts that the organisms are plastic, differences in growth rates occur, there are species variations, there may be randomly occurring single or multiple developmental centers in a single cell, and nutritional conditions have a pronounced effect on morphology.

Reproduction by filament formation has been described by many including Freundt (1960). Growth is initiated in an elementary body which is 250 to 300 nm in diameter. One or more exceedingly thin, optically homogeneous filaments are extruded. These filaments terminate in a very small refractile, club shaped or spherical body of the same dimension as the elementary body. This terminal body functions as a growth center for development of forked branches of new filaments. Truly lateral branching also occurs. The result of this stage is an apparent single celled mycelium appearing in 12 to 18 hours. This mycelium then is transformed into a chain of closely set, regularly spaced, strongly refractile spherical bodies lying in a cylindrical mycelium. There are no apparent transverse septa at this stage. Soon constrictions appear with eventual development of a chain of separate coccoid elements. This division into coccoid elements may occur simultaneously or gradually. The process is repeated from the individual coccoid elementary bodies (Fig. 2.7). This mode of reproduction is typical of *M. mycoides*. It can be observed in some other species but most do not give rise to long filaments but rather to extrusions which resemble buds. True filaments, if present, are very transitory and unstable. Included among those species in which filaments have been observed are *M. hominis*, *M. fermentans*, *M. pharyngis*, and *M. laidlawii*.

The mechanism involving budding or round body formation has been proposed by Dienes who summarized his views in 1963. An elementary body or viable granule, spherical or elongated and 100 to 300 nm in diameter, multiplies by division or extrusion of a thin but very short filament or bud on the end of which a new granule develops. These forms may then develop with age into large, flat, round or polygonal forms, 0.3 to 1.0 μm in size. The so-called large bodies can be assumed to be aggregates of granules arising from multiple centers of growth from a single organism and fail to disaggregate until a change occurs in environmental conditions (Dienes, 1960) (Fig. 2.6). Other morphologists have observed this type of reproduction. Clark (1965) has described hexadic fission in some species which may depict a type of budding from six centers of growth in an individual cell. Morton *et al.* (1954) observed single and multiple budlike projections in electron micrographs of dividing mycoplasmas (Fig. 2.7). Observation of sequential changes occurring in *M. gallisepticum* were made by Morowitz and Maniloff (1966). The post division cell of this species consists of a teardrop-shaped body containing a structural bleb at one end. Cell division commences with the appearance of an infrableb region at the opposite end of the cell which develops into a new bleb. The cell then elongates and nuclear material segregates into two parts separated by a band of ribosomes. A constriction appears in this ribosomal region followed by the formation of two daughter cells (Fig. 3.11). This sequence has been confirmed by Bernstein-Ziv (1969) who also noted the appearance of polysomes during logarithmic growth but only ribosomes during the lag phase. Polysomes and ribosomes migrate to the region of protein synthesis upon initiation of cellular growth. In all phases of the growth cycle polysomes and ribosomes are located near the cell membrane. This situation can be described best as a type of binary fission. There is additional evidence for binary fission in other species. Small coccoid cells of *M. arthritidis*, strain 39 elongate but remain connected by a thin membrane-bounded tubule. Although the cells stick together, division is binary in character (Maniloff, 1969). Kelton (1952) successfully achieved synchronous growth of two species, *M. gallinarum*, strain J and *M. gallisepticum*, strain S6, by prestarvation for serum supplement. The former species showed clear doubling at approximately 1-hour intervals. The other species showed an 85% increase in population in the first step and diminishing increases in succeeding steps. Employing glass surface as an anchor, Bredt (1968) observed division of *M. pneumoniae* by phase contrast microscopy either as binary fission or cellular elongation followed by disruption into two daughter cells. After separation the new cells moved away by a gliding motion to begin another

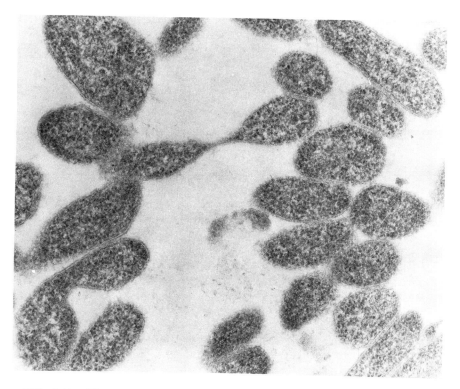

FIG. 3.11.   Electron micrograph of dividing *M. arthritidis*, strain 39. × 81,000.
Courtesy of J. Maniloff.

division. The gliding motion occurred only on the glass surface. Irregular
forms were observed to appear as a result of interaction of moving cells
with resting structures thereby simulating other modes of reproduction.
Furness and co-workers (Furness, 1968, 1969; Furness *et al.*, 1968a,b) have
analyzed the growth cycles of species derived from humans, *M. pneumoniae*,
M. orale, *M. arthritidis*, *M. pharyngis*, *M. salivarium*, and *M. fermentans*
by synchronous division and/or susceptibility to ultraviolet and x-irradiation. By use of light sonic treatment and filtration through millipore filters
single cell suspensions were obtained and confirmed by electron microscopy.
The rate of inactivation by irradiation is dependant upon the intensity of
radiations but independant of the concentration of the cells. Therefore
single-cell suspensions can be differentiated from aggregates by the exponential inactivation of singular colony forming units. Using this criterion,
M. arthritidis exists as single cells in the exponential phase of growth. *M.*

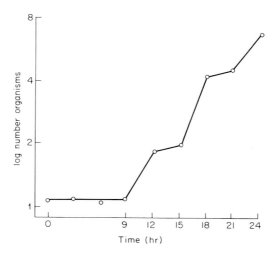

FIG. 3.12.   Synchronous division by *M. pneumoniae*. Courtesy of G. Furness. Copyright by Univ. Chicago Press. Adapted from Figure 1, Furness *et al.*, (1968b).

orale occurs as pairs of organisms, and *M. pneumoniae* as clusters of eight organisms. Other species occur as clusters of two of more single cells. All species appear to multiply by binary fission. Synchrony of single-cell suspensions was produced by prior chilling of the organisms. At least two cycles of doubling were observed with *M. orale* and *M. pneumoniae* (Fig. 3.12) before multiplication became random. Thus without doubt many mycoplasmal species can reproduce by binary fission. What remains is to explain budding and filament formation in terms compatible with a process similar to binary fission. This can be done but only on the basis of conjecture which probably will be unacceptable to all.

One must first exclude all those instances in which physical malformation of the organisms are produced either by manipulation, by aging, or by inadequate culture media. Secondly, the natural existence of filaments, budding forms, and round bodies cannot be denied since these have been observed by careful and experienced workers. Round bodies can be considered aggregates of individual cells which have been formed by binary fission but adhere to one another. Single bud formation can be viewed as binary fission in a situation where the plastic nature of the outer envelope allows inequality in size, shape, and the content of cytoplasmic constituents. Bud formation and short-filament formation can be considered different morphological manifestations of the plastic membrane which are dependant upon the nature of the fatty acids of the complex lipids or the presence or absence of sterol. Multiple short extrusions from a single cell may reflect organisms which have undergone several divisions without disaggregation. The size of the bud may be of no consequence. Long-filament formation is more difficult to rationalize. Two possibilities exist which can relate to binary fission. The initial formation of a long filament with a terminal bud may merely be cell elongation in its most radical extreme with each end containing nuclear material. Further extension from the new bud can be a repetition of the same process. The final appearance of chains of elementary bodies may be the result of continuing binary fission from either end. The filament then may consist of elementary bodies embedded in a matrix of polysaccharide which eventually is washed away leaving only the aggregated chains of coccoid elements. Needless to say additional studies of the filamentous forms need be done before they can be rationally included with those multiplying by binary fission. A second possibility is that tranverse septa formation is delayed because of the nature of the membrane or that these septa have not been observed for technical reasons. Molecular changes do occur during transformation of filaments into coccal forms. For example, there is an increase in diphosphatidyl glycerol as the cells mature. *Mycoplasma mycoides* grown with elaidate and behenate incorporates elaidate almost exclusively during exponential growth followed by behenate at late logarithmic phase or when filaments are transformed to coccal forms.

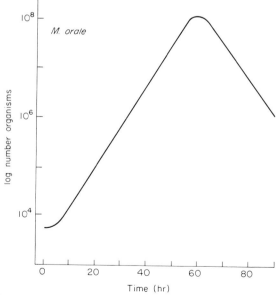

FIG. 3.13.   A typical growth curve during random division. Courtesy of G. Furness. Copyright by Univ. Chicago Press. Adapted from Figure 7, Furness (1968).

TABLE III.8

Generation Times of Mycoplasmas

Species	Mean generation time (hr)	Reference
M. arthritidis	3.3	Keller and Morton (1954)
M. arthritidis	1.7–2.4	Kelton (1960)
M. gallisepticum	0.8–1.0	Kelton (1960)
M. felis	1.0–1.5	Boatman and Kenny (1970)
M. pneumoniae	19 (est.)	Low and Eaton (1965)
M. pneumoniae	6	Furness et al. (1968b)
M. laidlawii	1.8	Kelton (1960)
T-strains	~1 (est.)	Ford (1962)
M. orale	3.3	Furness (1968)
Mycoplasma sp., goat strain Y	1.6–1.7	Rodwell (1969c)

Random multiplication of mycoplasmas leads to growth curves typical of bacteria (Fig. 3.13) (Kandler et al., 1956a,b; Keller and Morton, 1954; Kelton, 1960; Lecce and Morton, 1954; Low and Eaton, 1965; Lynn and Smith, 1958; Ford, 1962; Furness, 1968) The short stationary phase is notable and reflects the sensitivity of mycoplasmas to pH changes. Organisms harvested in this phase not only have decreased viability but also are enzymically inactive. Continuous cultivation has not been attempted. The generation times of a variety of species have been calculated (Table III.8). The variations probably are the result of inadequate nutrition rather than species differences.

E. CELL GROWTH

1. Measurement of Growth

Quantitation of growth by turbidimetry has been used frequently (Butler and Knight, 1960a; Keller and Morton, 1954; Rodwell, 1956; P. F. Smith, 1956; Tourtellotte, 1960). The sensitivity of this method is poor because of the small changes in turbidity. Increased sensitivity can be obtained by concentration of cultures at least tenfold (P. F. Smith, 1956). Some species, particularly M. laidlawii and M. mycoides, produce significant turbidity under optimal growth conditions and can be adequately quantitated by turbidimetry. However, these and other species tend to clump under suboptimal growth conditions rendering turbidity measurements useless. Furthermore, the organisms themselves or the temperature of incubation produce precipitates in the culture medium particularly those containing whole serum. Obviously this precipitate interferes not only with turbidity readings but also assays involving weight measurements. Light scattering has been employed successfully. The lower limit of sensitivity for *M. laidlawii* is 10^5 organisms per milliliter. The presence of serum in the medium lowers the sensitivity of the method (Wolf and Marcus, 1969).

The method of most probable number has been employed with *M. arthritidis* (Keller and Morton, 1954) and *M. gallisepticum* (Cleverdon and Morowitz, 1960). This technique is applicable to species capable of growth from minute inocula. It does not give an exact enumeration of the organisms and requires large numbers of tubes to reduce experimental error. Measurement of mean colony diameter of organisms grown under standardized conditions can give a quantitative measure of growth (P. F. Smith, 1956). This method requires maintenance of identical agar concentrations and prevention of colony crowding both of which reduce colonial size. Acid production by fermentative species and increase of pH by T strains are usuable methods (Purcell *et al.*, 1966; Taylor-Robinson *et al.*, 1966). Increase of pH with mycoplasmas possessing the arginine dihydrolase system is too erratic or minimal to be of value.

Growth of all species can be quantitatively assayed by measurement of

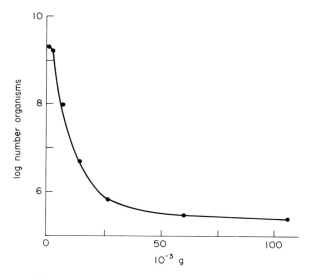

FIG. 3.14.   Effect of gravitational force on sedimentation of *M. arthritidis*.

dry weight (Butler and Knight, 1960a; P. F. Smith, 1963), DNA, or protein nitrogen (Lecce and Morton, 1954). These methods are not applicable to small volume cultures, can be tedious, and require certain precautions. As already mentioned, precipitates in the culture medium can interfere. All of the organisms must be sedimented. A force of at least 30,000 g is required to sediment 99.99% of the organisms (Fig. 3.14). Washing of cells must be done in solutions which will prevent lysis or leakage of cytoplasmic constituents. The requirement for high osmolality inserts the errors due to carryover of salts. Transfer to weighing vessels must be done with water or the appropriate corrections made. Dry weight measurements are not equatable to protein nitrogen from one species to another or to the same species grown under different conditions. Ratios of dry weight to protein nitrogen vary from 10 to 17, values far above the usual 6.25 for protein: protein nitrogen. Although dry weights are directly proportional to turbidities, neither turbidity nor dry weight are directly proportional to viable counts of organisms differing in age. This is due to loss of viability as organisms age.

Sedimentation counting as used for quantitation of viral particles is applicable to mycoplasmas (Clark, 1965; Anderson *et al.*, 1965). Organisms are sedimented onto glass slides or electron microscope grids in specially adapted centrifuge tubes. Counting is performed by light or electron microscopy. Results are comparable to viable counts.

The most common and probably the most accurate yet simple means of assay is dilution and plate count. Several variations of this method rest used for mycoplasmas by Keller and Morton (1954) have been devised (Butler and Knight, 1960a,b; Kelton, 1960: P. F. Smith, 1956). In general, serial tenfold dilutions are made in culture medium or phosphate buffered saline and 0.01 ml amounts of appropriate dilutions are spotted without spreading onto plates with dried agar surfaces. Sometimes very light sonication is used to break cell aggregates into single cells (Furness, 1968). After an appropriate incubation period, the plates are flooded with dilute Dienes' stain lacking maltose and the blue stained colonies counted at 20 × magnification. Improved visualization of the colonies in lieu of staining can be accomplished by coloring the bottom of the petri dish with transparent marking ink. Removal of debris which interferes with recognition of colonies at low magnification is possible by washing the stained agar surface with very dilute alkali. Although the error in this method is increased by clumping, immediate plating lessens this disadvantage. At most one obtains quantitation of colony forming units. Statistical analyses of several methods have been performed.

Even though numbers of individual organisms may exceed 10^{10} per ml culture medium, the small size of mycoplasmas results in yields considerably less than obtained with bacteria. Maximum yields of most optimally growing species ranges around 10 to 30 μg dry weight per ml. *M. mycoides* gives somewhat higher yields. These values are for cultures harvested at the peak of the logarithmic phase and are lower than those of stationary phase cultures.

2. Changes in Cellular Constituents During Growth

The patterns of nucleic acid composition during growth are similar to those observed in bacteria (Kandler *et al.*, 1956b; Lynn and Smith, 1958; S. C. Smith *et al.*, 1963). The DNA remains essentially constant throughout the growth cycle. There occurs a rapid increase in total RNA during the lag phase reaching its peak during the early logarthmic phase followed by a gradual decline during exponential growth. These findings are consistent with the known functions of nucleic acids.

Cellular protein content follows the pattern given by viable counts through both lag and logarithmic phases. During the early stationary phase a drop in protein and dry weight is observed followed by a rise of both parameters. This behavior probably reflects lysis or leakage of some of the organisms due to exhaustion of limiting nutrient, e.g., fatty acid, followed by a second wave of growth stimulated by cellular constituents released by lysis. Or ribosomal dissociation may be occurring with a resultant loss

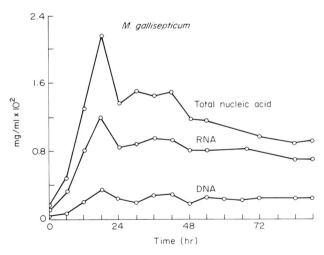

FIG. 3.15.   Changes in nucleic acid composition during growth. Courtesy of W. R. Dunlop. Copyright by American Society for Microbiology. Adapted from Figure 3, S. C. Smith *et al.* (1963).

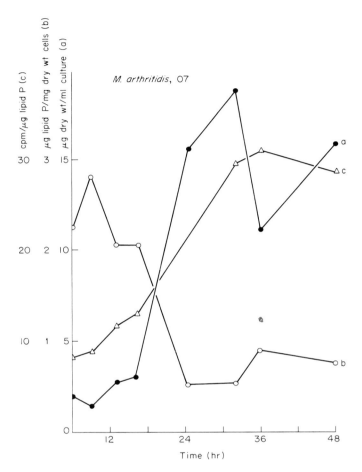

FIG. 3.16. Phospholipid changes during growth. Copyright by American Society for Microbiology. Figure 1, P. F. Smith and Koostra (1967).

of nucleic acid and protein from the cell without actual lysis (S. C. Smith *et al.*, 1963) (Fig. 3.15).

A similar pattern is seen with the sterol content (Lynn and Smith, 1960). Since sterol is associated solely with the cell membrane, lysis must account for this reduction. Liberation of sterol then allows for another short spurt of cell synthesis. The typical changes in total phospholipid composition are seen in Fig. 3.16. The changes in dry weight are the same as described above. During the lag phase some cell lysis occurs which is reflected in the phospholipids as an increase in specific activity. The same

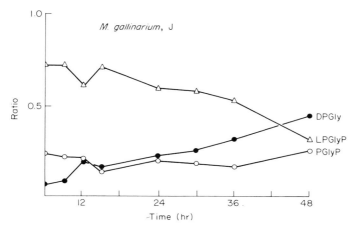

FIG. 3.17.   Changes in different species of phospholipids during growth. Copyright by American Society for Microbiology. Figure 3, P. F. Smith and Koostra (1967).

occurs in the early stationary phase. This increase in specific activity is due to contamination of viable intact cells with sedimentable membrane fragments which contain the bulk of cellular lipid. A gradual increase of total phospholipid measured as incorporation of ^{32}P follows the growth curve. Phospholipid phosphorus per unit dry weight decreases during exponential growth indicative of disproportionate increase in nonlipid cytoplasmic constituents, such as enzyme protein and RNA. Changes in the species of phospholipid in a typical mycoplasma, *M. gallinarum*, are shown in Figure 3.17. Phosphatidyl glycerophosphate remains relatively constant. Monoacyl phosphatidyl glycerophosphate decreases during the growth cycle while diphosphatidyl glycerol exhibits a concomitant increase (P. F. Smith and Koostra, 1967). A similar situation is seen in the limited number of other species examined. Turnover studies with goat strain Y indicate a sequence of labeling consistent with initial synthesis of diglyceride, followed by phosphatidyl glycerol synthesis, and eventually formation of diphosphatidyl glycerol (Plackett and Rodwell, 1970). Growth of this strain in the presence of elaidate and oleate results in equal incorporation of both acids. Growth with the unnatural mixture of elaidate and behenate results in early incorporation of elaidate with eventual incorporation of behenate in the late logarithmic or stationary phases.

No change is seen in the content of the triacyl glucose per unit dry weight during the growth cycle of *M. gallinarum*. This contrasts with the pattern seen with cholesteryl glucoside which decreases during logarithmic growth and increases during the stationary phase (Smith and Mayberry,

1968). Although the total glucosyl diglyceride content per unit dry weight of *M. laidlawii*, strain B does not change, the ratio of monoglucosyl to diglucosyl diglyceride decreases during exponential growth to about 1 and increases to 2 during the stationary phase (Shaw *et al.*, 1968). Aside from the cholesteryl glucoside, all of these lipid changes reflect membrane synthesis.

REFERENCES

Anderson, D. L., Pollack, M. E., and Brower, L. F. (1965). *J. Bacteriol* **90,** 1768.
Argaman, M., and Razin, S. (1964). *J. Gen. Microbiol.* **38,** 153.
Barile, M. F., Schimke, R. T., and Riggs, D. B. (1966). *J. Bacteriol* **91,** 189.
Bernstein-Ziv, R. (1969). *Can. J. Microbiol.* **15,** 1125.
Boatman, E. S., and Kenny, G. E. (1970). *J. Bacteriol.* **101,** 262.
Bredt, W. (1968). *Acta Pathol. Microbiol. Scand.* **32,** 321.
Butler, M., and Knight, B. C. G. (1960a). *J. Gen. Microbiol.* **22,** 478.
Butler, M., and Knight, B. C. G. (1960b). *J. Gen. Microbiol.* **22,** 483.
Castrejon-Diez, J., Fisher, T. N., and Fisher, E., Jr. (1962). *Biochem. Biophys. Res. Commun.* **9,** 416.
Castrejon-Diez, J., Fisher, T. N., and Fisher, E., Jr. (1963). *J. Bacteriol.* **86,** 627.
Clark, H. W. (1965). *J. Bacteriol.* **90,** 1373.
Cleverdon, R. C., and Morowitz, H. J. (1960). *J. Bacteriol.* **79,** 615.
DaMassa, A. J., and Adler, H. E. (1969). *Appl. Microbiol.* **17,** 310.
Dienes, L. (1960). *Ann. N. Y. Acad. Sci.* **79,** 356.
Dienes, L. (1963). *In* "Recent Progress in Microbiology" (N. E. Gibbons, ed.), pp. 511–517. Univ. of Toronto Press, Toronto.
Edward, D. G. ff. (1950). *J. Gen. Microbiol.* **4,** 311.
Edward, D. G. ff., and Fitzgerald, W. A. (1951). *J. Gen. Microbiol.* **5,** 576.
Edward, D. G. ff., and Fitzgerald, W. A. (1952a). *Vet. Rec.* **64,** 395.
Edward, D. G. ff., and Fitzgerald, W. A. (1952b). *J. Gen. Microbiol.* **6,** V.
Edward, D. G. ff., and Freundt, E. A. (1956). *J. Gen. Microbiol.* **14,** 197.
Fabricant, J. (1959). *Avian Dis.* **3,** 428.
Fabricant, C. G., VanDemark, P. J., and Fabricant, J. (1962). *Avian Dis.* **6,** 328.
Ford, D. K. (1962). *J. Bacteriol.* **84,** 1028.
Freundt, E. A. (1958). "The Mycoplasmataceae," 147 pp. Munksgaard, Copenhagen.
Freundt, E. A. (1960). *Ann. N. Y. Acad. Sci.* **79,** 312.
Furness, G. (1968). *J. Infec. Dis.* **118,** 436.
Furness, G. (1969). *Appl. Microbiol.* **18,** 360.
Furness, G., Pipes, F. J., and McMurtrey, M. J. (1968a). *J. Infec. Dis.* **118,** 1.
Furness, G., Pipes, F. J., and McMurtrey, M. J. (1968b). *J. Infec. Dis.* **118,** 7.
Gewirtz, M., and VanDemark, P. J. (1966). *Bacteriol. Proc.* pp. 45, 77.
Gill, J. W. (1962). *J. Bacteriol.* **83,** 213.
Hayashi, H., Fisher, H., and Söll, D. (1969). *Biochemistry* **8,** 3680.
Henrikson, C. V., and Panos, C. (1969). *Biochemistry* **8,** 646.
Henrikson, C. V., and Smith, P. F. (1964). *J. Gen. Microbiol.* **37,** 73.
Henrikson, C. V., and Smith, P. F. (1966a). *J. Bacteriol.* **92,** 701.
Henrikson, C. V., and Smith, P. F. (1966b). *J. Gen. Microbiol.* **45,** 73.

Kandler, O., Zehender, C., and Müller, J. (1956a). *Arch. Mikrobiol.* **24,** 209.

Kandler, O., Zehender, C., and Müller, J. (1965b). *Arch. Mikrobiol.* **24,** 219.

Keller, R., and Morton, H. E. (1954). *J. Bacteriol.* **67,** 129.

Kelton, W. H. (1960). *Ann. N. Y. Acad. Sci.* **79,** 422.

Kelton, W. H. (1962). *J. Bacteriol.* **83,** 948.

Kirk, R. G. (1966). RNA of *Mycoplasma gallisepticum.* Ph.D. Thesis, Yale Univ., New Haven, Connecticut.

Koostra, W. L., and Smith, P. F. (1969). *Biochemistry* **8,** 4794.

Kurzepa, H., Flinton, L., and VanDemark, P. J. (1969). *J. Bacteriol.* **99,** 908.

Lands, W. E. M. (1965). *J. Amer. Oil Chem. Soc.* **42,** 465.

Leach, R. H. (1962). *J. Gen. Microbiol.* **27,** 345.

Lecce, J. G., and Morton, H. E. (1954). *J. Bacteriol.* **67,** 62.

Low, I. E., and Eaton, M. D. (1965). *J. Bacteriol.* **89,** 725.

Lund, P. G., and Shorb, M. S. (1966). *Proc. Soc. Exp. Biol. Med.* **121,** 1070.

Lund, P. G., and Shorb, M. S. (1967). *J. Bacteriol.* **94,** 279.

Lynn, R. J. (1956). Nucleic acid metabolism of pleuropneumonia-like organisms. Ph.D. Thesis, Univ. Pennsylvania, Philadelphia, Pennsylvania.

Lynn, R. J. (1960). *Ann. N. Y. Acad. Sci.* **79,** 538.

Lynn, R. J., and Smith, P. F. (1958). *J. Bacteriol.* **74,** 811.

Lynn, R. J., and Smith, P. F. (1960). *Ann. N. Y. Acad. Sci.* **79,** 493.

McElhaney, R. N., and Tourtellotte, M. E. (1970a). *Biochim. Biophys. Acta* **202,** 120.

McElhaney, R. N., and Tourtellotte, M. E. (1970b). *J. Bacteriol.* **101,** 72.

Manchee, R. J., and Taylor-Robinson, D. (1969). *J. Bacteriol.* **100,** 78.

Maniloff, J. (1969). *J. Bacteriol.* **100,** 1402.

Morowitz, H. J., and Maniloff, J. (1966). *J. Bacteriol.* **91,** 1638.

Morton, H. E., Smith, P. F., and Leberman, P. R. (1951). *Amer. J. Syph. Gonor. Vener. Dis.* **35,** 361.

Morton, H. E., Lecce, J. G., Oskay, J. J., and Coy, N. H. (1954). *J. Bacteriol.* **68,** 697.

Neimark, H. C. (1964). *Nature (London)* **203,** 549.

Neimark, H. C., and Pickett, M. J. (1960). *Ann. N. Y. Acad. Sci.* **79,** 531.

Newing, C. R., and MacLeod, A. K. (1956). *Nature (London)* **177,** 939.

Panos, C., and Henrikson, C. V. (1969). *Biochemistry* **8,** 652.

Panos, C., and Rottem, S. (1970). *Biochemistry* **9,** 407.

Plackett, P. (1957). *Biochim. Biophys. Acta* **26,** 664.

Plackett, P. (1961). *Nature (London)* **189,** 125.

Plackett, P. (1967a). *Biochemistry* **6,** 2746.

Plackett, P. (1967b). *Ann. N. Y. Acad. Sci.* **143,** 158.

Plackett, P., and Rodwell, A. W. (1970). *Biochim. Biophys. Acta* **210,** 230.

Plackett, P., Marmion, B. P., Shaw, E. J., and Lemcke, R. M. (1969). *Aust. J. Exp. Biol. Med. Sci.* **47,** 171.

Plapp, R. (1963). *Zentralbl. Bakteriol., Abt. 1.* **191,** 415.

Pollack, J. D., and Tourtellotte, M. E. (1967). *J. Bacteriol.* **93,** 636.

Pollack, J. D., Razin, S., and Cleverdon, R. C. (1965). *J. Bacteriol.* **90,** 617.

Pollack, J. D., Somerson, N. L., and Senterfit, L. B. (1969a). *Bacteriol. Proc.* p. 32.

Pollack, J. D., Somerson, N. L., and Senterfit, L. B. (1969b). *J. Bacteriol.* **97,** 612.

Purcell, R. H., Taylor-Robinson, D., Wong, D., and Chanock, R. M. (1966). *J. Bacteriol.* **92,** 6.

Razin, S. (1962). *J. Gen. Microbiol.* **28,** 243.

Razin, S., and Cohen, A. (1963). *J. Gen. Microbiol.* **30,** 141.

Razin, S., and Knight, B. C. G. (1960). *J. Gen. Microbiol.* **22,** 492.

Razin, S., and Rottem, S. (1963). *J. Gen. Microbiol.* **33,** 459.

Razin, S., and Rottem, S. (1967). *J. Bacteriol.* **93,** 1181.

Razin, S., Knysznski, A., and Lifshitz, Y. (1964). *J. Gen. Microbiol.* **36,** 323.

Razin, S., Cosenza, B. J., and Tourtellotte, M. E. (1966a). *J. Gen. Microbiol.* **42,** 139.

Razin, S., Tourtellotte, M. E., McElhaney, R. N., and Pollack, J. D. (1966b). *J. Bacteriol.* **91,** 609.

Rodwell, A. W. (1956). *Aust. J. Biol. Sci.* **9,** 105.

Rodwell, A. W. (1960). *Ann. N. Y. Acad. Sci.* **79,** 499.

Rodwell, A. W. (1963). *J. Gen. Microbiol.* **32,** 91.

Rodwell, A. W. (1967). *Ann. N. Y. Acad. Sci.* **143,** 88.

Rodwell, A. W. (1968). *Science* **160,** 1350.

Rodwell, A. W. (1969a). *In* "The Mycoplasmatales and the L-Phase of Bacteria" (L Hayflick, ed.), pp. 413–450. Appleton, New York.

Rodwell, A. W. (1969b). *J. Gen. Microbiol.* **58,** 39.

Rodwell, A. W. (1969c). *J. Gen. Microbiol.* **58,** 29.

Rodwell, A. W., and Abbot, A. (1961). *J. Gen. Microbiol.* **25,** 201.

Rodwell, A. W., and Rodwell, E. S. (1953). *Nature (London)* **172,** 254.

Rodwell, A. W., and Rodwell, E. S. (1954a). *Aust. J. Biol. Sci.* **7,** 18.

Rodwell, A. W., and Rodwell, E. S. (1954b). *Aust. J. Biol. Sci.* **7,** 31.

Rodwell, A. W., and Rodwell, E. S. (1954c). *Aust. J. Biol. Sci.* **7,** 37.

Rottem, S., and Panos, C. (1969). *J. Gen. Microbiol.* **59,** 317.

Rottem, S., and Panos, C. (1970). *Biochemistry* **9,** 57.

Rottem, S., and Razin, S. (1964). *J. Gen. Microbiol.* **37,** 123.

Rottem, S., and Razin, S. (1966). *J. Bacteriol.* **92,** 714.

Rottem, S., and Razin, S. (1967). *J. Gen. Microbiol.* **48,** 53.

Schimke, R. T., and Barile, M. F. (1963). *J. Bacteriol.* **86,** 195.

Schimke, R. T., Berlin, C. M., Sweeney, E. W., and Carroll, W. R. (1966). *J. Biol. Chem.* **241,** 2228.

Shaw, N., Smith, P. F., and Koostra, W. L. (1968). *Biochem. J.* **107,** 329.

Shepard, M. C., and Lunceford, C. D. (1965). *J. Bacteriol.* **89,** 265.

Shepard, M. C., and Lunceford, C. D. (1967). *J. Bacteriol.* **93,** 1513.

Shklair, I. L., Mazzarella, M. A., Gutekunst, R. R., and Kiggins, E. M. (1962). *J. Bacteriol.* **83,** 785.

Smith, D. W. (1969). *Biochim. Biophys. Acta* **179,** 408.

Smith, D. W., and Hanawalt, P. C. (1968). *J. Bacteriol.* **96,** 2066.

Smith, P. F. (1955a). *J. Bacteriol.* **70,** 552.

Smith, P. F. (1955b). *Proc. Soc. Exp. Biol. Med.* **88,** 628.

Smith, P. F. (1956). *Appl. Microbiol.* **4,** 254.

Smith, P. F. (1957a). *J. Bacteriol.* **73,** 91.

Smith, P. F. (1957b). *J. Bacteriol.* **74,** 75.

Smith, P. F. (1957c). *J. Bacteriol.* **74,** 801.

Smith, P. F. (1959). *J. Bacteriol.* **77,** 682.

Smith, P. F. (1960a). *Ann. N. Y. Acad. Sci.* **79,** 543.

Smith, P. F. (1960b). *Ann. N. Y. Acad. Sci.* **79,** 508.

Smith, P. F. (1962). *J. Bacteriol.* **84,** 534.

Smith, P. F. (1963). *J. Gen. Microbiol.* **32,** 307.

Smith, P. F. (1964a). *Bacteriol. Rev.* **28,** 97.

Smith, P. F. (1964b). *J. Lipid Res.* **5,** 121.

Smith, P. F. (1966). *J. Bacteriol.* **92,** 164.

Smith, P. F. (1967). *Ann. N. Y. Acad. Sci.* **143,** 139.

Smith, P. F. (1968). *J. Bacteriol.* **95,** 1718.
Smith, P. F. (1969a). *Lipids* **4,** 331.
Smith, P. F. (1969b). *J. Bacteriol.* **99,** 480.
Smith, P. F. (1969c). *Bacteriol. Proc.* p. 121.
Smith, P. F., and Boughton, J. E. (1960). *J. Bacteriol.* **80,** 851.
Smith, P. F., and Henrikson, C. V. (1965a). *J. Bacteriol.* **89,** 146.
Smith, P. F., and Henrikson, C. V. (1965b). *J. Lipid Res.* **6,** 106.
Smith, P. F., and Henrikson, C. V. (1966). *J. Bacteriol.* **91,** 1854.
Smith, P. F., and Koostra, W. L. (1967). *J. Bacteriol.* **93,** 1853.
Smith, P. F., and Lynn, R. J. (1958). *J. Bacteriol.* **76,** 264.
Smith, P. F., and Mayberry, W. R. (1968). *Biochemistry* **7,** 2706.
Smith, P. F., and Morton, H. E. (1951). *J. Bacteriol.* **61,** 395.
Smith, P. F., and Morton, H. E. (1952). *Arch. Biochem. Biophys.* **38,** 23.
Smith, P. F., and Rothblat, G. H. (1960). *J. Bacteriol.* **80,** 842.
Smith, P. F., and Rothblat, G. H. (1962). *J. Bacteriol.* **83,** 500.
Smith, P. F., and Smith, M. R. (1970). *J. Bacteriol.* **103,** 27.
Smith, P. F., Lecce, J. G., and Lynn, R. J. (1954). *J. Bacteriol.* **68,** 627.
Smith, P. F., Koostra, W. L., and Mayberry, W. R. (1969). *J. Bacteriol.* **100,** 1166.
Smith, S. C., Dunlop, W. R., and Strout, R. G. (1963). *J. Bacteriol.* **86,** 880.
Taylor-Robinson, D., Purcell, R. H., Wong, D. C., and Chanock, R. M. (1966). *J. Hyg.* **64,** 91.
Tourtellotte, M. E. (1960). A comparative serologic and physiologic study of pleuro-pneumonia-like organisms. Ph.D. Thesis, Univ. Connecticut, Storrs, Connecticut.
Tourtellotte, M. E. (1969). *In* "The Mycoplasmatales and the L-Phase of Bacteria" (L. Hayflick, ed.), pp. 451–468. Appleton, New York.
Tourtellotte, M. E., and Jacobs, R. E. (1960). *Ann. N. Y. Acad. Sci.* **79,** 521.
Tourtellotte, M. E., Morowitz, H. J., and Kasimer, P. (1964). *J. Bacteriol.* **88,** 11.
Tourtellotte, M. E., Pollack, M. E., and Nalewaik, R. P. (1967). *Ann. N. Y. Acad. Sci.* **143,** 130.
VanDemark, P. J., and Smith, P. F. (1964a). *J. Bacteriol.* **88,** 122.
VanDemark, P. J., and Smith, P. F. (1964b). *J. Bacteriol.* **88,** 1602.
VanDemark, P. J., and Smith, P. F. (1965). *J. Bacteriol.* **89,** 373.
Warren, J. (1942). *J. Bacteriol.* **43,** 211.
Wolf, J. P., and Marcus, L. (1969). *Appl. Microbiol.* **18,** 4.
Woodson, B. A., McCarty, K. S., and Shepard, M. C. (1965). *Arch. Biochem. Biophys.* **109,** 364.

Relationship of Structure to Function 4

A. CYTOPLASMIC MEMBRANE

The existence of a single membrane enclosing the mycoplasmal cell offers a simple model for the study of membrane functions. These functions include permeation and transport processes, terminal respiration, and oxidative phosphorylation. Although the latter two functions have not been studied exclusively with membrane preparations, the evidence suggests that most of both are associated with the membrane. A limited number of enzymes are known to occur in the membrane (Table IV.1) and some of these appear to play roles in functions other than biosynthesis of structural components of the membrane.

1. Permeability

The general permeability properties of two species, *M. arthritidis* and *M. laidlawii*, are different (Spears and Provost, 1967). These conclusions are based on turbidity measurements of changes resulting from the rapid loss or uptake of water. At high osmolalities of nonpenetrating solutes, the cells become shrunken and turbidity increases; at low osmolalities the cells become swollen and turbidity decreases; at isoosmotic conditions no change is apparent. *Mycoplasma laidlawii* is impermeable to potassium and sodium chlorides, sucrose, and sodium acetate. It possesses a high degree of permeability to glucose, glycerol, and dimethylsulfoxide since increasing concentrations of these compounds do not induce large changes in turbidity. By contrast, *M. arthritidis* is impermeable to glucose, sucrose, sodium and potassium chlorides, and sodium acetate, but relatively perme-

TABLE IV.1

Enzymes Associated with Mycoplasmal Membranes

NADH$_2$ oxidase (variable)
Adenosine triphosphatase
Cholesterol esterase
Cholesteryl ester synthetase
α- and β-Glucosidases
Steryl glucoside synthetase
Phosphatidyl glucose synthetase
Mono- and diglucosyl diglyceride synthetases
Quinone reductase
Ferricyanide reductase
Lysophospholipase

---

able to glycerol and dimethylsulfoxide. Thus *M. laidlawii* appears more permeable than *M. arthritidis*, no doubt as a result of differences in membrane structure. Studies have been performed (R. N. McElhaney, personal communication) on the effects of varying the fatty acid composition of the complex lipids in *M. laidlawii* on the permeability of liposomes prepared from these lipids, of membranes and of the intact organisms to glycerol and erythritol. In general, permeability increases as the amount of unsaturated fatty acid increases. Organisms with the highest content of saturated fatty acids are the least permeable.

Studies on incorporation or transport of extracellular compounds into cells carried out over longer time periods are indicative of specific transport mechanisms. Crypticity of mycoplasmas to citrulline (P. F. Smith, 1957b), glutamic and aspartic acids (Tourtellotte, 1969), and phosphorylated long-chain isoprenoid compounds (Henrikson and Smith, 1966) are demonstrable of lack of transport systems for these compounds. Although osmotically impermeable to sodium acetate, mycoplasmas must possess a transport system for this compound. It is incorporated into fatty acids (Rottem and Razin, 1967) and into polyterpenes (P. F. Smith, 1963). The incorporation of acetate is temperature dependant, pH dependant, and is prevented by inhibition of energy generation. Palmitic and stearic but not oleic acids inhibit its incorporation, probably by their preferential uptake as preformed fatty acids obviating biosynthesis from acetate. Propionate and butyrate decrease acetate uptake, possibly by inhibiting acetokinase activity (Rottem and Razin, 1967).

Active transport of amino acids in *M. fermentans* and *M. hominis* and of sugars in *M. gallisepticum* and *M. laidlawii* have been demonstrated (Razin *et al.*, 1968; Rottem and Razin, 1969). The uptake of these compounds is temperature and pH dependant, follows saturation kinetics thereby obeying Michaelis-Menten kinetics, and is prevented by inhibition of energy production. L-Histidine uptake by *M. fermentans* is not entirely specific since it can be inhibited competitively by L-arginine and L-lysine. It accumulates at an intracellular concentration 200-fold the extracellular level. Efflux occurs at 37°C but not at 0°C and is accelerated by the presence of extracellular L-histidine. L-Methionine transport in *M. hominis* is highly specific. Separate transport systems exist in *M. gallisepticum* for D-glucose and α-methyl-D-glucoside and for D-mannose and D-fructose. Both systems are noninducible and stereospecific. The glucoside accumulates against a concentration gradient. Exit of the glucoside also is temperature dependant and is accelerated by energy supplied as oxidizable substrate. D-Glucose also accelerates glucoside exit. The general features of transport are consistent with active transport and with such processes in other cells.

The actual mechanism(s) of the transport processes are unknown. Turn-

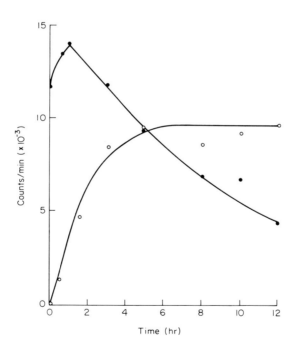

FIG. 4.1.   Turnover of ^{32}P in phospholipids of *M. laidlawii*. (●———●) Phosphatidyl glucose; (○———○) phosphatidyl glycerol. Copyright by American Oil Chemists Society. Figure 5, P. F. Smith (1969).

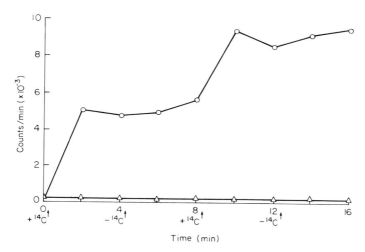

FIG. 4.2.   Absence of turnover of ^{14}C-glucose in glucosyl diglycerides of *M. laidlawii* during metabolism of glucose. (O——O) Diglucosyl diglyceride; (△——△) monoglucosyl diglyceride. Copyright by American Oil Chemists Society. Figure 3, P. F. Smith (1969).

over studies of lipid components suggest their role as carriers for some compounds, e.g., glucose and short-chain fatty acids. Prelabeling the phospholipids with ^{32}P during metabolism of glucose results in appearance of radioactivity in the "phosphatidyl glucose" of *M. laidlawii* but of very little radioactivity in the glycerophospholipids of *M. laidlawii* and *M. gallinarum*. Transfer to growth medium with excess unlabeled orthophosphate to dilute the ^{32}P results upon growth of the organisms in loss of label in the "phosphatidyl glucose" but a progressive increase in the label found in the glycerophospholipids (P. F. Smith, 1967, 1969) (Fig. 4.1). Pulse labeling with ^{14}C-glucose results in no appearance of label in the monoglucosyl diglyceride probably as a result of the lack of acceptor diglyceride. Diglucosyl diglyceride is increasingly labeled in the presence of ^{14}C-glucose and this label is not lost upon replacement of the labeled exogenous glucose with unlabeled glucose (Fig. 4.2). Similar results have been observed by McElhaney and Tourtellotte (1970) with the exception that no turnover of "phosphatidyl glucose" was observed during growth. These results have been taken as evidence of a structural role for these lipids.

Pulse labeling of *M. laidlawii* with ^{14}C-glucose does show turnover of glucose and fatty acids in certain lipids. Glucose in this organism is metabolized to acetate under aerobic conditions. The appearance of label in the extracellular acetate and liberated CO_2 follows the sequence of pulsing.

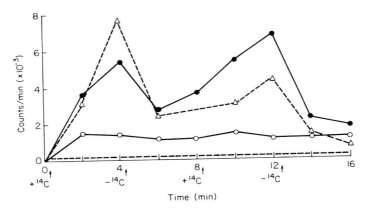

FIG. 4.3.   Turnover of glucose in carotenyl glucoside and acetate in carotenyl ester during metabolism of ^{14}C-glucose by *M. laidlawii* in absence and presence of metabolic inhibitors. (●——●) Carotenyl glucoside; (△- - -△) carotenyl ester; (○——○) carotenyl glucoside IAA (iodoacetamide); (1- - -1) carotenyl glucoside DOC (deoxy-corticosterone), carotenyl ester IAA, DOC. Copyright by American Oil Chemists Society. Figure 2, P. F. Smith (1969).

No labeling occurs in the free carotenol. The glucose moiety of carotenyl glucoside and the acetate moiety of the carotenyl ester become labeled during the short 4-minute pulse with ^{14}C-glucose and lose their labels upon replacement of the ^{14}C-glucose with unlabeled glucose (Fig. 4.3). The en-zymes capable of carrying out the synthesis and the removal of the glucose and acetate radicals are present in the membrane. Inhibition of glucose fermentation and glucosidase activity by iodoacetate depresses synthesis of the glucoside and inhibits completely the turnover of glucose. Under this condition no label appears in the ester. Inhibition of the utilization of glucose by deoxycorticosterone which has no effect on the glucosidase re-sults in no label appearing in either the glucoside or ester. These results have been taken as evidence for the participation of the carotenol in the case of *M. laidlawii* and the sterol in sterol-containing species as carriers of glucose into the cell and of the end product of glucose metabolism, ace-tate, out of the cell. The enzymes responsible for the synthesis and degrada-tion of the glucoside and ester are considered to be types of permeases. "Phosphatidyl glucose" turnover in the situation described also is seen in pulse labeling of metabolizing cells with ^{14}C-glucose (Fig. 4.4). With "phos-phatidyl glucose" both glucose and phosphate turn over. The equivalency of their rates is not known. The turnover of glucose in the lipids occurs at a rate compatible with the metabolism of glucose (Fig. 4.5). The disap-pearance of label from the lipids in prelabeled cells occurs at the same rate

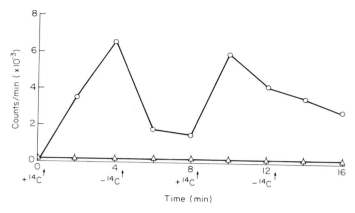

FIG. 4.4.   Turnover of "phosphatidyl glucose" during metabolism of ^{14}C-glucose by
M. laidlawii. (O——O) Phosphatidyl glucose; (△——△) phosphatidyl glycerol. Copyright by American Oil Chemists Society. Figure 4, P. F. Smith (1969).

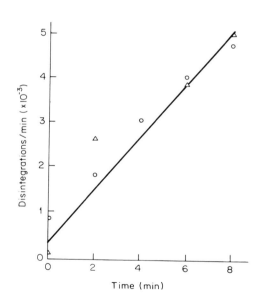

FIG. 4.5.   Rates of disappearance of ^{14}C-lipids labeled during metabolism of ^{14}C
glucose and appearance of $^{14}CO_2$ following chase with unlabeled glucose. (O) CO_2
(+ dpm); (△) total lipid (− dpm). Copyright by American Oil Chemists Society.
Figure 6, P. F. Smith (1969).

TABLE IV.2

Effect of Inhibitors on Glucose Utilization and β-Glucosidase of *M. laidlawii*[a]

Inhibitor	Glucose utilization[b]	β-Glucosidase[b]
Deoxycorticosterone	+	0
Estradiol	+	0
N-Ethylmaleimide	+	±
Iodoacetic acid	+	+
Uranyl nitrate	+	+
Phloridzin	+	0

[a] Data compiled from P. F. Smith (1969).

[b] + = inhibition; ± = partial inhibition; 0 = no inhibition.

as the appearance of labeled CO_2. A role for glucosidase in permeation also is suggested from inhibitor studies. Compounds which inhibit glucosidase activity also inhibit glucose utilization, whereas the reverse situation does not hold (Table IV.2). Deoxycorticosterone, which inhibits glucose utilization in mycoplasmas, also inhibits their growth (Shoenhard and Padgett, 1961). Glucose as well as amino acid and rubidium uptake in neurospora also are inhibited by deoxycorticosterone (Lester et al., 1958). Its relief in this system by cholesterol adds to the evidence for involvement of sterol and probably carotenol in permeation mechanisms.

Consideration of all the information known about sterols and carotenols in mycoplasmas has led to the development of a postulated permeability mechanism for glucose and short chain fatty acids (P. F. Smith, 1968). The present model is based upon a corpuscular model for membrane structure but can be adapted to a model incorporating a type of lamellar model, i.e., one envisioning not separate layers of lipid and protein but a mixed protein–lipid layer. It encompasses many of the aspects of the permease theory (Cohen and Monod, 1957), group translocation (Mitchell and Moyle, 1958), and mechanical propulsion by rotational movements (Danielli, 1954). A schematic diagram of this model is seen in Fig. 4.6. A represents a nontransporting segment of the membrane which is being approached by either substrate (S) or product (P) specific for that given site. The hydroxyl groups of the carotenol or dimer of planar sterol are free and the subunits are compressed due to the cation (Mg^{2+}) bound in the phospholipid bridge. The carotenol is included to serve as an example of a carrier lipid for glucose and acetate. Other compounds could be transported through the mediation of enzymes lining the pore. The condensed membrane could be sufficiently porous to account for simple diffusion of some substances such as water. In Fig. 4.6 B, substrate has become bonded

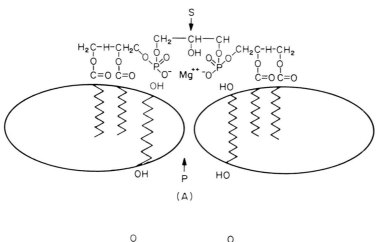

(A)

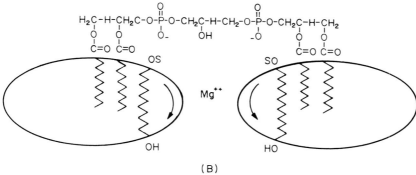

(B)

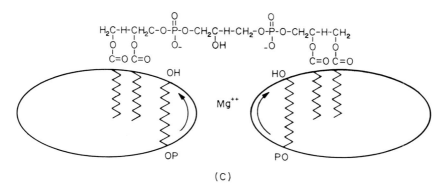

(C)

FIG. 4.6.   Model of proposed corpuscular segment of mycoplasmal membrane demonstrating permeation process (See text). Copyright by Academic Press, Inc. From P. F. Smith (1968).

to the outer hydroxyl group of the carotenol by the action of specific enzyme. In this case the substrate is glucose to account for the existence and the turnover of carotenyl glucoside. If the process is cation dependant the cation could be removed or used by the enzyme with the resultant expansion of the subunits forming a pore through which the substrate can enter. In this specific example the change in polarity of the carotenol by formation of the glycoside could initiate a rotational movement toward the interior of the cell (arrows) exposing the glucose radical to the inside where it can be cleaved by the glucosidase. Other substances conceivably could be transported by group translocation involving enzymes or other specific proteins lining the walls of the pore. Hence this specific example represents only a certain segment of the membrane. This mechanism does not preclude the possible role of allosteric transformations of proteins in mediation of transport across the membrane. There could exist also membrane segments lamellar in nature where other transport mechanisms prevail. Diagram C (Fig. 4.6) is similar to B except that the end product of metabolism is being transported out of the cell. In this specific case, acetate is bonded to the internal hydroxyl group through the mediation of the synthetase enzyme located in the membrane to form the carotenyl ester. A change in polarity opposite that occurring as a result of glycoside formation initiates a rotational movement toward the outside of the cell where acetate is released to the external medium by the action of the esterase. Other substances could be transported to the outside without the intervention of the lipid as carrier. In mycoplasmal species which oxidize short-chain fatty acids, the transport mechanism into the cell would be similar to the exit mechanism described for acetate in fermentative species. The postulated opening and closing of pores by expansion and contraction of the membrane could account for the shimmering movements during active transport (Kavanau, 1965).

This is only a postulated model designed to fit current data regarding membrane structure and permeability in mycoplasmas.

a. The hydroxyl groups of the carotenol and sterol are essential for growth but not incorporation into the membrane. These groups must be planar to the molecule, i.e., equatorial.

b. The lipids are found solely within the membrane which also contains the appropriate enzymes for the synthesis and degradation of the carotenyl or steryl glucoside and ester. Enzymes found in the membrane, e.g., ATPase and those involved in the synthesis of the glucoside, are dependant upon divalent cation.

c. The glucoside and glucosidase are found only in mycoplasmas capable of glucose metabolism. The principal fatty acid esterified to carotenol and sterol of fermentative species is acetate, the end product of glucose metabolism. In organisms utilizing short-chain fatty acids as an energy source the principal fatty acids in steryl esters are butyric, acetic, and propionic.

d. The glucoside and ester of carotenol and sterol turn over during metabolism of glucose and at a rate compatible with glucose fermentation.

e. Transport in and out of the cell is specific. Since it is enzyme mediated in this model, it would be temperature and pH dependant, would obey Michaelis-Menten kinetics, and require energy.

f. The model allows for easy traversal of a lipid barrier.

g. The model is compatible with the structural features of mycoplasmal membranes.

The problem of making a high-energy donor accesible to the surface of the membrane to permit synthesis of the glucolipids is unresolved. It is conceivable that ATP generated within the cytoplasm could transfer energy by the formation of UTP in the membrane.

2. Respiration

The limited number of different species studied generally can be classed either as fermentative, which appear to have a flavin-terminated respiratory chain, or nonfermentative, which contain some modification of a complete respiratory chain. As in any biological system no actual discontinuity exists as there is evidence for other types intermediate with respect to completeness of the respiratory chain. Many mycoplasmas have been shown capable of dye reduction giving a general indication of the presence of dehydrogenases. Methylene blue (Holmes and Pirie, 1932; Pirie and Holmes, 1933; Warren, 1942; Rodwell and Rodwell, 1954a, b); Kandler and Kandler, 1955) and the tetrazoliums, in particular triphenyltetrazolium (Somerson and Morton, 1953; Lecce and Morton, 1954), have been used most commonly. The use of these or other artificial or natural electron acceptors has resulted in the detection of a variety of dehydrogenases (oxidoreductases). These include NAD, NADP, and nonpyridine nucleotide-linked enzymes (Table IV.3).

Several mycoplasmas have been shown to oxidize $NADH_2$ and $NADPH_2$ (S. L. Smith et al., 1963; VanDemark and Smith, 1964; Pollack et al., 1965; Rodwell, 1967). Menadione and ferricyanide but not cytochrome c serve as acceptors for $NADH_2$ oxidation by M. gallisepticum. Menadione, indolphenol, and ferricyanide but not cytochrome c, hydrogen peroxide, nitrate, or oxidized glutathione can replace oxygen as the acceptor for $NADH_2$ oxidation by M. mycoides. These results indicate a similarity between these two species which apparently contain diaphorases and quinone reductase but no cytochrome c reductase. Menadione, indolphenol, and

TABLE IV.3

Known Dehydrogenases of Mycoplasmas

Acceptor	Substrate	Species	Reference[a]
NAD	Ethanol	M. arthritidis	1
	Glyceraldehyde	M. bovis	2
	3-phosphate	M. gallisepticum	3
	Glycerophosphate	M. bovis	2
	β-Hydroxybutyrate	M. arthritidis	4
	Lactate	M. mycoides	5
		M. gallisepticum	3, 6
		M. bovis	2
	Malate	M. arthritidis	4
NADP	Glucose 6-phosphate	M. gallisepticum	6
	Glyceraldehyde	M. gallinarum	7
	3-phosphate	M. laidlawii	8
		M. gallisepticum	6
	α-Glycerophosphate	M. gallisepticum	6
	Isocitrate	M. arthritidis	9
	Malate	M. bovis	2
	Proline	M. arthritidis	10
	Hydroxymethyl	M. laidlawii	11
	glutaryl CoA	M. gallinarum	11
Nonpyridine	Butyryl CoA	M. arthritidis	4
nucleotide	α-Ketoglutarate	M. arthritidis	4
linked	Lactate	M. arthritidis	1
	Succinate	M. arthritidis	9
	α-Glycerophosphate	M. mycoides	12

[a] Numbers refer to references as cited: 1, Lecce and Morton (1954); 2, Gewirtz and VanDemark (1966); 3, S. L. Smith et al. (1963); 4, VanDemark and Smith (1965); 5, Rodwell and Rodwell (1954b); 6, Tourtellotte (1960); 7, P. F. Smith, unpublished; 8, Castrejon-Diez et al. (1963); 9, VanDemark and Smith (1964); 10, P. F. Smith (1957a); 11, P. F. Smith and Henrikson (1965); 12, Rodwell (1967).

cytochrome c serve as acceptors for $NADH_2$ oxidation in M. arthritidis suggesting the additional presence of cytochrome c reductase. There is no evidence for an $NADH_2$-linked peroxidase in M. gallisepticum or M. mycoides. The $NADH_2$ oxidase of M. laidlawii is controlled by the level of ADP (Stopkie and Weber, 1967). The mechanism of this control may lie in the similarity of the structures of ADP and NAD both of which contain adenosine. The $NADH_2$ oxidase activity of M. laidlawii is membrane associated while it appears in the soluble fraction of a number of sterol requiring species (Pollack et al., 1965). In the latter case the activity may normally reside at or near the membrane but be very loosely bound. The NADH₂ oxidase of *M. gallisepticum* is associated with the particulate fraction (S. L. Smith *et al.*, 1963). The NADPH₂ oxidase activity of all mycoplasmas examined is found in the soluble fraction of the cells.

Direct evidence for the participation of flavins in the complex respiratory chain of *M. arthritidis* was obtained by VanDemark and Smith (1964). Resolution of the NADH₂ oxidizing enzymes was accomplished by treatment with trichloroacetic acid. Reactivation of NADH₂ oxidase was possible by the addition of flavin adenine dinucleotide (FAD) but not flavin mononucleotide (FMN). Diaphorase was reactivated by either FAD or FMN but the quinone reductase only by FMN. Other flavin-linked dehydrogenases in this species include those catalyzing the oxidation of succinate, lactate, and butyryl CoA.

Most mycoplasmal species are fermentative and possess a flavin-terminated respiratory chain. Those species examined include *M. mycoides*, *M. gallisepticum*, and *M. pneumoniae*. NADH₂ oxidase activity of *M. mycoides*, lost upon storage at −15°C, is restored by addition of FAD but not FMN and cysteine indicating the requirement of flavin for this oxidase (Rodwell, 1967). In *M. gallisepticum* lactate oxidation is stimulated by the addition of FMN or FAD (S. L. Smith *et al.*, 1963). The rate of oxidation of lactate by this organism is increased by increase of oxygen tension with maximum activity occurring in pure oxygen. This low affinity for oxygen is typical of a flavin-terminated respiratory chain. The average flavin content in *M. gallisepticum* is 2.1×10^{-10} mole/mg dry weight. Respiration in species with flavin-terminated systems results in the production of hydrogen peroxide. Addition of catalase enhances glucose and glycerol oxidation by *M. mycoides* (Rodwell, 1967) and *M. pneumoniae* (Low *et al.*, 1965). *Mycoplasma gallisepticum* accumulates nearly stoichiometric amounts of peroxide during NADH₂ oxidation (S. L. Smith *et al.*, 1963). However this is not the case for *M. mycoides* (Rodwell, 1967). Hydrogen peroxide has been identified as an end product of glucose metabolism in *M. pneumoniae* (Somerson *et al.*, 1965). The site of flavins is considered to be the membrane but only in *M. gallisepticum* has it been experimentally demonstrated. In this organism the quinone and ferricyanide reductases occur at this site.

Inhibitor studies on NADH₂ oxidation in *M. arthritidis* suggest a role for quinones in the respiratory pathway of this organism (VanDemark and Smith, 1964). NADH₂ oxidation is inhibited by amytal which inhibits the reduction of benzoquinones via flavoproteins; by antimycin A and BAL which block the oxidation of reduced quinones. Isolation and identification of quinones in mycoplasmas has not been successful. Gale *et al.* (1964) failed to find quinones in *M. gallisepticum*. Organic solvent extracts

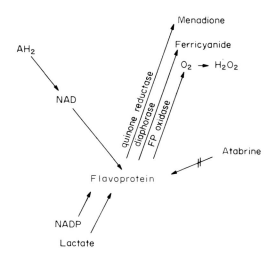

FIG. 4.7.   Respiratory pathway in fermentative species of mycoplasmas. Adapted from the work of P. J. VanDemark.

of *M. arthritidis* were separated into fractions which normally contain co-enzyme Q and vitamins K. These fractions are yellow and become colorless upon borohydride reduction. Their ultraviolet spectra exhibit a distinctive peak at 258 nm to 260 nm with shoulders at 270 nm and 290 nm. This spectrum is not typical of any of the known quinones involved in other respiratory chains. However, they appear quinonelike as they give a positive test with the Dam-Karrer assay. Extraction of *M. arthritidis* with diethyl ether or irradiation at 360 nm results in loss of $NADH_2$ oxidase activity. It is partially restored with coenzyme Q_6 and a lipid extract of the organism or by the addition of vitamin K_2 or menadione (VanDemark and Smith, 1964). It would appear that the nonfermentative *M. arthritidis* contains some type of quinone in its respiratory chain.

Cytochromes and heme compounds also occur in some mycoplasmas. In *M. arthritidis* spectrophotometric demonstration of cytochromes has been made (VanDemark and Smith, 1964). Difference spectra revealed absorption bands in the reduced state at 565, 532, and 429 nm, typical of b-type cytochromes and at 610 and 456 nm characteristic of an a-type cytochrome. In addition a terminal cytochrome oxidase was found which is capable of oxidizing reduced cytochrome c. In a bovine species, *M. bovis*, absorption bands at 553 and 425 nm typical of cytochrome c have been detected (VanDemark, 1969). Although no bands typical of cytochrome a were observed, carbon monoxide difference spectra revealed an absorption band

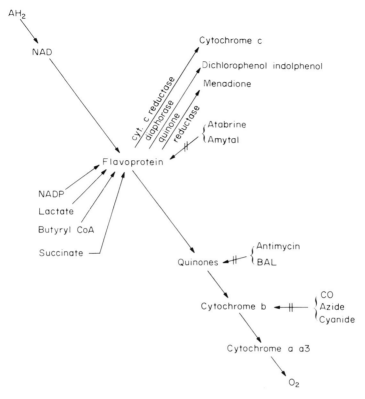

FIG. 4.8.   Respiratory pathway in nonfermentative species of mycoplasmas. Adapted from the work of P. J. VanDemark.

at 419 nm which is characteristic of cytochrome o, a terminal oxidase of certain bacteria. No cytochromes have been detected in two fermentative species, *M. mycoides* (Rodwell and Rodwell, 1954b) and *M. gallisepticum* (S. L. Smith *et al.*, 1963).

The hemoprotein, catalase, does not participate in electron transport but its presence may be indicative of the presence of other hematin respiratory pigments. A large majority of mycoplasmal species do not contain catalase, or catalase has not been deteteed by the techniques employed (Pirie, 1938; Kandler and Kandler, 1955; Weibull and Hammarberg, 1963; S. L. Smith *et al.*, 1963; Low *et al.*, 1965). It has been detected in *M. arthritidis* (Lecce and Morton, 1954) and a strain of *M. mycoides* (Rodwell and Rodwell, 1954b). Recent use of sensitive spectrophotometric and benzidine assays have resulted in the finding of catalase and heme-containing compounds in a variety of species including *M. iners, M. bovis,* and *M. arthritidis* (VanDemark, 1967). Catalase and heme-containing compounds are easily lost upon washing the cells which may account for some of the negative results in species eventually shown to contain catalase.

Inhibitor studies support the conclusion that some mycoplasmas possess a flavin-terminated pathway while others contain a complete respiratory chain. Pyruvate oxidation by the fermentative *M. mycoides* is insensitive to 2,4-dinitrophenol and azide consistent with the lack of cytochromes (Rodwell and Rodwell, 1954a,b). Lactate oxidation by *M. gallisepticum* is sensitive to atabrine but not to carbon monoxide, azide, or cyanide. On the other hand, ethanol oxidation by the nonfermentative *M. arthritidis* is cyanide sensitive (Lecce and Morton, 1954). Its respiration also is inhibited by atabrine, amytal, antimycin A, and azide (VanDemark and Smith, 1964). The probable respiratory chains of fermentative and nonfermentative species are shown in Figs. 4.7 and 4.8.

3. Oxidative Phosphorylation

Mycoplasmas which have a flavin-terminated pathway (facultative anaerobes) derive their energy by substrate phosphorylation. Those with a complete respiratory chain should derive their energy by oxidative phosphorylation. The site of this activity has not been established but could be presumed to occur in the membranous areas similar to bacteria. Oxidative phosphorylation has been demonstrated in *M. arthritidis* (VanDemark, 1967, 1969) as well as in an unclassified strain. Phosphorylation was followed by measurement of ^{32}P incorporation into ATP and by trapping ATP with hexokinase. P/O ratios were very low, 0.58 to 0.66, indicative of a very labile system similar to bacteria. The presence of serum albumin provides some protection. Dinitrophenol, azide, arsenate, and oligomycin, known uncouplers or inhibitors of oxidative phosphorylation, diminish or block completely the phosphorylation of ADP during $NADH_2$ oxidation. ATPase, an essential coupling factor for oxidative phosphorylation in other systems, occurs in association with the membranes of mycoplasmas (Pollack *et al.*, 1965).

B. THE GENOME

1. Limitations for Coding

The small size and free-living nature of mycoplasmas has encouraged their consideration as models for the study of DNA coding. Unfortunately technical difficulties have slowed progress in this area. Early irradiation data (Morowitz and Cleverdon, 1960) using ^{60}Co γ-rays gave multitarget survival curves due most likely to clumping of the organisms but nevertheless failing to distinguish mono- from polyploidy. More recent efforts have made use of suspensions of single cells produced by light sonication and filtration (Furness et al., 1968; Furness, 1968). Such suspensions exhibit single target survival curves with ultraviolet and x-irradiations. The single target curve is evidence for the occurrence of a single genome per mycoplasmal cell. Measurement of the ratio of DNA per cell to DNA per genome also indicates the occurrence of one genome per cell of M. arthritidis (Morowitz, 1969). Cells in the exponential phase have a range in ploidy of 1.2 to 1.5. A single cell immediately following division should show an average ploidy of 1.5 because of DNA replication.

The size of the genome varies from 444 to 1200 × 10^6 daltons. Morowitz (1969) has calculated the average cistron size for five species. For one of these, M. arthritidis, strain 39, there is a good degree of certainty. Assuming an average cistron encodes a protein of 40,000 molecular weight and the coding ratio of DNA to protein is 20:1, 800,000 daltons of DNA would constitute an average cistron. Thus the DNA of M. arthritidis, strain 39, could encode 637 cistrons and would represent the operation of 637 interrelated steps. With such a limited number, the possibility exists for a complete detailed analysis of the integrated functions of this organism. However this number is higher than originally assumed (Morowitz and Cleverdon, 1959) and does present a somewhat formidable problem even with these smallest of cells.

2. Mutability

Mutations are known to occur in mycoplasmas but only negligible work has been done in this area. Antibiotic resistant mutants of avian mycoplasmas arise in ovo (Osborn and Pomeroy, 1964) and in liquid culture medium (Domermuth, 1960). Spontaneous mutation on solid culture medium to resistance to chlorotetracycline, chloramphenicol, and erythromycin was observed with three species, M. laidlawii, M. gallinarum, and M. arthritidis, and to dihydrostreptomycin with these three species and M. hominis (Koostra et al., 1966). Surviving colonies of M. arthritidis, M. laidlawii, and M. gallinarum selected from media containing 400 μg per ml of streptomycin or erythromycin, 3 μg per ml of chloramphenicol, and 0.8 μg per ml of chlorotetracycline appear resistant upon subculture in these identical levels of antibiotics. However lengthening the incubation period results in outgrowth of mycoplasmas at these and higher concentrations of antibiotics. This is indicative of the nonlethality of the antibiotics and the probability that single step mutations do not occur. A more complex phenomenon undoubtedly occurs (B. Liska, personal communication). Precise mutation and reversion rates have not been calculated although the mutation rate is within the range of normal rates in other organisms. Temperature-sensitive conditional lethal mutants which grow only at 30°C but not at 40°C have been obtained from *M. laidlawii*, strain A (Folsome and Folsome, 1966). Induction of mutation was effected by exposure of exponentially growing cells to 2-aminopurine or 5-bromodeoxyuridine. Frequencies of appearance were 10^{-2} to 10^{-3}. Similar mutants have been produced from *M. pneumoniae* (Steinberg *et al.*, 1969). Mutations were induced with nitrosoguanidine and the resultant mutants grew at 32°C but not at 38°C. Frequencies were similar to those found with *M. laidlawii*. A variable degree of leakiness was observed at 37°C. In one mutant three defects other than temperature sensitivity were found.

3. Gene Transfer

Several unreported attempts have been made to demonstrate transformation or conjugation among mycoplasmas without success. *M. laidlawii*, strain A, is capable of binding in DNase resistant form high molecular weight double or single stranded homologous or heterologous DNA in amounts of 0.1 to 1.0 $\times$ 10^{-5} g per organism (Folsome, 1968). Binding is temperature dependant, occurring optimally at 40°C. It has been estimated that the maximum amount of DNA bound varies from 25 to 125 molecules 5 $\times$ 10^6 daltons in size. Unlabeled DNA competes for binding sites with ^{14}C-labeled DNA. Maximum binding requires high molecular weight DNA. The amount of DNA bound is dependant upon its concentration.

Attempts to transform streptomycin-sensitive cells to streptomycin resistance using DNA from homologous resistant organisms failed even under conditions of maximum DNA uptake. The appearance of resistant colonies was only two- to fourfold higher than spontaneous mutation (Folsome, 1968). Unreported attempts at transformation of antibiotic resistance and of competence for carotenoid biosynthesis gave similar results. However these negative findings should not be considered final as all the parameters which can be varied in transformation experiments have not been exhausted. Nor have mutants with double markers been used, a necessity for meaningful interpretation of results. Folsome (1968) has explained the inability of the organisms to undergo transformation as being due to the absence of one or more steps which occur between irreversible DNA uptake and genetic integration. In ultraviolet irradiated *M. laidlawii*, strain A, he found no caffeine-inhibitable dark repair mechanism although photoreactivation could occur. Other species, *M. gallisepticum*, *M. arth-ritidis*, and *M. laidlawii*, strain B also lack the caffeine-inhibitable repair mechanism. Thus Folsome considers the mycoplasmas examined to be similar to recombination deficient ultraviolet sensitive mutants of *E. coli* which lack a recombination mechanism. D. W. Smith and Hanawalt (1968) on the contrary have found a nonconservative mode of DNA replication similar to that of *E. coli* TAU-bar in ultraviolet irradiated *M. laidlawii*, strain B, strongly suggesting the presence of a dark repair system. Repair replication occurs to an equal extent both ahead of and behind normal replication. Visible light reduces the amount of repair replication consistent with an enzymic mechanism for photoreactivation. The amount of repair increases rapidly with dose at low doses of ultra-violet irradiation (5M ergs/mm^5) but more slowly, up to apparent satu-ration at 100 ergs/mm^5. (D. W. Smith and Hanawalt, 1969). In addition a small amount (1% per generation time) of nonconservative DNA replication occurs in normally growing *M. laidlawii*. Certainly there is too little information to assess the presence or absence of gene transfer mechanisms in mycoplasmas. With proper perseverance there is great likelihood that mechanisms similar to the bacteria will be found.

C. FUNCTION OF THE BLEB REGION

The bleb region described in *M. gallisepticum* is considered to have some function related to division (Morowtiz and Maniloff, 1966). Histochemical studies of ATPase have shown this activity to be localized in the bleb and infrableb regions and to be associated with the cell membrane. Acid phosphatase is localized in the infrableb region but not with the membrane (Munkres and Wachtel, 1967). This type of structure has been observed only in *M. gallisepticum* so its general occurrence among mycoplasmas is ill-defined. However this species has a more rigid membrane, so the find-ings may reflect merely the greater stability of this organism to manipula-tive procedures. The general shape of *M. gallisepticum* is seen in other species, i.e., lateral bleb formation.

REFERENCES

Castrejon-Diez, J., Fisher, T. N., and Fisher, E., Jr. (1963). *J. Bacteriol.* **86,** 627.
Cohen, G. N., and Monod, J. (1957). *Bacteriol. Rev.* **21,** 169.
Danielli, J. F. (1954). *Symp. Soc. Exp. Biol.* **8,** 502.
Domermuth, C. H. (1960). *Avian Dis.* **4,** 456.
Folsome, C. E. (1968). *J. Gen. Microbiol.* **50,** 43.

Folsome, C. E., and Folsome, J. (1966). *Bacteriol. Proc.* p. 37.

Furness, G. (1968). *J. Infec. Dis.* **118**, 436.

Furness, G., Pipes, F. J., and McMurtrey, M. J. (1968). *J. Infec. Dis.* **118**, 1.

Gale, P. H., Erickson, R. E., Page, A. C., Jr., and Folkers, K. (1964). *Arch. Biochem. Biophys.* **104**, 169.

Gewirtz, M., and VanDemark, P. J. (1966). *Bacteriol. Proc.* p. 45.

Henrikson, C. V., and Smith, P. F. (1966). *J. Gen. Microbiol.* **45**, 73.

Holmes, B. E., and Pirie, A. (1932). *Brit. J. Exp. Pathol.* **13**, 364.

Kandler, O., and Kandler, G. (1955). *Zentrolbl. Bakteriol.* Abt. 2 **108**, 383.

Kavanau, J. L. (1965). "Structure and Function in Biological Membranes," Vol. II. Holden-Day, San Francisco, California.

Koostra, W. L., Adams, J. N., and Smith, P. F. (1966). *J. Bacteriol.* **91**, 2386.

Lecce, J. G., and Morton, H. E. (1954). *J. Bacteriol.* **67**, 62.

Lester, G., Stone, D., and Hechter, O. (1958). *Arch. Biochem. Biophys.* **75**, 196.

Low, I. E., Eaton, M. D., and Proctor, P. (1965). *Bacteriol. Proc.* p. 77.

McElhaney, R. N., and Tourtellotte, M. E. (1970). *J. Bacteriol.* **101**, 72.

Mitchell, P., and Moyle, J. (1958). *Proc. Roy. Phys. Soc.* (*Edinburgh*) **27**, 61.

Morowitz, H. J. (1969). *In* "The Mycoplasmatales and the L-Phase of Bacteria" (L. Hayflick, ed.), pp. 405–412. Appleton, New York.

Morowitz, H. J., and Cleverdon, R. C. (1959). *Biochim. Biophys. Acta* **34**, 578.

Morowitz, H. J., and Cleverdon, R. C. (1960). *Radiat. Res.* **13**, 854.

Morowitz, H. J., and Maniloff, J. (1966). *J. Bacteriol.* **91**, 1638.

Munkres, M., and Wachtel, A. (1967). *J. Bacteriol.* **93**, 1096.

Osborn, O. H., and Pomeroy, B. S. (1964). *Exp. Chemother.* **3**, 363.

Pirie, A. (1938). *Brit. J. Exp. Pathol.* **19**, 9.

Pirie, A., and Holmes, B. E. (1933). *Brit. J. Exp. Pathol.* **14**, 290.

Pollack, J. D., Razin, S., and Cleverdon, R. C. (1965). *J. Bacteriol.* **90**, 617.

Razin, S., Gottfried, L., and Rottem, S. (1968). *J. Bacteriol.* **95**, 1685.

Rodwell, A. W. (1967). *Ann. N. Y. Acad. Sci.* **143**, 88.

Rodwell, A. W., and Rodwell, E. S. (1954a). *Aust. J. Biol. Sci.* **7**, 18.

Rodwell, A. W., and Rodwell, E. S. (1954b). *Aust. J. Biol. Sci.* **7**, 31.

Rottem, S., and Razin, S. (1967). *J. Gen. Microbiol.* **48**, 53.

Rottem, S., and Razin, S. (1969). *J. Bacteriol.* **97**, 787.

Schoenhard, D. E., and Padgett, G. A. (1961). *Bacteriol. Proc.* p. 125.

Smith, D. W., and Hanawalt, P. C. (1968). *J. Bacteriol.* **96**, 2066.

Smith, D. W., and Hanawalt, P. C. (1969). *J. Mol. Biol.* **46**, 57.

Smith, P. F. (1957a). *J. Bacteriol.* **74**, 75.

Smith, P. F. (1957b). *J. Bacteriol.* **74**, 801.

Smith, P. F. (1963). *J. Gen. Microbiol.* **32**, 307.

Smith, P. F. (1967). *Ann. N. Y. Acad. Sci.* **143**, 139.

Smith, P. F. (1968). *Advan. Lipid Res.* **6**, 69.

Smith, P. F. (1969). *Lipids* **4**, 331.

Smith, P. F., and Henrikson, C. V. (1965). *J. Bacteriol.* **89**, 146.

Smith, S. L., VanDemark, P. J., and Fabricant, J. (1963). *J. Bacteriol.* **86**, 893.

Somerson, N. L., and Morton, H. E. (1953). *J. Bacteriol.* **65**, 245.

Somerson, N. L., Walls, B. E., and Chanock, R. M. (1965). *Science* **150**, 226.

Spears, D. M., and Provost, P. J. (1967). *Can. J. Microbiol.* **13**, 213.

Steinberg, P., Horswood, R. L., and Chanock, R. M. (1969). *Bacteriol. Proc.* p. 33.

Stopkie, R. J., and Weber, M. M. (1967). *Biochem. Biophys. Res. Commun.* **28**, 1034.

Tourtellotte, M. E. (1960). A comparative serologic and physiologic study of pleuro-pneumonia-like organisms. Ph.D. Thesis, Univ. Connecticut, Storrs, Connecticut.

Tourtellotte, M. E. (1969). *In* "The Mycoplasmatales and the L-Phase of Bacteria" (L. Hayflick, ed.), pp. 451–468. Appleton, New York.

VanDemark, P. J. (1967). *Ann. N. Y. Acad. Sci.* **143,** 77.

VanDemark, P. J. (1969). *In* "The Mycoplasmatales and the L-Phase of Bacteria" (L. Hayflick, ed.), pp. 491–501. Appleton, New York.

VanDemark, P. J., and Smith, P. F. (1964). *J. Bacteriol.* **88,** 122.

VanDemark, P. J., and Smith, P. F. (1965). *J. Bacteriol.* **89,** 373.

Warren, J. (1942). *J. Bacteriol.* **43,** 211.

Weibull, C., and Hammarberg, K. (1963). *J. Bacteriol.* **85,** 498.

Interaction of Mycoplasmas with Their Environment

5

A. PHYSICAL ENVIRONMENT

1. Osmotic Stability

The absence of a rigid outer envelope should imply a high degree of sensitivity to the osmotic environment. This is not true, especially of mycoplasmas containing sterol in the cytoplasmic membrane. Nevertheless osmotic shock under specified conditions is the preferred method for isolation of the mycoplasmal membrane. Membranes thus prepared exhibit holes suggesting different degrees of stability or instability of various membrane sectors. The internal osmotic pressure of *M. arthritidis* has been estimated to be about 3 to 4 atm; that of *M. laidlawii*, 5 to 6 atm (Spears and Provost, 1967). The optimal tonicity of both solid and liquid culture media generally is about 10 atm (Leach, 1962). *Mycoplasma laidlawii* is capable of growth in media varying in osmotic pressure from 2.7 to 27 atm although the growth rate and amount of growth is reduced at the extreme values. *Mycoplasma gallinarum* and *M. mycoides* var. *capri* multiply at the lower value of 2.7 atm but growth ceases above 14 atm. Other species withstand a narrower range (6.8 to 14 atm). The organisms cannot be conditioned by growth in hypertonic or hypotonic medium.

No initial reduction in viable count occurs upon transfer of most species from an isotonic to a hypo- or hypertonic medium or from hypotonic to hypertonic environment or vice versa (P. F. Smith and Sasaki, 1958; Kim *et al.*, 1966). Continued exposure to a hypotonic environment at 37°C but not at 0°C results in increasing loss of turbidity and loss of viability (P. F.

Smith and Sasaki, 1958; Razin, 1964). This may be due to maintenance of the membrane in the form of a gel at low temperature. Maintenance of viability improves and is dependant upon increase in osmotic pressure as evidenced by the protective effect of sucrose. Optimum viability is obtained with 5 M sucrose (P. F. Smith and Sasaki, 1958). The pH of the suspending medium affects viability in hypotonic solutions, the optimum residing near neutrality (Razin, 1964). Species differences exist, with *M. laidlawii* and *M. bovigenitalium* being most sensitive and *M. mycoides*, *M. gallisepticum*, and *M. neurolyticum* being most resistant. The lipid composition of the culture medium and hence the lipid composition of the cytoplasmic membrane affect osmotic stability. Unsaturated long-chain fatty acids increase the osmotic stability of *M. laidlawii*, the cells of which appear more filamentous (Razin *et al.*, 1966). Trans isomers of monoenoic acids give rise to lower osmotic fragility than cis isomers (Rottem and Panos, 1969). Other species, when grown in increasingly higher concentrations of unsaturated fatty acids, become increasingly osmotically sensitive (Pollack *et al.*, 1969b). Conflicting reports exist as to the effect of cholesterol in the membrane (Razin, 1963a; Razin *et al.*, 1966). The greater osmotic stability of sterol requiring mycoplasmas points to a stabilizing effect for sterol. The relatively high lipid content of the membrane has been invoked as the basis for the unexpectedly high resistance to osmotic lysis. Osmotic fragility is greatest with cells in the logarithmic phase of growth.

The composition of the suspending medium can increase or decrease osmotic stability. Increasing viscosity has no effect (P. F. Smith and Sasaki, 1958). Divalent or polyvalent cations, spermine, and spermidine decrease reduction in turbidity and loss of cytoplasmic constituents (Razin, 1964; Rodwell, 1965). Protection by polyvalent cations has been postulated to occur by bridging of phospholipids and condensation of the membrane (P. F. Smith, 1968).

Spears and Provost (1967) have examined the osmotic and passive permeability properties of *M. laidlawii* and *M. arthritidis* which are prototypes of the sterol nonrequiring and sterol requiring mycoplasmas. Turbidity variations induced by various solutes at known levels of osmolality were measured with careful corrections for changes in refractive index by use of Ficoll solutions. Large turbidity increases in *M. laidlawii*, presumably reflecting osmotic influence on cell volume, are given by potassium and sodium chlorides, sodium acetate, and sucrose. Nonosmotic enhancement of turbidity also is induced in this species by sodium and potassium salts. Glucose, glycerol, and dimethylsulfoxide induce little or no change in turbidity. Only glycerol and dimethylsulfoxide have no effect on *M. arthritidis*. Aging of cultures or pretreatment with 5% *n*-butanol destroys the capacity to respond. Enhancement of overall turbidity of *M. laidlawii* but not of *M. arthritidis* suggests a cationic stabilization of the membrane of the former species. The turbidity changes induced by glucose, glycerol, and dimethylsulfoxide are greater in *M. laidlawii*. This may reflect a greater degree of permeability in this organism, a greater rigidity of the envelope of *M. arthritidis,* or more rapid or less restricted outflow of water in *M. arthritidis.* Neither organism exists with an internal osmotic pressure greater than the surrounding medium. Actually *M. arthritidis* has an osmotic pressure less than its external environment. This situation demands outflow of water. Such a phenomenon has been suggested as an explanation for the normal existence of many mycoplasmas in a filamentous state.

2. Alternate Freezing and Thawing

Repeated cycles of freezing and thawing results in almost complete lysis when the organisms are suspended in distilled water (P. F. Smith and Sasaki, 1958). Partial or complete protection against loss of viability, even after as many as twenty cycles, is seen when the organisms are suspended in growth medium, in increasing molarities of sucrose, and in saline (Taylor-Robinson *et al.*, 1968; Kim *et al.*, 1966; Razin and Argaman, 1963; P. F. Smith and Sasaki, 1958). Presumably the suspending medium may prevent the crystallization of ice inside the cells thereby reducing the shearing or cutting action. Amorphous ice having no sharp edges would be less deleterious.

3. Heat

The half life of all species examined with the possible exception of *M. hominis* (Taylor-Robinson *et al.*, 1968) is less than 2 minutes at temperatures of 50°C or greater. There is no survival after 7 to 10 minutes (P. F. Smith and Sasaki, 1958; Kim *et al.*, 1966). Half lives of various species at 37°C in saline at pH 7 amount to a few minutes with the exception of *M. pneumoniae* which maintains viability of 50% up to 5 hours. Similar effects are seen when the organisms are suspended in buffers or balanced salt solutions. Half lives of greater than 24 hours at 37°C are observed when the suspending fluid is the spent growth medium. At 4°C, survival in saline or buffers is extended to 7 days or more for *M. arthritidis.* Other species, such as those isolated from humans and *M. gallinarum,* exhibit half lives of a day or less. Survival time can be increased greatly by suspension in 50% glycerol–saline or 50% glycerol–culture medium. Lowering of pH below 7 is deleterious. Half lives at 25°C are intermediate to those at 4°C and 37°C. Viable organisms stored in culture medium can be recovered after ten months at −26°C. Little change in viability occurs after 12 months at $-65°C$ (Kelton, 1964). Under optimal conditions of pH and temperature in a protective suspending medium mycoplasmas possess a good capacity for survival.

4. Relative Humidity

Interest in airborne transmission of pathogenic mycoplasmas prompted a few studies on survival upon aerosolization. Survival depends upon the suspending medium and may account for differences noted by two groups using *M. gallisepticum* (Beard and Anderson, 1967; Wright *et al.*, 1968a). Optimum survival over a period of 5 hours at 27°C occurs at relative humidities (RH) of 10% and 90%. At least 90% loss in viability occurs at RH of 25% or greater. No organisms can be recovered at RH between 50% and 60%. *Mycoplasma meleagridis* behaves similarly. *Mycoplasma laidlawii* exhibits considerably more resistance which may reflect a characteristic for survival in its natural environment. Little loss in viability occurs at RH of 25% or lower and at RH of 75% or higher. Progressive death occurs at midrange RH reaching minimum survival at 40% where only 1% of the initial population remains viable. *Mycoplasma pneumoniae* is most sensitive at RH of 60% and 80%. Best survival occurs at very low or very high RH. However some survival is evident at most RH values and may reflect the capability of *M. pneumoniae* to produce contagious respiratory disease (Wright *et al.*, 1968b; Kundsin, 1968). Survival decreases at all values of RH in the presence of ultraviolet light. This reduction is dramatic at RH of 25%. Some protection against the lethal effects of ultraviolet light is afforded by an RH of 95%. The relationship between RH and ultraviolet irradiation is second order for *M. pneumoniae* supporting a theory of indirect, possibly multiple site injury resulting from ultraviolet irradiation (Wright and Bailey, 1969). Information of this sort is valuable for practical purposes but the effects of many parameters complicate meaningful analysis. Particle size, suspending medium, means of aerosolization, age of organisms, and temperature interact to give different results (Wright *et al.*, 1969). In general, mycoplasmas seem to behave in a fashion similar to bacteria.

5. Freeze-Drying

All species of mycoplasmas survive lyophilization in culture medium but, with the exception of the T strains, a one to four log drop in viable counts results (P. F. Smith and Sasaki, 1958; Kelton, 1964; Taylor-Robinson *et al.*, 1968). Strain differences are more variable than species differences. Use of distilled water as the suspending medium permits no survival.

Least reduction in viability occurs when the organisms are lyophilized in a medium high in protein content, such as equal volumes of skim milk and inactivated horse serum (Morton, 1963).

6. Sedimentation

The small size of mycoplasmas is reflected in the centrifugal forces needed for sedimentation. For all species a force of 25,000 g will sediment greater than 99% of the organisms. The typical effect of increasing centrifugal force on the disappearance of organisms from the supernatant medium is shown in Fig. 3.14. Few if any species sediment without the application of force. The appearance of a sediment in cultures often is used as a criterion of bacterial contamination. Gravitational force has little effect on viability.

7. Filtration

The earliest investigators used filtration through Berkfeld, Chamberland, and Jena glass filters to demonstrate the viral nature of mycoplasmas (Bordet, 1910; Elford, 1938; Klieneberger-Nobel, 1962). Use of gradacol membranes of standardized average pore diameter permitted Klieneberger to estimate the size of the minimal reproductive unit to be 120 to 180 nm. Greater than 99% of the cells of *M. agalactiae* are retained by gradacol membranes with an average pore diameter of 420 nm (Klieneberger-Nobel, 1962). Four species, *M. laidlawii*, *M. gallisepticum*, *M. gallinarum*, and *M. arthritidis*, will pass through millipore filters with an average pore diameter of 0.22 μm but few if any pass through a filter with an average pore diameter of 0.10 μm (Morowitz *et al.*, 1963). All filtration experiments assume rigid particles. The plasticity of mycoplasmas would allow passage through pores of diameter smaller than the natural morphological form by distortion of their shape. Nevertheless particle sizes determined by filtration are equivalent to sizes estimated by electron microscopy.

8. Irradiation

Mycoplasmas are very susceptible to lysis by sonic irradiation (P. F. Smith and Sasaki, 1958; Kim *et al.*, 1966). At 9 Kc greater than 99% killing occurs in 30 minutes. With the exception of *M. pharyngis*, which is more sensitive, all species examined display similar sensitivities. The initial concentration of organisms and the type of suspending medium do not have any pronounced effect. Loss of viability follows the general pat-

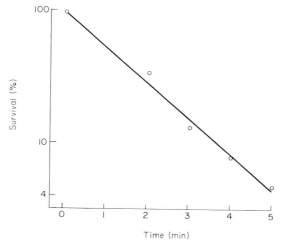

FIG. 5.1. Decay curve for *M. orale* subjected to sonic oscillation (10 kc). Courtesy of G. Furness. Copyright by Univ. Chicago Press. Adapted from Figure 2, Furness (1968).

tern of exponential decay (Fig. 5.1). Increase of frequency of radiation to 10 Kc results in a five- to sixfold decrease in time required for 99.99% killing. Increase to 20 Kc reduces this time even further to 2 minutes or less. Prolonged sonication results not only in rupture of the organisms but also fragmentation of the membranes. Controlled sonication can be used for preparation of membranes.

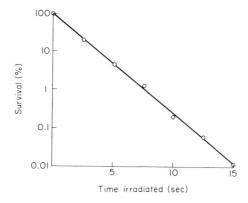

FIG. 5.2. Decay curve for *M. pneumoniae* subjected to ultraviolet irradiation. Courtesy of G. Furness. Copyright by Univ. Chicago Press. Adapted from Figure 1, Furness *et al.* (1968a).

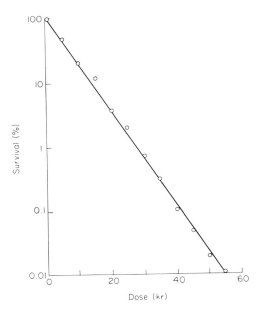

FIG. 5.3. Effect of x-ray dose on survival of *M. pneumoniae*. Courtesy of G. Furness. Copyright by Univ. Chicago Press. Adapted from Figure 4, Furness *et al.* (1968a).

The effect of irradiation with visible light on viability has not been examined. The ATPase of *M. laidlawii* is partially inactivated by visible light generated by a tungsten lamp when the organisms are in contact with toluidine blue. The ATPase of cells deficient in colored carotenoid pigments is inactivated to a greater degree than in normally pigmented cells. This greater photodynamic inactivation in the absence of pigments has been used to suggest a protective role for carotenoid pigments, especially since the normal habitat of *M. laidlawii* would subject it to solar irradiation (Rottem *et al.*, 1968).

Inactivation by ultraviolet and x-irradiation is exponential (Figs. 5.2 and 5.3) (Furness *et al.*, 1968a,b; Furness, 1968). This rate of inactivation is dependant upon the use of single cell suspensions. Nonexponential inactivation can be attributed to clumping of the organisms. Susceptibility is high. For example, *M. pneumoniae* undergoes 99% inactivation in 7.5 seconds by an ultraviolet light source delivering 220 µwatts/cm²/sec and by 30,000 r of x-ray. Inactivation rates are independant of cell concentration but dependant upon intensity of irradiation. Use has been made of inactivation curves to demonstrate the existence of various species as single cells or clumps of cells and to demonstrate division by binary fission.

Mycoplasma laidlawii exhibits extreme sensitivity to ultraviolet irradiation, estimated to be 13-fold that of *E. coli* (Folsome, 1968). There occurs not only a drastic reduction of DNA synthesis but also degradation of DNA which is exponential at rates which increase with dose of ultraviolet light. Irradiation also leads to dose-dependant lysis (D. W. Smith and Hanawalt, 1969).

The 1/e dose of gamma irradiation from ^{60}Co for *M. gallisepticum* is estimated to be 20,300 r (Morowitz and Cleverdon, 1960). Although the curve obtained is suggestive of a triple target it is possible that clumps of organisms rather than single cells were irradiated. The ultraviolet light inactivation curves reported by P. F. Smith (1967) also might be explained by clumping.

B. CHEMICAL ENVIRONMENT

1. Hydrogen Ion Concentration

Most mycoplasmas prefer a pH slightly alkaline to 7.0. Although variations occur as to species growth occurs with most over a range of pH 6.8 to 9.2 (Edward, 1950). This range is extended as far as pH 5.5 to 10.0 for *M. hominis*, *M. salivarium*, and *M. fermentans* although growth becomes greatly diminished at these extremes (Shepard and Lunceford, 1965). *Mycoplasma pneumoniae* requires an alkaline pH. In partially defined media growth occurs best between pH 7.5 and 8.0 (Rodwell and Abbot, 1961; Razin and Cohen, 1963; P. F. Smith, 1955). The T strains are an exception. Multiplication is maximal at pH 6.0 with no growth occurring beyond pH 8.0. At very low or very high pH loss of viability occurs rapidly and lysis ensues, particularly at alkaline pH (P. F. Smith and Sasaki, 1958; Razin and Argaman, 1963). Acid production by fermentative species ultimately results in death of the organisms unless the medium is well buffered. In *M. laidlawii* and *M. arthritidis* reduction of pH is followed by a reduction in phosphatidyl glycerol content and a concomitant rise in aminoacyl phosphatidyl glycerol (P. F. Smith and Koostra, 1967; Koostra and Smith, 1969). This quantitative alteration in lipid composition has been suggested to reflect an attempt by the organisms to buffer against acid by the production of more negatively charged groups. There is no real proof for this speculation. Formation of acid in cultures of *M. pneumoniae* results in loss of ability to induce formation of the tetrazolium reduction inhibition antibody and to act as antigens in immunodiffusion tests (Pollack *et al.*, 1969a). The T strains require careful attention to buffering because of their sensitivity to alkaline pH and their propensity to produce an alkaline environment by ammonia production from urea (Shepard and Lunceford, 1967; Ford and MacDonald, 1967).

2. Gaseous Environment

Gaseous requirements for growth ultimately reflect the respiratory physiology of the organisms. Those species with a cytochrome-terminated respiratory pathway should grow better aerobically while those lacking the cytochromes should grow best under anaerobic or microaerophilic conditions, especially if peroxides are formed. This has not proven to be entirely true although the respiratory physiology has been examined in only a limited number of species. For example, *M. pneumoniae*, which ferments glucose and forms peroxides, appears to be a strict aerobe (Low and Eaton, 1965); *M. salivarium*, which is nonfermentative, requires an anaerobic environment upon initial isolation but adapts to grow aerobically after transfer in pure culture (Shklair *et al.*, 1962). Most species grow equally well aerobically or anaerobically or in the presence of added carbon dioxide (Edward, 1950; Morton *et al.*, 1951). Greater yields of *M. mycoides* can be obtained by aeration (Rodwell and Rodwell, 1954; Newing and MacLeod, 1956). Added carbon dioxide is required or beneficial for initial isolation from humans, poultry, and rodents (Ford, 1962; Fabricant, 1959; Warren, 1942). Growth of established species does not require added carbon dioxide. Gaseous requirements are altered by the nature of the culture medium. Carbon dioxide improves growth of some species of human origin when grown in a suboptimal medium (Morton *et al.*, 1951). Both glucose and pyruvate are required by *M. gallisepticum* for anaerobic growth (Gill 1962). Glucose is not attacked by *M. mycoides* under anaerobic conditions thereby requiring the presence of other carbon and energy sources (Rodwell, 1960). Cultivation of *M. mycoides* and selected other species under aerobic conditions requires an increase in glycerol content, the addition of sodium lactate, and reduction of the level of phosphate to maintain proper tonicity of the medium (Rodwell, 1969). The necessity for added glycerol in the medium might reflect the reduction in glycerol available for lipid synthesis from glycolysis as a result of its being metabolized to acetate. Carbon dioxide is fixed by *M. arthritidis* into yet undefined cellular components (P. F. Smith and Henrikson, 1965).

3. Antibiotic Agents

Characteristically mycoplasmas are resistant to antibiotics which interfere with bacterial cell wall synthesis (Table V.1). An exception is *M. neurolyticum*. It is inhibited by concentrations of penicillin as low as 40

TABLE V.1

Inhibitory Levels of Various Antibiotics

Antibiotic	Inhibitory range μg/ml
Chloramphenicol[a]	0.1–8.0
Chlorotetracycline[a]	0.1–8.0
Demethylchlorotetracycline[a]	0.004–2.0
Erythromycin[a]	0.004–40.0
Kanamycin[a]	0.5–40.0
Nystatin[a]	>200
Oxytetracycline[a]	0.02–8.0
Polymyxin[a]	>1000
Spiramycin[a]	0.02–40.0
Streptomycin[a]	0.5–1000
Tylosin[a]	0.004–0.5
Bacitracin[b]	>600 units
Neomycin[b,c]	2–20
Penicillin[b]	>20,000 units
Filipin[d]	0.5
Amphotericin B[d]	3
Fungichromin[d]	10

[a] Newnham and Chu (1965).   [c] Leberman et al. (1952).
[b] Ward et al. (1958).   [d] Lampen et al. (1963).

units/ml (Hottle and Wright, 1966; Wright, 1967). Cultures remain viable for many days in the presence of penicillin. The inhibitory action is removed by washing or addition of penicillinase. The mode of action of penicillin on *M. neurolyticum* is not known. No analyses have been performed with this organism to assess the presence or absence of peptidoglycan. Conceivably penicillin could have a different mode of action. Extremely high concentrations of penicillin, i.e., 20,000 units/ml, will inhibit other species of mycoplasmas (Ward et al., 1958). Like penicillin, cycloserine and polymyxin are noninhibitory at the usual bacteriostatic levels. Bacitracin and other polypeptide antibiotics which interfere with bacterial cell wall synthesis also are without effect on mycoplasmas.

The so-called "small" polyene antibiotics (34 to 37 carbon atoms) are inhibitory while the "large" polyenes are not (Lampen et al., 1963). The "small" polyenes include filipin, amphotericin B, and fungichromin; the "large," nystatin and N-acetyl candidin. In addition to the molecular size of the antibiotic, inhibition is dependant upon the presence of sterol in the membrane. *Mycoplasma laidlawii*, a sterol nonrequiring mycoplasma, is refractory to the polyenes when grown in the absence of sterol but becomes susceptible when grown under conditions permitting incorporation of sterol into the membrane (Weber and Kinsky, 1965; Feingold, 1965). All polyene antibiotics become bound mycoplasma membranes which contain sterol (Lampen *et al.*, 1963; Razin, 1963b). Restriction of inhibitory action to the "small" polyenes is thought to be their capacity to penetrate into the membrane. The molecular dimensions of the small polyenes approximates the dimensions of the hydrophobic inner layer of the membrane thereby allowing for a better fit into the membrane. The "large" polyenes would be partially excluded. The "small" polyenes would be afforded a better opportunity to disrupt the membrane.

Other antibiotics which exert a disruptive action on lipoprotein membranes usually are inhibitory to mycoplasmas. These include the tyrocidines (Hatch, 1949). Surprisingly, the polymyxins are not inhibitory (Newnham and Chu, 1965). These antibiotics would be expected to inhibit as they bind to cytoplasmic membranes and disrupt the osmotic barrier. Their specificity for gram-negative bacteria might suggest the requirement for some lipoprotein component of the gram-negative bacterial wall in addition to or together with the cytoplasmic membrane in order for growth inhibition to occur.

Those antibiotics which interfere with more general and fundamental biological functions, such as protein and nucleic acid biosynthesis, are inhibitory to mycoplasmas. The broad spectrum antibiotics, i.e., the tetracyclines and chloramphenicol, the streptomycin family, and tylosin are inhibitory at low concentrations (Table V.1). Rather high concentrations of erythromycin are required for growth inhibition. Exceptions are species isolated from poultry and *M. pneumoniae* (Newnham and Chu, 1965; Slotkin *et al.*, 1967; Crawford, 1967). Resistant mutants arise to streptomycin, chloramphenicol, erythromycin, and chlortetracycline. As with the bacteria, stepwise mutants appear to streptomycin (Koostra *et al.*, 1966).

4. Chemotherapeutic Agents

Early reports on the effectiveness of arsenicals in the treatment of *M. agalactiae* infections in sheep and mycoplasmal infections of rodents (Bridre *et al.*, 1928; Findlay *et al.*, 1940) have not been substantiated by recent studies. A series of polyvalent arsenicals stovarsol, 3-nitro, 4-

hydroxy-phenylarsonic acid, arsanilic acid, aldarsone, carbarsone, try-parsamide, exhibited no effect *in vitro* or on mycoplasmal infections of chick embryos (Yamamoto and Adler, 1956; Adler *et al.*, 1956). *In vitro* inhibition of a variety of species by neoarsphenamine required 2 to 1000 μg/ml (Newhamn and Chu, 1965).

Colloidal gold and insoluble organic gold compounds, calcium aurothio-glycollate and calcium aurothiomalate, do not inhibit growth or alter pathogenicity, but the organic gold compounds display some therapeutic effect in mycoplasmal infected mice (Findlay *et al.*, 1940; Sabin and Warren, 1940a,b). Aurothiomalate does inhibit growth of mycoplasmas of human origin at concentrations of 16 to 128 μg/ml (Robinson *et al.*, 1952).

Sulfonamides, antimonials, salicylates (Findlay *et al.*, 1940), and iso-nicotinyl hydrazones (Yamamoto and Adler, 1956) are without effect. Nitrofurans as a group vary widely in their inhibitory levels (0.1 to 1000 μg per ml) but are effective against avian, animal, and saprophytic species (Domermuth, 1958; Turner, 1960; Newnham and Chu, 1965). A variety of thio compounds exert a bacteriostatic effect. Most are effective at levels of 100 μg/ml and include dithiocarbaminate and its derivatives, thioamides, thiooxamide and its derivatives, thiobiuret and its derivatives, and hetero-cyclic ring compounds containing nitrogen, carbon, and sulfur (Hagellock and Liebermeister, 1951).

Several antiprotozoal agents are inhibitory to many species of myco-plasmas (Newnham and Chu, 1965; Robinson *et al.*, 1959). These include quinine hydrochloride, chloroquin diphosphate, atabrine hydrochloride, ethidium bromide, prothidium bromide, and antrycide. Growth inhibition by atabrine results from its effect on respiration. Cortisone is without effect, but steroid inhibitors benzmalecene and triparanol prevent growth of *M. laidlawii* (Shifrine *et al.*, 1961). This inhibition can be explained as interference with carotenoid biosynthesis which proceeds in part via the pathway of sterol biosynthesis. A variety of other compounds which inhibit sterol biosynthesis [α(para-chlorophenoxy)isobutyric acid, farnesenic acid, vanadium trichloride, β-diethylaminoethyldiphenylpropyl acetate, phenethyl biguanide chlorpropamide, tolbutamide, geraniol, farnesol, nerolidol, citronellol, and citronellal[5]] inhibit the growth of *M. laidlawii* grown in the absence of sterol (P. F. Smith and Henrikson, 1966). Deoxy-corticosterone inhibits growth (Butler and Knight, 1960a; Schoenhard and Padgett, 1961) probably by disruption of the lipid-protein interac-tions in the cytoplasmic membrane. Various 3-keto derivatives of cho-lesterol actually stimulate growth whereas increasingly unsaturated 3-ketosteroids exhibit increasing inhibitory activity (Butler and Knight, 1960a). A series of 200 steroids have been tested against *M. gallisepticum*. Several were found inhibitory at concentrations of 5 to 100 μg/ml, some were without effect, and a few elicited a growth response 10- to 100-fold greater than cholesterol (Muftic and Redmann, 1968).

5. Dyes

Studies on effects of certain dyes have been prompted by the desire to develop selective culture media for mycoplasmas and to aid in visualization of colonies by vital staining. Species of human origin exhibit higher resistance to basic fuchsin (10 to 20 μg/ml), Nile blue A (10 μg/ml), thionin (25 to 100 μg/ml), brilliant green (5 to 25 μg/ml), and especially crystal violet (>10 μg/ml) than bacteria (P. F. Smith et al., 1950). Tetrazolium salts are not inhibitory and under anaerobic conditions are reduced (Somerson and Morton, 1953). The colonies stained by the reduced dyes require photography with special filters for visualization. Chlorazol black E vitally stains mycoplasmal colonies and not only aids in their visualization but also increases the diameter of the colonies. The mechanism underlying this increase in colony diameter may reflect stimulation of growth or accumulation of dye on the cytoplasmic membranes (Berliner et al., 1969). Brilliant cresyl blue and acridine orange are valueless for vital staining because of their toxicity. Toluidine blue participates in the photodynamic inactivation of ATPase in M. laidlawii (Rottem et al., 1968).

6. Inorganic Salts and Heavy Metals

Inorganic salts exert effects other than supplying growth requirements. Divalent cations provide a stabilizing effect on the membranes thereby preventing leakage of cytoplasmic constituents and loss of turbidity (Rodwell, 1965; Razin, 1964). Inorganic ions also are toxic to mycoplasmas This effect was shown first as loss of viability upon making dilutions of the organisms in saline or steam-distilled water (Butler and Knight, 1960b). Deionization of the water or treatment with chelating agents (diethyldithiocarbamate, ethylenediaminetetraacetic acid, or 8-hydroxyquinoline) improved survival. Salts of Mg^{2+}, Zn^{2+}, Co^{2+}, and Fe^{2+} in concentrations from 1 to 100 $\times$ 10^{-6} M inhibit the Y strain (Rodwell, 1967). Ferric ammonium sulfate at a concentration of 30 $\times$ 10^{-6} M inhibits M. laidlawii, strain A (Razin and Cohen, 1963). Phosphate at levels of 0.04 M or greater are deleterious to M. laidlawii, strains A and B. Many species are inhibited by 0.04 to 0.06 M potassium chloride although K$^+$ is required for growth (Gill, 1962; Leach, 1962; Razin and Cohen, 1963; Rodwell, 1967). Care must be taken in interpretation of these findings as trace metal contaminants rather than the stated salts may have contributed to or been the sole cause for inhibition of growth. Potassium tellurite and sodium azide are inhibitory for species of human origin at levels of 5 μg/ml (P. F. Smith et al., 1950). Thallium and gold are the only heavy metals examined for growth inhibitory properties of their salts. Differential susceptibility of mycoplasmas and bacteria to thallium, usually as the acetate, serves as an aid in isolation of mycoplasmas from bacterial containing specimens (Edward, 1947; Morton and Lecce, 1953). Thallium acts as do the mercurials by binding to sulfhydryl groups. Competition is noted between thallium and sulfhydryl compounds, such as glutathione and 2-mercaptoethanol. For some reason mycoplasmas can withstand higher concentrations than most bacteria with the exception of the streptococci. Although growth is reduced, most mycoplasmas multiply at concentrations up to 2 mg/ml. T strains are more susceptible to inhibition by thallium (Taylor-Robinson et al., 1968).

7. Surfactants

Mycoplasmas are particularly sensitive to compounds which lower surface tension. Lytic effects of bile salts first was noted by Tang et al. (1935) and Seiffert (1937). Pure bile salts are inhibitory at a concentration of 10^{-5} M (P. F. Smith and Sasaki, 1958; P. F. Smith and Lynn, 1958). Increasing the number of hydroxyl groups on the molecule results in decreasing inhibitory activity. Thus, cholic acid is the least inhibitory, deoxycholate is intermediate, and lithocholate the most inhibitory of the three.

Soaps are inhibitory to growth in the range of 10^{-3} to 10^{-4} M (Keller et al., 1952). Salts of unsaturated fatty acids usually are lytic at lower concentrations than salts of saturated fatty acids. Protein and sterol protect against the lethal effect of soaps (P. F. Smith and Boughton, 1960).

The ease with which mycoplasmal membranes can be lysed by detergents has been capitalized upon to disaggregate purified membranes. Intact cells are equally susceptible. Cationic detergents produce visible lysis only within a narrow range (3 to 7 $\times$ 10^{-5} M). At higher concentrations no change or even an increase of turbidity is noted. This may represent absence of lysis or aggregation of cellular particles by virtue of the excess positively charged detergent ions (Razin and Argaman, 1963). Anionic detergents readily lyse mycoplasmas at concentrations of 10^{-5} M or greater. The degree of lysis is dependant upon the concentration of organisms. Pretreatment of cells with uranyl nitrate protects against lysis. Nonionic detergents are required in higher concentrations. Even their maximal lytic effect is much less than with anionic detergents. Phospholipids (P. F. Smith

and Lynn, 1958) and Tweens (Razin and Argaman, 1963) also lyse mycoplasmas but at relatively high concentrations.

8. Enzymes

Lysozyme has no lytic effect as would be expected from the absence of
bacterial cell wall (Razin and Argaman, 1963). Variable effects are seen
with proteolytic enzymes. Initial studies showed very little lysis by trypsin,
bromelin, and papain unless the organisms were pretreated by heat denaturation or exposure to trimethylamine (Razin and Argaman, 1963;
Morowitz et al., 1962; P. F. Smith, 1967). Subsequent studies on intact
cells and membranes of M. laidlawii demonstrated reduction in turbidity
as a result of treatment with trypsin and chymotrypsin. Cellulase was without effect (P. F. Smith et al., 1969). Since no attempts were made to demonstrate release of cytoplasmic constituents these and most other studies on
lytic effects of various agents can merely presume membrane damage.

A variety of lipolytic enzymes can cause loss of viability and reduction
in turbidity. Pancreatic lipase induces lysis (Razin and Argaman, 1963).
Phospholipase C and the θ-hemolysin of Clostridium welchii do not affect
M. mycoides (Rodwell, 1956). Lysis of M. laidlawii results from exposure
to phospholipase A (Crotalus adamanteus venom) but not to wheat germ
lipase, phospholipase C from Clostridium welchii, or phospholipase D from
cabbage (P. F. Smith et al., 1969). Extracts of normal tissues from humans,
mice, rats, and cultured cells are lytic for M. neurolyticum. Evidence
suggests it to be phospholipase A producing lysolecithin which is lytic
(Kaklamanis et al., 1969). Negative effects of lipolytic enzymes should
be interpreted with caution as many of these enzymes require substrates
in micellar form and interaction with specific cations. The lipoprotein
nature of the mycoplasmal membrane should suggest susceptibility to
degradation by both proteolytic and lipolytic enzymes provided the appropriate sites are available to the enzymes. The lytic effect of alkaline phosphatase from E. coli indicates a role for terminal phosphate groups in the
maintenance of membrane structure. The possible existence of phospho-
proteins in the membrane should not be dismissed. Staphylococcal α-toxin
induces lysis of mycoplasmas regardless of whether they contain sterol or
not (Bernheimer and Davidson, 1965). The mechanism of action of this
hemolysin is unknown. It does not possess proteolytic activity. Streptolysin
S lyses a few species which contain sterol. Lytic activity of streptolysin O
is dependant upon the presence of sterol in the membrane. However only
species requiring sterol are susceptible. Unlike the situation with the polyenes, growth of M. laidlawii in the presence of cholesterol does not render
it susceptible to lysis. The reason for this is unclear. Mycoplasma neurolyti-

cum is less susceptible to lysis by streptolysin O. This greater stability may reflect a difference in the molecular structure of its cytoplasmic membrane or the existence of vestigial wall components suggested by its sensitivity to penicillin.

9. Miscellaneous Chemical Agents

Sterol-containing mycoplasmas are lysed by digitonin (P. F. Smith and Rothblat, 1960; Razin and Argaman, 1963). *Mycoplasma laidlawii* is refractory to digitonin unless it is grown in the presence of sterol.

Primary alcohols induce lysis. On a molar basis the longer the chain length, the less alcohol is required. This pnenomenon with mycoplasmas is identical to that found with bacterial protoplasts (Gilby and Few, 1960). The thermodynamic activity coefficients calculated from the solubility of an alcohol in culture medium and the growth-inhibitory concentration (Lamanna and Mallette, 1965) are similar for a series of alcohols with carbon chain length varying from 2 to 28 (P. F. Smith, unpublished).

Chelating agents do not induce lysis but cause leakage of intracellular constituents (Rodwell, 1965). Nitrogen mustard (Robinson *et al.*, 1952), phenol (Shoetensack, 1936), oxidizing agents such as hydrogen peroxide and potassium permanganate (Seiffert, 1937; Warren, 1942), and β-propiolactone (Roberts, 1964) are inhibitory. Sulfated polysaccharides normally present in agar presumably render some lots of agar toxic to mycoplasmas (Lynn and Morton, 1956). The addition of diethylaminoethyl dextran renders such lots nontoxic apparently by binding to the sulfated polysaccharides (Tauraso, 1967).

Viral infections of mycoplasmas are suspected. Gourlay (1970) found that filtrates from cultures of *M. laidlawii* isolated from the bovine nasal passage cause plaque formation on lawns of these mycoplasmas. The agent passes filters with average pore diameter of 10 nm, is heat sensitive (100°C, 30 minutes) and is inactivated by ultraviolet irradiation. A four to five logarithmic increase in titer is noted after each passage. Plaques are 2 to 3 mm in diameter. Dugle and Dugle (1971) demonstrated a satellite DNA, accounting for 38% of the total DNA in *M. laidlawii*. The buoyant density of this DNA is 1.685 (G + C, 25%; 38×10^6 daltons) in contrast to the major DNA component which has a buoyant density of 1.695 (G + C, 35%; 99×10^7 daltons). These authors interpret their finding as evidence for a viral nature for the satellite DNA. An average of eleven viral particles per cell was calculated. If these represent viral particles, they are very small. Furthermore, their mode of infection must be unique for microbial viruses since mycoplasmas are devoid of the usual attachment sites for phage.

C. HOST-PARASITE INTERACTIONS

1. Pathogenicity

a. MYCOPLASMAL INFECTIONS

Mycoplasmas are relatively poor pathogens. A few exceptions are *M. mycoides*, var. *mycoides* which causes bovine pleuropneumonia, *M. mycoides*, var. *capri*, the infectious agent of contagious caprine pneumonia, and *M. neurolyticum* which by virtue of a toxin produces neurological disorders in mice. The usual mycoplasmal infection results in invasion of epithelial cells lining the respiratory or genitourinary tracts.

Respiratory infections are the most common and are seen in many species of animals. These include, in addition to the bovine, ovine, and caprine pleuropneumonias, primary atypical pneumonia of man caused by *M. pneumoniae*, chronic respiratory disease of fowl caused by *M. gallisepticum* and *M. meleagridis*, chronic pneumonia of swine due to *M. hyopneumoniae*, and infectious catarrh of rodents due primarily to *M. pulmonis*. The typical gross pathology is consistent with an inflammatory response, i.e., congestion, edema, and the formation of a serous exudate which may become purulent in the event of secondary bacterial invasion. In the more acute cases of bovine pleuropneumonia, there appears a serofibrinous pleurisy and edema of the interlobular septa of the lungs. The cellular response consists of a thickening of the mucosa due to subepithelial infiltration of lymphocytes and large mononuclear phagocytes. Lymphoid hyperplasia together with petechial to diffuse hemorrhage is common. Leukocytic exudate is found in bronchi and to a lesser extent in the alveoli. Although it is generally true that mycoplasmas invade epithelial cells (Fig. 5.4), there is a notable lack of intracellular organisms in *M. pulmonis* infections of gnotobiotic mice (Piercy, 1960; Olesiuk and VanRoekel, 1960; Fabricant, 1969; Lutsky and Organick, 1966; Organick *et al.*, 1966; Organick and Lutsky, 1968). Other species have been found associated with respiratory disease but their contribution to the pathology is not established (*M. bovirhinis* in cattle, *M. hominis* in humans, and *M. hyorhinis* in swine).

The T strains found in the genital tracts of man and cattle and *M. bovigenitalium* of cattle are found associated with inflammatory processes. In humans the T strains are considered responsible for some cases of nonspecific urethritis (Shepard, 1967) and possibly for reproductive failure (Kundsin *et al.*, 1967). Although *M. bovigenitalium* is common to the bovine male genital tract it is suspected to be involved in inducing in-

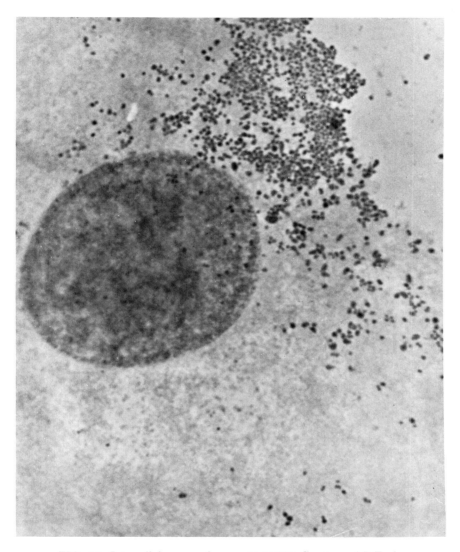

FIG. 5.4. Intracellular mycoplasmas. $\times$ 44,000. Courtesy of J. Fogh.

fertility in the female (Edward and Fitzgerald, 1952). The role of certain mycoplasmas in the production of mastitis is firmly established. These include *M. agalactiae* in cattle, sheep, and goats and *M. bovimastitis* and *M. bovigenitalium* in cattle. Infections of joints and articular tissues are seen in many animals. *Mycoplasma mycoides* and several unclassified species produce arthritis in cattle (Cottew and Leach, 1969). *Mycoplasma granularum* and *M. hyorhinis* infected swine exhibit arthritis and polyserositis (Switzer, 1969). Synovitis in poultry is caused by *M. synoviae* (Olson *et al.*, 1964). Purulent arthritis of rats results from infection with *M. arthritidis*. In this disease the tibiotarsal or radiocarpal joints of front or hind limbs become swollen, progressing into large edematous swelling of the entire leg. Although the disease may regress at this stage, the skin commonly ulcerates with the discharge of purulent fluid. Besides the pathological effects seen in soft tissue, there occurs frequently abscess formation and destruction of all structures of the joint including capsule, synovial membrane, and sometimes cartilage and bone. The arthritic disease is usually the most severe in the rat but gradations of these symptons are seen in arthritic diseases of other animals (Tully, 1969). *Mycoplasma pulmonis* produces polyarthritis of mice whereas rats are refractory to this organism (Barden and Tully, 1969). Conjunctivitis is another outcome of mycoplasmal infections in rodents, cattle, and man. A special situation characterizes *M. neurolyticum* infections of mice. The production of a toxin by this organism is manifested in the animal by neurological symptoms which are given the name of rolling disease. Animals exhibit rapid rotation on the long axis of the body either continuously or sporadically with eventual paralysis ascending from the hindlegs. Animals progress into a comatose state followed by death. The organisms are found in the brain at autopsy (Tully, 1969).

Production of experimental disease in most instances requires more than simple injection of the infectious agent. Even among the most virulent of the mycoplasmas special procedures are required. For example, production of typical bovine pleuropneumonia requires exposure of susceptible animals to aerosols (Cottew and Leach, 1969). The natural occurrence of rolling disease in mice requires the presence of latent mycoplasmas in the mouse injected with infectious tissue. After several passages the concentration of organisms becomes sufficient to produce symptoms. Relatively large doses of artificially grown *M. neurolyticum* given intravenously quickly produce the neurotoxic response (Tully, 1969). Most mycoplasmas exhibit a species specificity with respect to pathogenesis. Thus bovine strains are innocuous for man, avian strains are without effect on rodents, and so on. The most severe infections are associated often with other infectious organisms. Murine hepatitis virus and trachoma agent enhance the cerebral toxicity of murine mycoplasmas (Nelson, 1957; Lemcke, 1961); *Pasteurella pneumotropica* augments murine pneumonia due to *M. pulmonis* (Brennan *et al.*, 1969); *E. coli* (Gross, 1956) and *Klebsiella pneumoniae* (Gianforte *et al.*, 1960) aid in the natural and experimental production of chronic respiratory disease in chickens. Stress alone can activate latent infections (Lemcke, 1961).

Mycoplasmal infections frequently give rise to multiple symptomatology. *Mycoplasma hyorhinis* infections can produce nasal turbinate atrophy and pneumonia in addition to polyserositis and arthritis in swine; mycoplasmas are implicated in Reiter's disease of humans with its triad of symptoms: arthritis, conjunctivitis, and urethritis; *M. pulmonis* infections give rise to rhinitis, otitis media, and pneumonia.

The isolation of mycoplasmas from the bone marrow of humans with leukemias has stirred speculation as to their role in cancer (Barnard, 1925; Murphy *et al.*, 1967). Isolation of microorganisms from diseased hosts is insufficient criterion for establishment of the etiology of the disease. Extra caution is in order with mycoplasmas as these organisms form part of the normal microbial flora of most animals and man. Controlled studies have shown no definite relationship between mycoplasmas and murine leukemia (Tully and Rask-Nielsen, 1967) and human leukemias (Leach and Butler, 1966; Barile, 1967).

Mycoplasma-like forms have been observed in electron micrographs of corn-stunt diseased plants, their leaf hopper vectors (Doi *et al.*, 1967; Granados *et al.*, 1968), and yellows-type diseased plants and their insect vectors (Heimbeck, 1954; Ploaie and Maramorosch, 1969; Hirumi and Maramorosch, 1969). As with claims for mycoplasmal involvement in leukemias extreme caution should be invoked. Until the presumed agents have been subjected to analysis by Koch's postulates or some modification therof there can be no proof of a causal relationship for mycoplasmas in these diseases. A first step has been made by the isolation of the agent of corn stunt essentially free of plant tissue, its maintenance and apparent increase in number on artificial culture medium, and reinfection of healthy plants via the leaf hopper vector, *Dalbulus elimatus* (Chen and Granados, 1970).

b. FACTORS INVOLVED IN PATHOGENESIS

i. Galactan of M. mycoides. Hot phenol extracts of *M. mycoides* elicit in rabbits a febrile response accompanied by a leukopenia and followed by a leukocytosis (Villemot *et al.*, 1962). However a considerable quantity of the purified galactan (1 mg) is necessary to show any febrile response although smaller doses (1 μg) induces a leukocytic response. Intravenous injection of the galactan in some cattle elicits an anaphylactoid reaction within a few minutes characterized by an increase in respiratory rate, coughing, and salivation. Animals recover within an hour (Hudson *et al.*, 1967). It is questionable whether endotoxic activity is a property of the galactan or of some impurity. The galactan itself induces no antibody response unless injected with Freund's adjuvant. Simultaneous injection of galactan and *M. mycoides* prolongs the mycoplasemia with localization of the infection in joints. The galactan appears in urine and other body fluids of infected cattle (Gourlay, 1962, 1965; Gourlay and Palmer, 1965). Since this material is haptenic in character (Plackett *et al.*, 1963) it could aid infection by binding circulating antibody. This phenomenon is exemplified by the eclipse of the agglutination and complement-fixation reactions seen with sera from animals with severe cases of bovine pleuropneumonia (Turner, 1962). The galactan itself is not a specific virulence factor of *M. mycoides* as galactans from avirulent strains behave similarly (Hudson *et al.*, 1967). However it may be involved in an allergic reaction as suggested by its cross reactivity with a galactan found in bovine lung (Shifrine and Gourlay, 1965; Gourlay and Shifrine, 1966).

ii. Neurotoxin of M. neurolyticum.   The neurotoxin is produced only by logarithmically growing cultures and is lost by drop in pH and in the stationary phase of growth. Filtrates of cultures free of organisms have a toxicity equivalent to the whole cultures. Nonproliferating cells and organisms suspended in nonnutritive media fail to elaborate additional toxin (Tully, 1969). Inhibition of its production by puromycin and aureomycin suggests that active protein synthesis is necessary for its formation (Thomas and Bitensky, 1966a; Thomas, 1967). Freeze-thawing destroys the toxin and its preservation at $-70°C$ is only partially successful. It is thermolabile at 45° to 50°C (Tully, 1964). Its resistance to physical factors is greater in contact with the organisms than in cell-free culture filtrates. Sephadex filtration suggests that the toxic material in culture filtrates is a protein (absorption maximum, 275 to 280 nm) of molecular weight in excess of 200,000. However, similar material can be obtained from other nonneurotoxic mycoplasmas. Its protein nature is confirmed by its inactivation with trypsin (Thomas *et al.*, 1966a). The site of toxin formation in the cell is unknown. It is yet to be determined whether the toxin is exotoxic in nature or whether it is an integral component of some cellular structure such as membrane.

The pathogenicity of *M. neurolyticum* is directly associated with neurotoxin production. Intravenous introduction of toxin results in its rapid fixation to vascular receptors followed by transportation to the central nervous system. Introduction of viable organisms can result either in localized adsorption to tissue cells or cellular circulatory elements with the released toxin being transported to the central nervous system or direct transport of the organisms to the central nervous system where toxin can be elaborated. The toxin can adsorb to the leukocyte membrane. Specific antibody is capable of neutralization of the toxin (Thomas *et al.*, 1966a;

Thomas and Bitensky, 1966a). Since antibody is ineffective 2 minutes after introduction of the toxin, it is presumed that toxin has already become bound to tissue receptors. Symptoms appear rapidly after the toxin reaches the central nervous system. The target site in the brain is suspected to be a ganglioside (Thomas, 1967). Focal lesions develop in the cerebrum and cerebellum particularly deep in the cerebral cortex and underlying white matter. The accumulation of vesicles, distension of astrocytes, and the appearance of large quantities of intracellular fluid suggest a disruptive action on astrocyte membranes. Although electron micrographs show no overt damage it is conceivable that the lesions are too minute to be visible. Alterations in permeability of cell membranes need not be accompanied by overt physical damage. Compression of nerve cells and axons by distended astrocytes and disruption of the blood brain barrier are sufficient to account for the characteristic symptoms of the disease. In tissue cultures *M. neurolyticum* exhibits a cytopathogenic effect but there is no established relationship between this effect and neurotoxin (Tully, 1969).

Mycoplasma gallisepticum also is capable of elaborating neurotoxic activity for turkey poults (Thomas *et al.*, 1966b). This toxic component is inactivated by heat (50°C), freezing and thawing, and specific antibody. In contrast to the neurotoxin of *M. neurolyticum* this toxic activity appears associated only with living organisms and probably exerts its action on blood vessels rather than on the central nervous system.

iii. Hemolysins. Hemolytic activity of mycoplasmas first was studied by Suchanova (1955) who found it associated with both viable and nonviable organisms. Hemolysis of erythrocytes from many species of animals now is recognized as a general characteristic of most mycoplasmal species (Cole *et al.*, 1968; Sachdev *et al.*, 1968). Hemolysis by all species appears to be due to peroxides. Because of its medical importance *M. pneumoniae* has been studied most extensively. The type of hemolysis (α or β) and the degree of hemolysis is affected by the cultural conditions and the species of erythrocyte (Somerson *et al.*, 1965a; Sachdev *et al.*, 1968). The hemolysis now is proven to be associated only with viable metabolizing cells. It is inactivated by catalase and peroxidase. Heat denaturation of these enzymes or their inhibition with 3-amino-1,2,4-triazole destroys the inactivating capacity (Somerson *et al.*, 1965b). The hemolytic activity is heat labile and diffuses through dialysis membranes. β-Hemolysis results from destruction of the erythrocytes and is seen with *M. pneumoniae* and *M. laidlawii*. α-Hemolysis observed with some species, *M. gallisepticum*, *M. neurolyticum*, and *M. pulmonis*, is the result of methemoglobin formation due to peroxide excretion by these organisms (Thomas and Bitensky, 1966b).

The significance and function of peroxide formation in pathogenesis re-

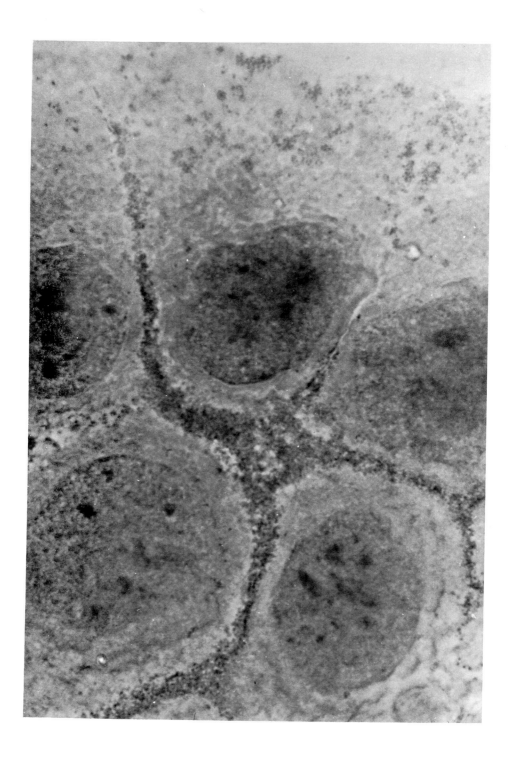

mains in the realm of speculation. Mycoplasmas, in particular *M. pneumoniae*, possess the ability to adsorb to erythrocytes (DelGuidice and Pavia, 1964) and tracheal epithelial cells (Sobeslavsky *et al.*, 1968). It is postulated that such close association allows the secreted peroxide to damage the tissue cell membranes without being inactivated by the catalase or peroxidase of the extracellular body fluids. Catalase-deficient mice exhibit less resistance to production of pneumonia by *M. pulmonis* than normal mice (Brennan and Feinstein, 1969). Suggested reasons why peroxides of virulent mycoplasmas are of pathological significance are the greater capacity of these organisms to adsorb to tissue cells and to produce quantitatively more peroxide.

iv. Cytopathogenicity. α. Adsorption of mycoplasmas to tissue cells (Fig. 5.5). Different species of mycoplasmas possess varying capacities to adsorb to erythrocytes (DelGuidice and Pavia, 1964; Manchee and Taylor-Robinson, 1968, 1969), tracheal epithelial cells (Sobeslavsky *et al.*, 1968), and spermatozoa (Taylor-Robinson and Manchee, 1967). This adsorption can be inhibited by specific antisera. The sites of adsorption on the tissue cells have been established as sialic acid residues (Gesner and Thomas, 1966; Sobeslavsky *et al.*, 1968). Hemadsorption and hemagglutination is inhibited by mucoproteins containing sialic acid, by sialic acid, and by pretreatment of erythrocytes with neuraminidase. In addition, adsorption sites on tracheal epithelial cells are removed or blocked by receptor-destroying enzyme or pretreatment with influenza B virus. The site on the mycoplasmal membrane which binds to the sialic acid residues has not been established. It has been suggested to be lipid or lipoprotein, possibly the lipid hapten responsible for complement-fixing activity of some mycoplasmas. Close apposition of mycoplasmas to tissue cells affords the organisms the opportunity to exert a cytopathogenic action.

β. Interference with normal metabolism of tissue cells. Mycoplasmal-infected tissue cells exhibit an altered amino acid metabolism which mirrors the metabolism neither of mycoplasmas nor of tissue cells alone (Powelson, 1961). The predominant change is the rapid depletion of the culture medium of arginine (Kenny and Pollock, 1963; Schimke and Barile, 1963) and glutamine (Castrejon-Diez *et al.*, 1963). One result of this depletion is retardation of growth and eventual death of the tissue cells. Infection with T strains induces degenerative cytopathogenicity (Shepard, 1958). These organisms alone among the mycoplasmas possess a very active urease giving rise to ammonia and a strongly alkaline pH (Shepard and Lunce-

FIG. 5.5. Localization of mycoplasmas at the surfaces of cultured tissue cells. × 2660. Courtesy of J. Fogh.

ford, 1967) both of which would be toxic to tissue cells. Mycoplasmal-infected L cells are incapable of incorporating thymidine and uridine forcing the cells to synthesize these nucleosides de novo (Nardone *et al.*, 1965). Alteration of the pathway for synthesis of pyrimidines in fibroblasts occurs upon mycoplasmal infection. Normally the fibroblasts utilize bicarbonate for pyrimidine synthesis. Infecting mycoplasmas supply arginine deiminase and ornithine transcarbamylase which make available the guanidino carbon of arginine as carbamyl phosphate. Carbamyl phosphate serves as precursor for carbamyl aspartate which lies on the pathway to pyrimidines (Woodson *et al.*, 1965). Thus the synthesis of pyrimidines in infected tissue cells involves the coordinate utilization of carbamyl phosphate-synthesizing enzymes of the mycoplasmas and the pyrimidine-synthesizing enzymes of the host cell. Some species of mycoplasmas which are capable of glucose fermentation can produce a considerable quantity of acid which could induce cytopathogenicity. However, acid production is not the sole explanation for cytopathogenicity of these species since *M. laidlawii* has no effect while *M. gallisepticum* is cytopathogenic (Butler and Leach, 1964).

γ. Destruction of cellular components. Infected FL human amnion cells decrease in number following an initial period of normal division after infection. The surviving population increases at a greatly reduced rate which cannot be altered by increasing the arginine concentration of the medium (Fogh *et al.*, 1965). These alterations in growth pattern are accompanied by a gradual reduction of chromosome number, an increase in chromosomal abberations, and the production of structural rearrangements of the chromosomes (Fogh and Fogh, 1965), particularly in dicentric and teleocentric chromosomes. Frequently the infected cells give the appearance of "leopard cells" due to the nuclei containing clumped chromatin (Stanbridge *et al.*, 1969). Most of the chromosomal changes are irreversible even upon ridding the cells of mycoplasmas (Fogh and Fogh, 1967). Chromosomal changes are reflected in the instability of the DNA of the host cells. Radioactive thymidine which becomes incorporated into the DNA is subsequently released into the medium as acid-soluble material Randall *et al.*, 1965). Breakdown of host cell DNA may be the direct result of DNases which are contained in mycoplasmas. Mycoplasmas introduced into lymphocyte cultures inhibit phytohemagglutinin-stimulation of mitosis (Morton *et al.*, 1968; Spitler *et al.*, 1968). There is complete inhibition of DNA and RNA synthesis. The most probable explanations are the depletion of arginine which is a precursor of nucleic acids or degradation of nucleic acids by mycoplasmal nucleases.

These alterations in the metabolic character of tissue cells and the changes induced in cellular structures pose a variety of practical problems. For example, suppression of viral growth has been observed (Somerson and Cook, 1965); nutritional requirements of tissue cells become altered; any metabolic studies on tissue cells may reflect mixed metabolism by tissue cells and mycoplasmas; there is interference with karyotyping and maintenance of a single karyotype.

Mycoplasma pneumoniae is capable of altering the antigenic determinants on human erythrocytes (P. J. Schmidt *et al.*, 1965; C. B. Smith *et al.*, 1967). Treatment of erythrocytes with mycoplasmas leads to destruction of the I agglutinogen, probably by enzymic digestion. Since cold agglutinins are specific for the I antigen, it has been suggested that the alteration of this antigen by mycoplasmas renders it nonrecognizable as self. Hence antibody is synthesized against it and becomes detectable as cold agglutinin. The absence of the I antigen in leukemic individuals and its destruction by mycoplasmas probably is circumstantial.

Exposure of lymphocytes from humans infected with *M. pneumoniae* to the antigens of this organism results in their transformation to large blast-like cells. Lymphocytes from noninfected humans do not give this response (Leventhal *et al.*, 1968).

2. Immunological Response to Mycoplasmas

a. Antigens

i. General aspects. A multiplicity of antigens can be presumed from starch-gel and polyacrylamide-gel patterns of whole organisms and cytoplasmic membranes (Fowler *et al.*, 1963, 1967; Rottem and Razin, 1967). Agar gel double diffusion and immunoelectrophoretic techniques confirm the antigenic complexity of mycoplasmas (Taylor-Robinson *et al.*, 1963; Lemcke, 1965; Argaman and Razin, 1969). Probably the more specific antigens are located at the cell surface and in the cytoplasmic membrane. Specificity does exist in soluble antigens. For example, the tetrazolium reduction inhibition antigen of *M. pneumoniae* is membrane associated while the complement fixing antigen is located in the soluble fraction (Pollack *et al.*, 1969b). This separation of antigens is no clear proof of their original sites. Variations in antigenic composition and specificity has been used to differentiate species and subtypes of mycoplasmas isolated from humans (Taylor-Robinson *et al.*, 1963; Lemcke, 1965), swine (Dinter *et al.*, 1965), poultry (Yamamoto and Adler, 1958), rabbits (Deeb and Kenny, 1967), cattle (Cottew and Leach, 1969), and many others. Most studies have employed viable whole cells as antigens without too much regard for quantitation. Soluble antigens are usually poor immunogens. Disrupted cells elicit the production of fewer precipitating antibodies than viable whole cells although no difference is noted with the complement-fixing antibody response (Lynn, 1967a). The use of Freund's adjuvant aids in production of higher antibody titers as does the route of injection. However, when comparisons are made using quantitatively identical doses of protein, mycoplasmal antigens are as immunogenic as bacterial antigens.

ii. Specific antigens. The nature of specific antigenic determinants in mycoplasmas has been studied only in a limited number of species. With the exception of *M. mycoides* and *M. pneumoniae* knowledge of the nature of antigens is restricted to their gross chemical class, such as lipid, carbohydrate, or protein.

α. Mycoplasma mycoides. A polysaccharide, initially isolated in crude form (Kurotchkin, 1937) and shown to be ethanol soluble, heat stable, active in precipitin reactions, and liberated into the culture medium or body fluids of infected animals (Dafaalla, 1957), has been identified as a galactan (Buttery and Plackett, 1960; Plackett and Buttery, 1964; Plackett *et al.*, 1963). The galactan was purified by extraction with hot aqueous phenol and precipitation from 70% ethanol followed by high speed centrifugation. It is almost homogeneous in gel diffusion tests but at least two minor components are detectable. Physicochemical analyses revealed an optical rotation of -150 degrees, and susceptibility to acid hydrolysis and periodate oxidation. Although galactose constitutes most of the reducing sugar component, about 1% is accounted for as glucose. The major linkage is -6-O-$β$-D-galactofuranosyl-1, based upon chemical properties and the structure of the disaccharide found after partial acid hydrolysis. Heating with alkali does not affect its inhibition of the indirect hemagglutination reaction. Such material can no longer sensitize erythrocytes for this reaction. Alkali treatment liberates long-chain fatty acids suggesting that some of the hydroxyl groups are esterified. Fatty acids are necessary for binding of the polysaccharide to the erythrocyte surface. The galactan is active in precipitin, complement fixation, and indirect hemagglutination reactions although it is nonantigenic and nonpyrogenic (Cottew, 1960, 1962). The serological reactions are inhibited by oligosaccharides composed of -6-O-$β$-D-galactofuranosyl units but not by those composed of -6-O-$β$-D-galactopyranosyl units. Hence the antigenic specificity appears to be determined by the galactofuranosyl structure. However, some *M. mycoides* antisera react with polysaccharides containing glucopyranose linkages such as barley glucan and type II pneumococcal polysaccharide indicating the existence of other specific antigenic determinants in the organism.

The minor components contaminating the galactan probably are glycolipids as deduced from the alkali lability of both sensitizing and inhibitory properties in indirect hemagglutination. The major glycolipid of *M. my-*

coides is 1-*O*-β-D-galactofuranosyl diglyceride (Plackett, 1967). Undoubtedly very small amounts of glycolipids with more hexose units exist in the organism. These glycolipids could exhibit haptenic activity similar to the glycolipids of *M. pneumoniae*. The cross reactions seen between *M. mycoides* and several bacterial species (Gourlay and Shifrine, 1966; Shifrine and Gourlay 1967) including *Corynebacterium xerosis*, *Aeromonas hydrophila*, and *E. coli* in agar gel precipitation and *Streptococcus* and *Pneumococcus*, type XIV in complement fixation probably are due to identical glycolipids. Likewise, the relationship between *M. mycoides* and *M. pneumoniae* seen in complement fixation, immunofluorescence, and growth-inhibition tests probably is due to identical glycolipid components (Lemcke *et al.*, 1965). The galactan does not appear to be related to protecive antigens (Hudson *et al.*, 1967).

β. *Mycoplasma pneumoniae*. First indication of a lipoidal antigen was the successful extraction of a complement-fixing fraction by chloroform or ether (Kenny and Grayston, 1965). These extracts were immunogenic. Partitioning with chloroform–methanol and aqueous potassium chloride resulted in loss of immunogenicity but retention of complement-fixing activity. Subsequent studies on various chemical fractions revealed that complement-fixing activity was associated with lipoidal components from the membrane while precipitin activity was associated with polysaccharide components (Prescott *et al.*, 1966; Sobeslavsky *et al.*, 1966, 1967). Lemcke *et al.* (1968) found complement-fixing and gel-precipitating activities in chloroform–methanol extracts. These were heat stable, resistant to lipase and protease, but sensitive to periodate oxidation and alkaline methanolysis. These extracts were poor immunogens. Since this material is immunogenic when associated with protein (Sobeslavsky *et al.*, 1966), it appears that the lipoidal portion imparts the specificity to the antigen and behaves as a hapten. Subsequent analyses (Beckman and Kenny, 1968; Lemcke *et al.*, 1967) showed the presence of the sugars, glucose and galactose, glycerol, fatty acid esters, and possibly phosphate. Proof of the glycolipid nature of the specific antigenic determinant was made by Plackett *et al.* (1969) who found a series of compounds which became labeled when the organisms were grown in radioactive substrates. These lipids for which the exact structures have yet to be determined consist of digalactosyl and trigalactosyl diglycerides, a dihexosyl diglyceride containing both glucose and galactose, and a trihexosyl diglyceride containing both hexoses which probably is a mixture of two or more glycolipids. Demonstration of serological activity of these lipids necessitates the preparation of a micellar form of the glycolipid together with auxiliary lipids such as egg lecithin, synthetic phosphatidyl choline, or phosphatidyl ethanolamine. Auxiliary lipids alone exhibit no reactivity in the complement-fixation reaction. The serological activity shown by phosphatidyl glycerol (Prescott *et al.*, 1969) probably is due to its auxiliary effect on trace amounts of glycolipids contaminating the preparation. Cross reactivity of antisera to *M. pneumoniae* occurs with other glycolipids such as lactosylceramide (cytolipin H), digalactosyl diglyceride from spinach, and diglucosyl diglyceride from *Streptococcus* MG (Plackett *et al.*, 1969). Whole cell antigens and the lipid hapten of *M. pneumoniae* react with antisera to *Streptococcus* MG (Marmion and Hers, 1963; Marmion *et al.*, 1967; Lind, 1968). It would appear that several lipid haptens possess the ability to react in complement fixation reactions, the exact specificity of each not yet being firmly established.

The role of these haptens when combined with protein in immunity to *M. pneumoniae* is not known. Apparently the lipoprotein complexes stimulate the production of antibodies which fix complement, inhibit growth of the organisms (measured as tetrazolium reduction inhibition), and function in the indirect hemagglutination reaction. Growth-inhibiting antibody is considered protective since a correlation exists between its concentration and protection against illness due to *M. pneumoniae* (Senterfit and Jensen, 1966, 1967).

Other antigens found in *M. pneumoniae* include uncharacterized lipids and proteins, a polysaccharide (Sobeslavsky *et al.*, 1966, 1967), a phenol-soluble antigen and a component precipitable from ethanol extracts with acetone (Marmion *et al.*, 1967).

Formation of the tetrazolium reduction inhibitory antigen is dependant upon maintenance of a slightly alkaline pH. It is destroyed if cultures are allowed to become acidic (Pollack *et al.*, 1969a). This antigen is sensitive to lipases.

γ. *Mycoplasma laidlawii.* The diglucosyl diglyceride [1-(*O*-α-D-glucopyranosyl-(1 → 2)-*O*-α-D-glucopyranosyl)-2,3-diacyl-D-glycerol] of this organism (Shaw *et al.*, 1968) behaves as a specific hapten (Plackett and Shaw, 1967). It is identical to the diglucosyl diglyceride of *Streptococcus* MG and cross reacts with this organism as well as *M. pneumoniae* (Marmion *et al.*, 1967) in complement-fixation reactions. The serological activity of the monoglucosyl diglyceride has not been examined. There appear to exist glycolipids with longer hexose chains which probably impart antigenic specificity. These are poorly extractable into lipid solvents and could account for the association of antibody stimulatory activity with the defatted membranes observed by Kahane and Razin (1969). However there is no reason to assume the absence of specific protein antigens.

δ. *Mycoplasma neurolyticum.* The neurotoxin of this organism is a thermolabile protein which can be inactivated by trypsin. It elicits the formation of specific antibody which is protective for mice if given before injection of the toxin. It is ineffective when given 3 minutes after the injection of toxin indicating rapid binding of toxin to tissue sites (Thomas, 1967). Identical sites on the toxin molecule for both tissue and for antibody reaction are indicated. The tissue site for toxin binding is thermostable, resistant to trypsin, but destroyed by periodate oxidation suggestive of a ganglioside. The possibility of the active binding site on the toxin being lipoidal has not been ruled out.

ε. Bovine arthritis strain. An unclassified mycoplasma which is the causative agent of bovine arthritis contains a serologically active glucan. The predominant linkage in this polysaccharide is -2-O-β-D-gluco-pyranosyl-1.

ζ. Partially characterized antigens from other species. *Mycoplasma fermentans* contains a chloroform–methanol soluble antigen exhibiting specificity. Other species of human origin (*M. hominis*, *M. pharyngis*, *M. orale*, *M. salivarium*, and *M. arthritidis*) and *M. pulmonis* contain non-specific lipoidal antigens (Kenny, 1967; Deeb and Kenny, 1967). *Mycoplasma arthritidis* contains no glycolipids (P. F. Smith and Koostra, 1967). In all liklihood nonspecificity of lipoidal antigens in this and other species is due to absence of glycolipids. Specific antigens of these species are heat labile. Antigens of *M. hominis* which give rise to antibodies functional in metabolic inhibition and indirect hemagglutination are associated with protein. No lipid or polysaccharide antigens occur (Hollingdale and Lemcke, 1969). The antigens of *M. pulmonis* consist of heat labile, cross related, water-soluble components and heat stable, subtype specific, water-soluble components. These latter antigens are precipitable with trichloro-acetic acid, stable to periodate oxidation, but inactivated by pronase, suggesting a protein nature.

Heterogenetic antigens common to *M. arthritidis* and rat tissue have been postulated (Cole *et al.*, 1969). Infection of rats with this organism fails to produce antibody functional in metabolic inhibition and indirect hemagglutination. On the other hand antibodies of these types are produced by rats exposed to nonmurine species. Yet complement-fixing antibody and resistance to challenge are produced in rats exposed to *M. arthritidis*.

Antigens which exhibit the greatest specificity appear to be lipoproteins in which the specific antigenic determinants are glycolipids. In the absence of a cell wall glycolipids offer the best molecules which can exist with a variety of components (sugars) and in a variety of linkages. Although they are present in bacteria their location in the cytoplasmic membrane and the occurrence of other components with specific antigenic structure in walls and capsules overshadows their immunological activity.

b. Formation of Antibody Against Mycoplasmas

i. The course of antibody formation. An antibody response to infection by or to experimental introduction of mycoplasmas has been demonstrated in many species of animals and man. Random sampling of sera from humans of different age groups shows an increasing titer of tetrazolium reduction inhibitory activity with increasing age. Complement-fixing antibody is transient in appearance and bears no correlation with indirect hemagglutination (Taylor-Robinson *et al.*, 1965). Immunological competence probably appears very early since agglutinating and hemagglutination-inhibitory activities and resistance to challenge are seen in chickens immunized neonatally (Roberts and Olesiuk, 1966). Significantly greater antibody response is obtained when the immunizing preparation consists of viable organisms and when introduced in Freund's adjuvant or in the foot pad of rabbits. Higher titers of complement-fixing and growth-inhibiting antibodies and more precipitin lines in agar gel diffusion result from injection of viable cells than from disrupted organisms (Lynn, 1967a).

The course of antibody formation has been followed in the rabbit, cattle, and human volunteers. In rabbits the size of antigen dose has no effect if immunization is carried out over an extended time period. However, sera taken after 7 days show greater complement-fixing and growth-inhibitory activities with larger antigen doses. An increase in complement fixing titer and the number of precipitin bands occurs up to 3 weeks followed by a drop in both. Growth-inhibitory antibody shows a general increase with time (Table V.2). All serological activities examined with the exception of growth inhibition are associated with the 7 S fraction (IgG). One fraction containing 19 S (IgM) globulin which exhibits growth inhibitory activity also contains a 7 S component (Lynn, 1967a,b). Riggs *et al.* (1967) also find growth-inhibitory antibody associated with IgG and IgM. Thus essentially all antibody produced by rabbits against mycoplasmas appears to be 7 S globulin. Further confirmation of these results is their lack of alteration by treatment of serum with 2-mercaptoethanol before chromatographic separation.

Antibody is formed in cattle against *M. bovigenitalium* by inoculation into the udder but not by intranasal or intravaginal instillation. Only 19 S antibodies are formed. Antibody first appears in 2 weeks, persists for 7 weeks, and then rapidly declines (Roberts, 1968).

Infection via the respiratory route of human volunteers with *M. hominis* results in a gradual increase of indirect hemagglutinating antibody reaching a maximum in 3 weeks (Taylor-Robinson *et al.*, 1966). This antibody persists for at least 16 weeks. No rise in complement-fixing antibody occurs.

A variety of antibodies are produced in humans following infection with

TABLE V.2

Serological Activity of Antisera to *M. arthritidis*, strain 39[a]

Antibody type (DEAE fraction)	Values at day 7			Values at day 20			Values at day 44		
	CF[b]	Pptn. bands[c]	Growth inhibition[d]	CF	Pptn. bands	Growth inhibition	CF	Pptn. bands	Growth inhibition
IgG	20	0	+	2560	3	+	640	2	+
IgG	160	0	ND	1280	1	+	160	1	+
IgG	40	0	ND	160	0	+	80	0	+
IgG	40	0	ND	20	0	ND	20	0	ND
IgG	80	0	ND	20	0	ND	0	0	±
IgG, IgM	0	0	+	0	0	+	0	0	+

[a] Data adapted from Lynn (1967a,b).

[b] Reciprocal of highest dilution of serum permitting 50% binding of complement in presence of 50 μg antigen protein.

[c] Number of precipitin bands; antigen concentration was 100 μg protein/ml.

[d] 3-mm Zone or greater is considered positive. ND = not done.

M. pneumoniae. Complement-fixing antibody is associated with both IgG (Fernald *et al.*, 1967) and IgM (N. J. Schmidt *et al.*, 1966). Indirect hemagglutination, growth inhibition, and cold agglutinins are associated with IgM. The IgG fraction contains complement-fixing and growth-inhibitory activities. Antibody associated with IgM disappears rapidly over a period of 6 months with the exception of complement-fixing antibody which persists. Growth inhibitory activity persists as IgG. Passive transfer of immunity has been demonstrated (Cole *et al.*, 1969).

ii. Types of antibodies produced. Antibodies of both 19 S and 7 S are produced depending upon the species of animal examined. These antibodies are active in a variety of serological reactions including hemagglutination of both fresh and tanned erythrocytes, complement fixation, growth inhibition, metabolic inhibition, precipitation, agglutination, and immunofluorescence. Fractionation procedures have not been highly successful in separating antibodies with different serological activities. Most antibodies appear to be directed against components of the cytoplasmic membrane. There exist more than one type of antibody active in certain reactions such as complement fixation and growth inhibition. One type of antibody can be reactive in more than one type of reaction. The specificity and the inhibitory nature of the growth-inhibitory antibody suggest a role for it in immunity. Metabolic inhibition and growth inhibition have been assumed to be due to the same antibody. This generalization may be hazardous since most antibodies against enzymes are not directed against the active sites on enzymes. The varied results indicative of a role for heat-stable and heat-labile normal serum components as adjuncts to growth inhibition suggest a more complicated phenomenon than is assumed. Nevertheless correlations do exist between the presence of metabolic inhibiting activity and resistance to infection (C. B. Smith *et al.*, 1967). Likewise such a correlation has been demonstrated with antibody measured by indirect immunofluorescence (Taylor-Robinson *et al.*, 1966).

c. ANTIGEN–ANTIBODY INTERACTIONS

i. Agglutination. Many species of mycoplasmas, particularly those of avian origin, possess the capacity to adsorb to and agglutinate erythrocytes. This agglutination is inhibited specifically by antibody and is used as the basis for hemagglutination-inhibition test (Jungherr *et al.*, 1953). Although this method is sensitive and specific it has never been fully developed and tested for mycoplasmas other than those of avian origin.

Indirect hemagglutination of tanned erythrocytes upon which antigens are adsorbed has found extensive use with species of mycoplasmas derived from cattle (Cottew, 1960) and humans (Tully, 1963). Sonically disrupted organisms or soluble antigens such as the galactan of *M. mycoides* are adsorbed to the surface of tannic acid treated erythrocytes. This procedure renders the antigens particulate and the subsequent agglutination in the presence of specific antiserum visible. Adsorption of the antigens to the erythrocyte appears to occur through the mediation of long-chain fatty acid residues. This method is specific but difficult to standardize.

Latex agglutination employs the same principle as indirect hemagglutination except for the substitution of inert latex particles as antigen carrier. This method is specific and only slightly less sensitive than indirect hemagglutination. Both indirect methods obviate the difficulties encountered by autoagglutination seen frequently with whole cell preparations (Morton, 1966).

Simple agglutination of mycoplasmas has not been widely accepted because of autoagglutination, the requirement for large amounts of antigen, and the difficulty in assessing agglutination of such small particles.

ii. Precipitation. Agar gel double diffusion and this method coupled with gel electrophoresis have yielded a dozen or more distinct bands. However, three to four is usually the rule. These techniques have proven useful in determination of antigenic relationships between different mycoplasmas (Taylor-Robinson *et al.*, 1963; Lemcke, 1965). This method requires soluble and diffusible antigens. Standard tube precipitin tests have been used but have found little application.

iii. Complement fixation. This test has been used widely with all species of mycoplasmas except those of avian origin (Card, 1959; Lemcke, 1965; Chanock *et al.*, 1962). Its sensitivity and specificity is not considered as great as other tests such as growth inhibition and indirect agglutination. Many mycoplasmal antigens are highly anticomplementary. It has been found very useful in assessing the serological activity of specific lipid haptens (Lemcke *et al.*, 1967).

iv. Antibody-inhibition tests. Growth inhibition without the requirement for complement (Edward and Fitzgerald, 1954) and with a requirement for complement (P. F. Smith and Morton, 1953) has proven to be highly sensitive and specific. The requirement of heat stable and heat labile serum components for its expression or stimulation has not been resolved. Use of the growth-inhibitory antibody has been made to rid tissue cultures of contaminating mycoplasmas (Pollock and Kenny, 1963).

Measurement of growth inhibition by assessing depression of metabolism of glucose, arginine, or urea assumes inhibition of growth (Jensen, 1963; Taylor-Robinson *et al.*, 1966; Purcell *et al.*, 1966a,b). Growth inhibition in these tests is measured as absence of change of pH to acid in the case of glucose fermentative organisms and to an alkaline reaction in the case of organisms hydrolyzing urea or degrading arginine or lack of reduction of triphenyltetrazolium which acts as a terminal electron acceptor. Inhibition of the cytopathogenic action of certain mycoplasmas occurs with antibody plus a heat-labile serum component (Eaton *et al.*, 1962). Growth inhibition by antibody is considered the most specific serological test and has found wide use in separation of species.

The heat-labile serum component which is necessary for or stimulates growth inhibition by antibody is thought to be complement. It can be removed or destroyed by treatment of serum with ethylenediaminetetraacetic acid, ammonium hydroxide, antigen–antibody precipitates, zymosan, and anti b_1C/b_1A globulin (Riggs *et al.*, 1967; Barker and Patt, 1967). Thus it would appear that complement components $C'1$ and $C'3$ may constitute the heat labile accessory fator. If other components of complement are involved the mechanism of growth inhibition may be immune lysis as a result of damage to the cytoplasmic membranes. Antibody-induced growth inhibition of *M. mycoides* and *M. gallisepticum* is temperature dependant occurring only between 30° and 37°C (Domermuth and Gourlay, 1967; Gourlay and Domermuth, 1967; Barker and Patt, 1967). This may reflect enzymic activity associated with complement action. Both heat-labile and heat-stable nonspecific inhibitors have been found (Fernald *et al.*, 1967; R. J. Lynn, personal communication). Specific heat-stable inhibitors are considered to be antibody. Expression of inhibition depends upon species of mycoplasmas as well as the method for demonstrating growth inhibition (Purcell *et al.*, 1969).

Both indirect and direct fluorescent staining have been used to demonstrate various species of mycoplasmas in smears of liquid cultures, on solid culture media, and in infected tissue cells.

REFERENCES

Adler, H. E., Yamamoto, R., and Cordy, D. R. (1956). *Cornell Vet.* **46,** 206.
Argaman, M., and Razin, S. (1969). *J. Gen. Microbiol.* **55,** 45.
Barden, J. A., and Tully, J. G. (1969). *J. Bacteriol.* **100,** 5.
Barile, M. F. (1967). *Ann. N. Y. Acad. Sci.* **143,** 557.
Barker, L. F., and Patt, J. K. (1967). *J. Bacteriol.* **94,** 403.
Barnard, J. E. (1925). *Lancet* **2, 117.**
Beard, C. W., and Anderson, D. P. (1967). *Avian Dis.* **11,** 54.
Beckman, B. L., and Kenny, G. E. (1968). *J. Bacteriol.* **96,** 1171.
Berliner, M. D., Kundsin, R. B., and Allred, E. N. (1969). *J. Bacteriol.* **99,** 1.
Bernheimer, A. W., and Davidson, M. (1965). *Science* **148,** 1229.
Bordet, J. (1910). *Ann. Inst. Pasteur Paris* **24,** 161.
Brennan, P. C., and Feinstein, R. N. (1969). *J. Bacteriol.* **98,** 1036.
Brennan, P. C., Fritz, T. E., and Flynn, R. J. (1969). *J. Bacteriol.* **97,** 337.
Bridre, J., Donatien, A., and Hilbert, D. (1928). *C. R. Acad. Sci. (Paris)* **187,** 262.
Butler, M., and Knight, B. C. G. (1960a). *J. Gen. Microbiol.* **22,** 470.
Butler, M., and Knight, B. C. G. (1960b). *J. Gen. Microbiol.* **22,** 483.
Butler, M., and Leach, R. H. (1964). *J. Gen. Microbiol.* **34,** 285.
Buttery, S. H., and Plackett, P. (1960). *J. Gen. Microbiol.* **23,** 357.
Card, D. H. (1959). *Brit. J. Vener. Dis.* **35,** 27.
Castrejon-Diez, J., Fisher, T. N., and Fisher, E., Jr. (1963). *Proc. Soc. Exp. Biol. Med.* **112,** 643.
Chanock, R. M., James, N. D., Fox, H. H., Turner, H. C., Mufson, M. A., and Hayflick, L. (1962). *Proc. Soc. Exp. Biol. Med.* **110,** 884.
Chen, T., and Granados, R. R. (1970). *Science* **167,** 1633.
Cole, B. C., Ward, J. R., and Martin, C. H. (1968). *J. Bacteriol.* **95,** 2022.
Cole, B. C., Cahill, J. F., Wiley, B. B., and Ward, J. R. (1969). *J. Bacteriol.* **98,** 930.
Cottew, G. S. (1960). *Aust. Vet. J.* **36,** 54.
Cottew, G. S. (1962). *Nature (London)* **194,** 308.
Cottew, G. S., and Leach, R. H. (1969). *In*" TheMycoplasmatales and the L-Phase of Bacteria" (L. Hayflick, ed.), pp. 527–570. Appleton, New York.
Crawford, Y. E. (1967). *In* "A Microbial Enigma" (C. Panos, ed.), pp. 1–70. World Publ., Cleveland, Ohio.
Dafaalla, E. N. (1957). *Bull. Epizootic Dis. Africa* **5,** 135.
Deeb, B. J., and Kenny, G. E. (1967). *J. Bacteriol.* **93,** 1416.
DelGuidice, R. A., and Pavia, P. (1964). *Bacteriol. Proc.* p. 71.
Dinter, Z., Danielsson, D., and Bakos, K. (1965). *J. Gen. Microbiol.* **41, 77.**
Doi, Y., Terenaka, M., Yora, K., and Asuyama, H. (1967). *Ann. Phytopathol. Soc. Japan* **33,** 259.
Domermuth, C. H. (1958). *Avian Dis.* **4,** 456.

Domermuth, C. H., and Gourlay, R. N. (1967). *J. Gen. Microbiol.* **47,** 289.

Dugle, D. L., and Dugle, J. R. (1971). *Can. J. Microbiol.* **17,** 433.

Eaton, M. D., Farnham, A. E., Levinthal, J. D., and Scala, A. R. (1962). *J. Bacteriol.* **84,** 1330.

Edward, D. G. ff. (1947). *J. Gen. Microbiol.* **1,** 238.

Edward, D. G. ff. (1950). *J. Gen. Microbiol.* **4,** 311.

Edward, D. G. ff., and Fitzgerald, W. A. (1952). *Vet. Rec.* **64,** 395.

Edward, D. G. ff., and Fitzgerald, W. A. (1954). *J. Pathol. Bacteriol.* **68,** 23.

Elford, W. J. (1938). *In* "Handbuch der Virusforschung" (R. Doerr and C. Hallauer, eds.), Vol. 1., p. 126, Wien.

Fabricant, J. (1959). *Avian Dis.* **3,** 428.

Fabricant, J. (1969). *In* "The Mycoplasmatales and the L-Phase of Bacteria" (L. Hayflick, ed.), pp. 621–641. Appleton, New York.

Feingold, D. S. (1965). *Biochem. Biophys. Res. Commun.* **19,** 261.

Fernald, G., Clyde, W. A., Jr., and Denney, F. (1967). *J. Immunol.* **98,** 1028.

Findlay, G. M., Mackenzie, R. D., and MacCallum, F. O. (1940). *Brit. J. Exp. Pathol.* **21,** 13.

Fogh, J., and Fogh, H. (1965). *Proc. Soc. Exp. Biol. Med.* **119,** 233.

Fogh, J., and Fogh, H. (1967). *Proc. Soc. Exp. Biol. Med.* **126,** 67.

Fogh, J., Hahn, E., III, and Fogh, H. (1965). *Exp. Cell Res.* **39,** 554.

Folsom, C. E. (1968). *J. Gen. Microbiol.* **50,** 43.

Ford, D. K. (1962). *J. Bacteriol.* **84,** 1028.

Ford, D. K., and MacDonald, J. (1967). *J. Bacteriol.* **93,** 1509.

Fowler, R. C., Coble, D. W., Kramer, N. C., and Brown, T. McP. (1963). *J. Bacteriol.* **86,** 1145.

Fowler, R. C., Coble, D. W., Kramer, N. C., Pai, R. R., Serrano, B. A., and Brown, T. McP. (1967). *Ann. N. Y. Acad. Sci.* **143,** 641.

Furness, G. (1968). *J. Infec. Dis.* **118,** 436.

Furness, G., Pipes, F. J., and McMurtrey, M. J. (1968a). *J. Infec. Dis.* **118,** 1.

Furness, G., Pipes, F. J., and McMurtrey, M. J. (1968b). *J. Infec. Dis.* **118,** 7.

Gesner, B., and Thomas, L. (1966). *Science* **151,** 590.

Gianforte, E. M., Skamser, L. M., and Brown, R. G. (1960). *Ann. N. Y. Acad. Sci.* **79,** 713.

Gilby, A. R., and Few, A. V. (1960). *J. Gen. Microbiol.* **23,** 27.

Gill, J. W. (1962). *J. Bacteriol.* **83,** 213.

Gourlay, R. N. (1962). *Nature (London)* **195,** 99.

Gourlay, R. N. (1965). *Res. Vet. Sci.* **6,** 263.

Gourlay, R. N. (1970). *Nature (London)* **225,** 1165.

Gourlay, R. N., and Domermuth, C. H. (1967). *Ann. N. Y. Acad. Sci.* **143,** 325.

Gourlay, R. N., and Palmer, R. F. (1965). *Res. Vet. Sci.* **6,** 255.

Gourlay, R. N., and Shifrine, M. (1966). *J. Comp. Pathol.* **76,** 417.

Granados, R. R., Maramorosch, K., and Shikata, E. (1968). *Proc. Nat. Acad. Sci.* **60,** 841.

Gross, W. B. (1956). *Poultry Sci.* **35,** 765.

Hagellock, G., and Liebermeister, K. (1951). *Z. Naturforsch. B* **6,** 147.

Hatch, M. H. (1949). "A Symposium on Current Progress in the Study of Venereal Diseases," p. 183. U. S. Govt. Printing Office, Washington, D.C.

Heimbeck, L. S. (1954). "On the Etiology of Brown Roots, Yellowing and Wilt Due to B Type (Dienes) L (Klieneberger) Forms of Bacteria with Special Reference to Pea Wilt," 40 pp. Dreyers Forlag, Olso.

Hirumi, H., and Maramorosch, K. (1969). *J. Virol.* **3**, 82.

Hollingdale, M. R., and Lemcke, R. M. (1969). *J. Hyg.* **67**, 585.

Hottle, G. A., and Wright, D. N. (1966). *J. Bacteriol.* **91**, 1834.

Hudson, J. R., Buttery, S., and Cottew, G. S. (1967). *J. Pathol. Bacteriol.* **94**, 257.

Jensen, K. E. (1963). *J. Bacteriol.* **86**, 1349.

Jungherr, E. L., Luginbuhl, R. E., and Jacobs, R. E. (1953). *Proc. Amer. Vet. Med. Ass.*, p. 303.

Kahane, I., and Razin, S. (1969). *J. Bacteriol.* **100**, 187.

Kaklamanis, E., Thomas, L., Stavropoulos, K., Borman, I., and Boshwitz, C. (1969). *Nature (London)* **221**, 860.

Keller, R., Smith, P. F., and Morton, H. E. (1952). *J. Gen. Microbiol.* **7**, 313.

Kelton, W. H. (1964). *J. Bacteriol.* **87**, 588.

Kenny, G. E. (1967). *Ann. N. Y. Acad. Sci.* **143**, 676.

Kenny, G. E., and Grayston, J. T. (1965). *J. Immunol.* **95**, 19.

Kenny, G. E., and Pollock, M. E. (1963). *J. Infec. Dis.* **112**, 7.

Kim, K. S., Clyde, W. A., Jr., and Denney, F. W. (1966). *J. Bacteriol.* **92**, 214.

Klieneberger-Nobel, E. (1962). "Pleuropneumonia-Like Organisms (PPLO) Mycoplasmataceae," 157 pp. Academic Press, New York.

Koostra, W. L., and Smith, P. F. (1969). *Biochemistry* **8**, 4794.

Koostra, W. L., Adams, J. N., and Smith, P. F. (1966). *J. Bacteriol.* **91**, 2386.

Kundsin, R. B. (1968). *Appl. Microbiol.* **16**, 143.

Kundsin, R. B., Driscoll, S. G., and Ming, P. L. (1967). *Science* **157**, 1573.

Kurotchkin, T. J. (1937). *Proc. Soc. Exp. Biol. Med.* **37**, 21.

Lamanna, C., and Mallette, M. F. (1965). "Basic Bacteriology," pp. 912–915. Williams & Wilkins, Baltimore, Maryland.

Lampen, J. O., Gill, J. W., Arnow, P. M., and Magana-Plaza, I. (1963). *J. Bacteriol.* **86**, 945.

Leach, R. H. (1962). *J. Gen. Microbiol.* **27**, 345.

Leach, R. H., and Butler, M. (1966). *J. Bacteriol.* **91**, 934.

Leberman, P. R., Smith, P. F., and Morton, H. E. (1952). *J. Urol.* **68**, 399.

Lemcke, R. M. (1961). *J. Hyg.* **59**, 401.

Lemcke, R. M. (1965). *J. Gen. Microbiol.* **38**, 91.

Lemcke, R. M., Shaw, E. J., and Marmion, B. P. (1965). *Aust. J. Biol. Med. Sci.* **43**, 761.

Lemcke, R. M., Marmion, B. P., and Plackett, P. (1967). *Ann. N. Y. Acad. Sci.* **143**, 691.

Lemcke, R. M., Plackett, P. Shaw, E. J., and Marmion, B. P. (1968). *Aust. J. Exp. Biol. Med. Sci.* **46**, 123.

Leventhal, B. G., Smith, C. B., Carbone, P. P., and Hersh, E. M. (1968). *In* "Proceedings of the Third Annual Leucocyte Conference," (W. O. Rieke, ed.), Appleton, New York.

Lind, K. (1968). *Acta Pathol. Microbiol. Scand.* **73**, 237.

Low, I. E., and Eaton, M. D. (1965). *J. Bacteriol.* **89**, 725.

Lutsky, I. I., and Organick, A. B. (1966). *J. Bacteriol.* **92**, 1154.

Lynn, R. J. (1967a). *Ann. N. Y. Acad. Sci.* **143**, 654.

Lynn, R. J. (1967b). *In* "A Microbial Enigma," (C. Panos, ed.), pp. 211–259. World Publ., Cleveland, Ohio.

Lynn, R. J., and Morton, H. E. (1956). *Appl. Microbiol.* **4**, 339.

Manchee, R. J., and Taylor-Robinson, D. (1968). *J. Gen. Microbiol.* **50**, 465.

Manchee, R. J., and Taylor-Robinson, D. (1969). *J. Bacteriol.* **98**, 914.

Marmion, B. P., and Hers, J. F. (1963). *Amer. Rev. Resp. Dis.* **88** (Part 2), 198.

Marmion, B. P., Plackett, P., and Lemcke, R. M. (1967). *Aust. J. Exp. Biol. Med. Sci.* **45**, 163.

Morowitz, H. J., and Cleverdon, R. C. (1960). *Radiat. Res.* **13**, 854.

Morowitz, H. J., Tourtellotte, M. E., Guild, W. R., Castro, E., and Woese, C. (1962). *J. Mol. Biol.* **4**, 93.

Morowitz, H. J., Tourtellotte, M. E., and Pollack, M. E. (1963). *J. Bacteriol.* **85**, 134.

Morton, H. E. (1963). *Bacteriol. Proc.* p. 51.

Morton, H. E. (1966). *J. Bacteriol.* **92**, 1196.

Morton, H. E., and Lecce, J. G. (1953). *J. Bacteriol.* **66**, 646.

Morton, H. E., Smith, P. F., and Leberman, P. R. (1951). *Amer. J. Syph. Gonor. Vener. Dis.* **35**, 361.

Morton, H. E., Copperman, R., and Lam, G. T. (1968). *J. Bacteriol.* **95**, 2418.

Muftic, M., and Redmann, U. (1968). *Zentralbl. Bakteriol. (Orig.)* **206**, 228.

Murphy, W. H., Ertel, I. J., Bullis, C., and Zarofonetis, C. J. D. (1967). *Proc. Soc. Exp. Biol. Med.* **124**, 366.

Nardone, R. M., Todd, J., Gonzalez, P., and Gaffney, E. V. (1965). *Science* **149**, 1100.

Nelson, J. B. (1957). *J. Exp. Med.* **106**, 179.

Newing, C. R., and MacLeod, A. K. (1956). *Nature (London)* **177**, 939.

Newnham, A. G., and Chu, H. P. (1965). *J. Hyg.* **63**, 1.

Olesiuk, O. M., and VanRoekel, H. (1960). *Ann. N. Y. Acad. Sci.* **79**, 727.

Organick, A. B., and Lutsky, I. I. (1968). *J. Bacteriol.* **95**, 2310.

Olson, N. O., Adler, H. E., DaMassa, A. J., and Corstvet, R. E. (1964). *Avian Dis.* **8**, 623.

Organick, A. B., Siegesmand, K. A., and Lutsky, I. I. (1966). *J. Bacteriol.* **92**, 1164.

Piercy, S. E. (1960). *Ann. N. Y. Acad. Sci.* **79**, 665.

Plackett, P. (1967). *Biochemistry* **6**, 2746.

Plackett, P., and Buttery, S. H. (1964). *Biochem. J.* **90**, 201.

Plackett, P., and Shaw, E. J. (1967). *Biochem. J.* **104**, 61.

Plackett, P., Buttery, S., and Cottew, G. S. (1963). *In* "Recent Progress in Microbiology," (N. E. Gibbons, ed.), pp. 535–547. Univ. of Toronto Press, Toronto.

Plackett, P., Marmion, B. P., Shaw, E. J., and Lemcke, R. M. (1969). *Aust. J. Exp. Biol. Med. Sci.* **47**, 171.

Ploaie, P., and Maramorosch, K. (1969). *Phytopathology* **59**, 536.

Pollack, J. D., Somerson, N. L., and Senterfit, L. B. (1969a). *J. Bacteriol.* **97**, 612.

Pollack, J. D., Somerson, N. L., and Senterfit, L. B. (1969b). *Bacteriol. Proc.*, p. 32.

Pollock, M. E., and Kenny, G. E. (1963). *Proc. Soc. Exp. Biol. Med.* **112**, 176.

Powelson, D. M. (1961). *J. Bacteriol.* **82**, 288.

Prescott, B., Sobeslavsky, O., Caldes, G., and Chanock, R. M. (1966). *J. Bacteriol.* **91**, 2117.

Prescott, B., Chernick, S. S., James, W., Caldes, G., and Chanock, R. M. (1969). *Bacteriol. Proc.*, p. 94.

Purcell, R. H., Taylor-Robinson, D., Wong, D., and Chanock, R. M. (1966a). *J. Epidemiol.* **84**, 51.

Purcell, R. H., Taylor-Robinson, D., Wong, D., and Chanock, R. M. (1966b). *J. Bacteriol.* **92**, 6.

Purcell, R. H., Chanock, R. M., and Taylor-Robinson, D. (1969). *In* "The Mycoplasmatales and the L-Phase of Bacteria," (L. Hayflick, ed.), pp. 221–264. Appleton, New York.

Randall, C. C., Gafford, L. G., Gentry, G. A., and Lawson, L. A. (1965). *Science* 149, 1098.

Razin, S. (1963a). *J. Gen. Microbiol.* 33, 471.

Razin, S. (1963b). *Biochim. Biophys. Acta* 78, 771.

Razin, S. (1964). *J. Gen. Microbiol.* 36, 451.

Razin, S., and Argaman, M. (1963). *J. Gen. Microbiol.* 30, 155.

Razin, S., and Cohen, A. (1963). *J. Gen. Microbiol.* 30, 141.

Razin, S., Tourtellotte, M. E., McElhaney, R. N., and Pollack, J. D. (1966). *J. Bacteriol.* 91, 609.

Riggs, S., Sharp, J. T., and Carpenter, R. R. (1967). *Ann. N. Y. Acad. Sci.* 143, 784.

Roberts, D. H. (1964). *Brit. Vet. J.* 120, 479.

Roberts, D. H. (1968). *J. Hyg.* 66, 585.

Roberts, D. H., and Olesiuk, O. M. (1966). *J. Infec. Dis.* 116, 490.

Robinson, L. B., Wichelhausen, R. H., and Brown, T. McP. (1952). *J. Lab. Clin. Med.* 39, 290.

Robinson, L. B., Brown, T. McP., and Wichelhausen, R. H. (1959). *Antibiot. Chemother.* 9, 111.

Rodwell, A. W. (1956). *Aust. J. Biol. Sci.* 9, 105.

Rodwell, A. W. (1960). *Ann. N. Y. Acad. Sci.* 79, 499.

Rodwell, A. W. (1965). *J. Gen. Microbiol.* 40, 227.

Rodwell, A. W. (1967). *Ann. N. Y. Acad. Sci.* 143, 88.

Rodwell, A. W. (1969). *In* "The Mycoplasmatales and the L-Phase of Bacteria" (L. Hayflick, ed.), pp. 413–450. Appleton, New York.

Rodwell, A. W., and Abbot, A. (1961). *J. Gen. Microbiol.* 25, 201.

Rodwell, A. W., and Rodwell, E. S. (1954). *Aust. J. Biol. Sci.* 7, 18.

Rottem, S., and Panos, C. (1969). *J. Gen. Microbiol.* 59, 317.

Rottem, S., and Razin, S. (1967). *J. Bacteriol.* 94, 359.

Sabin, A. B., and Warren, J. (1940a). *J. Bacteriol.* 40, 823.

Sabin, A. B., and Warren, J. (1940b). *Science* 92, 535.

Rottem, S., Gottfried, L., and Razin, S. (1968). *Biochem. J.* 109, 707.

Sachdev, K. S., Trojan, I., and Flamm, H. (1968). *Zentralbl. Bakteriol. (Orig.)* 208, 294.

Schimke, R. T., and Barile, M. F. (1963). *J. Bacteriol.* 86, 195.

Schmidt, N. J., Lennette, E. H., Dennis, J., and Gee, P. S. (1966). *J. Immunol.* 97, 95.

Schmidt, P. J., Barile, M. F., and McGinniss, M. H. (1965). *Nature (London)* 205, 371.

Schoenhard, D. E., and Padgett, C. A. (1961). *Bacteriol. Proc.*, p. 125.

Seiffert, G. (1937). *Zentrabl. Bakteriol. (Orig.)* 140, 168.

Senterfit, L. B., and Jensen, K. E. (1966). *Proc. Soc. Exp. Biol. Med.* 122, 786.

Senterfit, L. B., and Jensen, K. E. (1967). *Ann. N. Y. Acad. Sci.* 143, 461.

Shaw, N., Smith, P. F., and Koostra, W. L. (1968). *Biochem. J.* 107, 329.

Shepard, M. C. (1958). *J. Bacteriol.* 75, 351.

Shepard, M. C. (1967). *Ann. N. Y. Acad. Sci.* 143, 505.

Shepard, M. C., and Lunceford, C. D. (1965). *J. Bacteriol.* 89, 265.

Shepard, M. C., and Lunceford, C. D. (1967). *J. Bacteriol.* 93, 1513.

Shifrine, M., and Gourlay, R. N. (1965). *J. Comp. Pathol.* 75, 381.

Shifrine, M., and Gourlay, R. N. (1967). *Ann. N. Y. Acad. Sci.* 143, 317.

Shifrine, M., Adler, H. E. Aaronson, S., and Hutner, S. H. (1961). *Bacteriol. Proc.*, p. 125.

Shklair, I. L., Mazzarella, M. A. Gutekunst, R. R., and Kiggins, E. M. (1962). *J. Bacteriol.* 83, 785.

Shoetensack, H. M. (1936). *Kitasato Arch. Exp. Med.* 13, 175.

Slotkin, R. I., Clyde, W. A., Jr., and Denny, F. W. (1967). *Amer. J. Epidemiol.* 86, 225.

Smith, C. B., McGinniss, M. H., and Schmidt, P. J. (1967). *J. Immunol.* **99,** 333.
Smith, D. W., and Hanawalt, P. C. (1969). *J. Mol. Biol.* **46,** 57.
Smith, P. F. (1955). *Proc. Soc. Exp. Biol. Med.* **88,** 628.
Smith, P. F. (1967). *In* "A Microbial Enigma" (C. Panos, ed.), pp. 71–163. World Publ., Cleveland, Ohio.
Smith, P. F. (1968). *Advan. Lipid Res.* **6,** 69.
Smith, P. F., and Boughton, J. E. (1960). *J. Bacteriol.* **80,** 851.
Smith, P. F., and Henrikson, C. V. (1965). *J. Bacteriol.* **89,** 146.
Smith, P. F., and Henrikson, C. V. (1966). *J. Bacteriol.* **91,** 1854.
Smith, P. F., and Koostra, W. L. (1967). *J. Bacteriol.* **93,** 1853.
Smith, P. F., and Lynn, R. J. (1958). *J. Bacteriol.* **76,** 264.
Smith, P. F., and Morton, H. E. (1953). *Proc. Soc. Exp. Biol. Med.* **83,** 65.
Smith, P. F., and Rothblat, G. H. (1960). *J. Bacteriol.* **80,** 842.
Smith, P. F., and Sasaki, S. (1958). *Appl. Microbiol.* **6,** 184.
Smith, P. F., Morton, H. E., and Leberman, P. R. (1950). *Proc. Soc. Exp. Biol. Med.* **74,** 552.
Smith, P. F., Koostra, W. L., and Mayberry, W. R. (1969). *J. Bacteriol.* **100,** 1166.
Sobeslavsky, O., Prescott, B., James, W. D., and Chanock, R. M. (1966). *J. Bacteriol.* **91,** 2126.
Sobeslavsky, O., Prescott, B., and Chanock, R. M. (1967). *Ann. N. Y. Acad. Sci.* **143,** 682.
Sobeslavsky, O., Prescott, B., and Chanock, R. M. (1968). *J. Bacteriol.* **96, 695**.
Somerson, N. L., and Cook, M. K. (1965). *J. Bacteriol.* **90,** 534.
Somerson, N. L., and Morton, H. E. (1953). *J. Bacteriol.* **65,** 245.
Somerson, N. L., Purcell, R. H., Taylor-Robinson, D., and Chanock, R. M. (1965a). *J. Bacteriol.* **89,** 813.
Somerson, N. L., Walls, B. E., and Chanock, R. M. (1965b). *Science* **150,** 226.
Spears, D. M., and Provost, P. J. (1967). *Can. J. Microbiol.* **13,** 213.
Spitler, L., Cochrum, K., and Fudenberg, H. H. (1968). *Science* **161,** 1148.
Stanbridge, E., Onen, M., Perkins, F. T., and Hayflick, L. (1969). *Exp. Cell Res.* **57,** 397.
Suchanova, M. (1955). *Cesk. Hyg. Epidemiol. Mikrobiol. Immunol.* **4,** 32.
Switzer, W. R. (1969). *In* "The Mycoplasmatales and the L-Phase of Bacteria" (L. Hayflick, ed.), pp. 607–620. Appleton, New York.
Tang, F. F., Wei, H., McWhirter, D. L., and Edgar, J. (1935). *J. Pathol. Bacteriol.* **40,** 392.
Tauraso, N. (1967). *J. Bacteriol.* **93,** 1559.
Taylor-Robinson, D., and Manchee, R. J. (1967). *Nature (London)* **215,** 404.
Taylor-Robinson, D., Somerson, N. L., Turner, H. C., and Chanock, R. M. (1963). *J. Bacteriol.* **85,** 1261.
Taylor-Robinson, D., Ludwig, W. M., Purcell, R. H., Mufson, M. A., and Chanock, R. M. (1965). *Proc. Soc. Exp. Biol. Med.* **118,** 1073.
Taylor-Robinson, D., Sobeslavsky, O., Jensen, K. E., Senterfit, L. B., and Chanock, R. M. (1966). *Amer. J. Epidemiol.* **83,** 287.
Taylor-Robinson, D., Williams, M. H., and Haig, D. A. (1968). *J. Gen. Microbiol.* **54,** 33.
Thomas, L. (1967). *Ann. N. Y. Acad. Sci.* **143,** 218.
Thomas, L., and Bitensky, M. W. (1966a). *J. Exp. Med.* **124,** 1089.
Thomas, L., and Bitensky, M. W. (1966b). *Nature (London)* **210,** 963.

Thomas, L., Aleu, F., Bitensky, M. W., Davidson, M., and Gesner, B. (1966a). *J. Exp. Med.* **124,** 1067.

Thomas, L., Davidson, M., and McCluskey, R. T. (1966b). *J. Exp. Med.* **123,** 897.

Tully, J. G. (1963). *Proc. Soc. Exp. Biol. Med.* **114,** 704.

Tully, J. G. (1964). *J. Bacteriol.* **88,** 381.

Tully, J. G. (1969). *In* "The Mycoplasmatales and the L-Phase of Bacteria" (L. Hayflick, ed.), pp. 571–606. Appleton, New York.

Tully, J. G., and Rask-Nielsen, R. (1967). *Ann. N. Y. Acad. Sci.* **143,** 345.

Turner, A. W. (1960). *Aust. Vet. J.* **36,** 221.

Turner, A. W. (1962). *Aust. Vet. J.* **38,** 401.

Villemot, J. M., Provost, A., and Queval, R. (1962). *Nature (London)* **193,** 906.

Ward, J. R., Madoff, S., and Dienes, L. (1958). *Proc. Soc. Exp. Biol. Med.* **97,** 132.

Warren, J. (1942). *J. Bacteriol.* **43,** 211.

Weber, M. M., and Kinsky, S. C. (1965). *J. Bacteriol.* **89,** 306.

Woodson, B. A., McCarty, K. S., and Shepard, M. C. (1965). *Arch. Biochem. Biophys.* **109,** 364.

Wright, D. N. (1967). *J. Bacteriol.* **93,** 185.

Wright, D. N., and Bailey, G. D. (1969). *Can. J. Microbiol.* **15,** 1449.

Wright, D. N., Bailey, G. D., and Hatch, M. T. (1968a). *J. Bacteriol.* **95,** 251.

Wright, D. N., Bailey, G. D., and Hatch, M. T. (1968b). *J. Bacteriol.* **96,** 970.

Wright, D. N., Bailey, G. D., and Goldberg, L. J. (1969). *J. Bacteriol.* **99,** 491.

Yamamoto, R., and Adler, H. E. (1956). *Amer. J. Vet. Res.* **17,** 538.

Yamamoto, R., and Adler, H. E. (1958). *J. Infec. Dis.* **102,** 243.

Significance of
Mycoplasmas as Cells 6

This final short chapter is devoted to my own thoughts and speculations concerning mycoplasmas as a biological entity. Although some may seem ephemeral all have some supportive evidence either real or circumstantial. The only justification for this chapter is the possible stimulation it might provide to use mycoplasmas as models for investigations of unsolved biological and pathological phenomena.

A. THE SIMPLEST CELLULAR MODEL

Mycoplasmas are the smallest free-living organisms known. This fact alone should suggest their value in the study of basic biological phenomena since the complexity of structures and functions is diminished. There is little if any space in mycoplasmas avialable for redundancy. Their minuteness almost demands efficiency. Drawbacks for their use are the low yields and the complexity of culture media. Low yields in mass must be expected because of the inherent small size of the organisms. One may obtain only one-fiftieth to one-hundredth of the cell crop of a bacterium such as $E.\ coli$ yet the number of organisms in the original culture can exceed 10^{10} per milliliter. Yet there is no cell wall which accounts for half or more of the weight of a bacterial sediment. The yield of mycoplasmas consists primarily of membrane. Recent advances have led to the development of defined culture media for an increasing number of mycoplasmal species. Certainly this number will expand rapidly.

The area of a mycoplasmal cell, assuming a spherical shape, varies from about 0.8 to 2 μ^2 and the volume from 0.07 to 0.25 μ^3. Contained within this cell is a double helical circle of DNA varying in size from 440 to 1200 $\times$ 10^6 daltons allowing coding for 600 to 1500 genes. Even though these are large numbers when considered in terms of their complete elucidation, they are almost an order of magnitude lower than for the usual bacterium. Assuming that one gene codes for one protein, the simplest mycoplasmal cell should contain approximately 600 different proteins. Even at this stage of studies on mycoplasmas where no concerted effort has been made to identify systematically all of the enzyme and nonenzymic proteins well over a hundred could be listed. So it is conceivable that mycoplasmas could offer the most suitable object for a first complete analysis of the genetic code.

Such an analysis necessitates considerable knowledge of the genetics of mycoplasmas, an area almost devoid of study and results. Although the first attempts have been discouraging success should be predicted. The DNA of mycoplasmas is not unique either as to structure, function, or replication. Mutations are seen. Natural mutants of a given species must exist for a wide variety of strains occur within a species. An example is *M. laidlawii*. Neither strain A nor strain B can synthesize unsaturated fatty acids yet the former requires an unsaturated acid for growth. The glucosidase of strain B is specific for the β configuration while strain A appears specific for the α configuration. Both strains are very closely related on the basis of serology and DNA-DNA homology. More careful selection of mutants and a wider selection of methodology should enable the demonstration of genetic transfer and ultimately gene mapping.

Mycoplasmas already have found a niche in the rapidly developing area of biological membranes. Exponential phase mycoplasmas contain but one membranous structure, that surrounding the organism. It constitutes 60 to 70% of their dry weight and is composed almost exclusively of lipoproteins. No obvious bacterial wall components are present in the usual mycoplasma as observable morphologically or chemically. The membrane appears as a typical trilaminar structure similar to other biological membranes. Mycoplasmas offer a simple uncluttered cell with a naked singular membrane for study of structure and function. Isolation and purification of sufficient quantities of membranes is an easy task. These advantages are augmented further by the simplicity of the lipids in some species and by the ease of alteration of lipid composition. In general only acidic lipids are found. In some species only one phospholipid, phosphatidyl glycerol, is apparent although a small amount of diphosphatidyl glycerol may occur. Others contain one to three glycerophospholipids together with glycolipids, accounted for almost entirely by two related compounds such as mono- and diglycosyl diglycerides. The apolar lipids of some species such as *M. laidlawii* are an uncomplicated group of carotenoids. Species which require sterol contain the sterol supplied to them together with this sterol in its esterified form or this ester plus a glucoside. Appropriate selection of organism can give one of surprising simplicity, e.g., *M. arthritidis* containing phosphatidyl glycerol, a trace of diphosphatidyl glycerol, cholesterol, and cholesteryl esters of short-chain fatty acids. In addition to the requirement for sterol many species also are incapable of fatty acid biosynthesis. These characteristics allow the investigator to alter systematically not only the neutral lipid components of the membrane but also the fatty acid composition of the polar lipids. Even the quantity of sterol can be regulated. The mycoplasmal membrane can be seen as the first step toward complexity from artificial model membranes. The effects of lipid composition on the structure of membranes already has yielded information about stability and phase transitions. Likewise alterations in permeability of the membrane have been shown to be dependant upon the quantity of sterol and the nature of the fatty acids of the complex lipids. The role of cations in control of membrane structure and permeation have been examined only cursorily. This simplicity and flexibility of composition should suggest many new approaches toward the elucidation of the structure and function of biological membranes.

There exists considerable doubt as to the naturalness of reaggregated membranes produced after detergent lysis. However, if such material is shown to closely resemble the original membrane, it may be possible to reconstruct it with only one lipid component such as diphosphatidyl glycerol. Delipidized membranes are solubilized by acidic lipids and form aggregates in the presence of divalent cation.

Lipid function is another area readily attacked by use of mycoplasmas. Lipid alterations in metabolizing and growing cells should give an indication of their function. Since the lipids of mycoplasmas are restricted to the membrane it may be possible to study such aspects of membrane transport in isolated membrane vesicles.

B. EVOLUTIONARY DEVELOPMENT

A resemblance between mycoplasmas and bacteria cannot be denied. Neither contain mitochondria, and their nuclear material is not bounded by an internal membrane. Division by mycoplasmas is best described as binary fission similar to true bacteria. The aberrations observed in dividing mycoplasmas undoubtedly are the result of plasticity due to the absence of a rigid outer wall. Mesosomes occur in many bacteria as an internal structure. However these are a recent discovery having been overlooked or considered as artifacts in earlier cytological studies. They disappear upon protoplast formation apparently evaginating to appear as a segment of the protoplast membrane. Mesosomes have not been described in mycoplasmas. Yet in the stationary phase internal membrane-bounded vesicles and dense cytoplasmic bodies are seen. Could these be similar to the mesosomes or are they really artifacts? Judgment should not be hasty. On the other hand the lack of rigidity of the cell may preclude the cytological observance of mesosomes since they could form part of the cytoplasmic membrane as with bacterial protoplasts.

Resemblances also extend to the molecular level. The base composition of DNA of mycoplasmas falls within the range encompassing the bacteria. Although no homology between the DNA's of mycoplasmas and bacterial species has been successfully demonstrated, too few have been examined. Random selection of a few bacterial and mycoplasmal species would not be expected to yield positive findings because of the chance involved. The recent discovery of deletion of a portion of the chromosome of *Streptococcus* upon L transformation suggests that more than subtle changes occur. Deletion of segments of genome could account for the smaller size of mycoplasmal DNA, the greater efficiency of its use, and loss of redundancy. RNA of mycoplasmas resembles the RNA of bacteria rather than of higher forms of life; this conclusion is based upon the sensitivity of protein synthesis to macrolide antibiotics.

There are many indications that mycoplasmas attempt cell wall synthesis. One species, *M. neurolyticum*, is sensitive to low concentrations of penicillin indicative of the presence of vestigial wall containing portions of a peptidoglycan. Another species, *M. gallisepticum*, accumulates a peptide containing four amino acids common to peptidoglycan. Aminoacyl esters of phosphatidyl glycerol of the two species examined, *M. laidlawii* and *M. arthritidis*, consist primarily of those with glycine, alanine, glutamic acid, and lysine, four amino acids common to peptidoglycan. Furthermore, *M. laidlawii* also synthesizes a D-alanyl phosphatidyl glycerol. In view of the unknown function of aminoacyl esters of phosphatidyl glycerol, could these lipids serve as carriers or intermediates in the biosynthesis of cell wall? If so, would not such components be expected to accumulate in organisms with a block in the pathway for wall biosynthesis? All mycoplasmas examined are capable of decarboxylating α,ϵ-diaminopimelic acid, a wall constituent of some bacteria. This inherent enzymic activity must indicate some prior exposure or genetic knowledge of the existence of such a molecule. A lipid currently termed "phosphatidyl glucose" but having the most probable structure of a glycerophosphoryl diglucosyl diglyceride occurs in large quantity in *M. laidlawii*. Phosphoglucolipids of identical structure are suspected to occur in trace amounts in staphylococci and streptococci. This molecular structure minus the fatty acyl residues has the general appearance of structural units of teichoic acids. Indeed a fragment from alkaline hydrolysis of a bacterial teichoic acid has this particular sequence of components. Could this be another instance of a mycoplasma attempting to synthesize wall unsuccessfully, thereby resulting in the accumulation of an intermediate? Some species of mycoplasmas synthesize copious quantities of galactan or glucan, polysaccharides similar to bacterial capsules and slime.

The lipids of mycoplasmas as with the bacteria are associated solely with the cytoplasmic membrane. Furthermore there is a great similarity in the structure of mycoplasmal and bacterial lipids. Many cocci synthesize carotenoid pigments as do certain mycoplasmas. These carotenoids are capable of replacing the sterol requirement of mycoplasmas having such a requirement because of blocks in the biosynthetic pathway to polyterpenes. Carotenyl glucosides occur in *Flavobacterium* as well as *M. laidlawii*. Large amounts of neutral lipids composed of glycosyl diglycerides are found in both gram-positive bacteria and mycoplasmas. Specifically the glucosyl diglycerides of *M. laidlawii* are identical to those of *Streptococcus*. The galactosyl diglyceride of *M. mycoides* resembles those of *Staphylococcus*. The triacyl glucose of *M. gallinarum* has its counterpart in the tetraacyl glucose of *Streptococcus faecalis*. These and glycosyl diglycerides with longer hexose chains account for serological specificity of mycoplasmal antigens which cross react with bacterial antisera. Ceramide hexoses are suspected to occur in another mycoplasma and could be identical to those found in the bacterial genus, *Bacterioides*. The polar lipids of mycoplasmas are totally acidic in nature similar to those found in many gram-positive bacteria. These consist of glycerophospholipids. In one species a ceramide phosphoryl glycerol similar in structure to a sphingolipid found in *Bacterioides* is seen. Mycoplasmas prefer lactobacillic and *cis*-vaccenic acids, fatty acids common to bacteria, rather than oleic or linoleic acids.

This wide range of counterparts of bacteria and mycoplasmas extends beyond similarities in nucleic acid composition, lipid structure and antigenic cross reactivity to include metabolic character. Homolactic fermentation of glucose is the common metabolic pathway in fermentative species of mycoplasmas analogous to the behavior of streptococci and lactobacilli. The respiratory pathway in these organisms is flavin terminated and under aerobic conditions gives rise to the production of peroxides. The respiratory pathway in nonfermentative species of mycoplasmas is cytochrome terminated. In at least one of these species examined cytochrome o, a bacterial cytochrome, has been detected. Arginine is degraded and synthesized by the common bacterial mechanisms. Lysine is formed by the decarboxylation of diaminopimelic acid and not through the intermediate formation of α-aminoadipate.

One is correct in assuming that more common points relate the mycoplasmas to bacteria than to any other biological organism. Hence mycoplasmas must either be evolutionary precursors of bacteria or degenerate bacteria. Philosophical arguments can be advanced for both possibilities. The more rational possibility, for me, is the second mentioned. The major basis for this selection resides in the fact that bacteria can be induced to undergo transformation to the L phase under the influence of toxic environmental factors. Although these L forms are not identical to mycoplasmas they are very similar and may represent one stage in a degenerate evolution from bacterium to mycoplasma.

The natural habitat of mycoplasmas is in some host. Even those which are found outside hosts probably originally resided within since these species are found in materials contaminated with animal or plant excrement or tissues, such as manure, sewage, leaves, and compost. Assuming that mycoplasmas arose from bacteria a host would be the most appropriate environment to explain the mechanism of their origin. L transformation has been demonstrated *in vitro* and probably *in vivo* for many bacterial genera. It occurs as the result of exposure of the bacterium to a wide variety of toxic agents including antibiotics which inhibit bacterial wall biosynthesis, antisera which are directed primarily against wall components, and to high concentrations of amino acids, particularly those found in bacterial walls. Several well-defined stages of the transformation have been described. First, the bacteria are transformed to a wall-less or wall-deficient form which readily reverts to the original bacterium upon removal of the inducing agent. This stage is nonmutational since 100% conversion to the wall-less form and 100% reversion to the bacterial form can occur. These are transitional forms and give rise to the B type L colonies. Upon repeated transfer in the presence of inducing agent there appears the second stage of L transformation, the true L phase organism which gives rise to the A type colonies. These forms do not revert to the original bacterium when the inducing agent is removed. They can under certain conditions be encouraged to revert. Mutational changes or more radical genome deletion has occurred. Most of these forms require an environment of high osmolality as well as an increased cation concentration. Repeated culture lessens their capacity to revert to the original bacterium. Repeated culture in decreasing salt concentration results in their being "trained" or selected to withstand lower cation concentration and decreasing osmolality. These are the changes observed *in vitro*. Similar changes are suspected to occur *in vivo*. The differences between *in vivo* and *in vitro* environments could allow the production of L-phase organisms indistinguishable from mycoplasmas. This could be a short-term result or require long-term growth *in vivo* as the L phase with the eventual selection of organisms incapable or rarely capable of reversion.

The basis for selection would be survival in an environment perilous to microorganisms bounded by a bacterial wall. The absence of a wall would offer many advantages for survival. The organisms are less foreign to the host with the resultant lessened stimulation of antibody formation against them. The deeper one penetrates into the organism, the less distinction between the organism and the host. Antibiotics and chemotherapeutic agents directed against walls or other external bacterial components become ineffective. The wall-less organisms lack the virulence factors and hence are less noxious to the host. Mycoplasmas are capable of taking up residence in the cytoplasm of the host's cells removing them from direct action of other host immune factors and antibiotics which act at sites other than wall synthesis, e.g., the tetracyclines. The growth rate of the wall-less organisms is much slower than of the parent bacterium obviating an overwhelming infection. In short a state of almost true parasitism is established. The organisms in being selected for survival in the host have lost many of their synthetic functions and their armament for extrahost survival and so have become more dependant upon existence within the host.

One can visualize also that mycoplasmas represent an evolutionary stage in the development of more complex organisms possibly intermediate between viruses and bacteria. In this situation the wide variety of mycoplasmas could be considered as evolutionary precursors of the wide variety of bacteria. The genome is smaller because the organisms have not yet developed coding for many proteins and enzymes found in bacteria. The developing capability to form walls can be seen in some as the formation of extracellular peptides containing typical wall amino acids, in the formation of probable teichoic acid intermediates, and in the synthesis of polysaccharides which could eventually become capsular structures or slime. Mycoplasmas found outside hosts could be considered forms further along in development as attested by their increasing self-dependence. They have developed the capacity to synthesize polyterpenes and are no longer dependant upon host-supplied sterol for membrane formation. Those still residing within hosts consist of an array representing different developing capacities for polyterpene biosynthesis. A type of binary fission is operational and will become fully developed upon acquisition of a wall.

C. MYCOPLASMA-HOST CELL INTERACTIONS

An overt damaging or lethal effect on a host by mycoplasmas is the exception rather than the rule. Most infections by these organisms are inapparent and any effect on the host is subtle. Reasons for believing that mycoplasmas reside in hosts in a state of nearly true parasitism have been advanced above. Therefore it is the author's contention that the significance of mycoplasmal infections lies not in acute infectious disease but rather in more subtle effects on the host. These include their possible role as reservoirs of acute infectious disease, latency of infectious disease, immunological abberrations, and in diseases of undetermined etiology.

If one presumes that mycoplasmas arise from bacteria as a result of an effort to survive in a hostile environment, several possible roles for them become apparent. For the sake of simplicity let us trace what might happen in a hypothetical example. A host becomes infected with a bacterium. The host can react in several ways. It is overwhelmed and dies from the infection; it recognizes the bacterium as foreign and removes it by nonspecific resistance factors; the bacterium is accepted and becomes part of the host's normal flora; a limited infection results with the host developing specific antibody which aids the host in removing the bacterium; man intervenes and treats the host with antibiotic or chemotherapeutic agents. In the first instance the bacterium destroys its environment; in the second, the host denies its environment to the bacterium; in the third, both host and parasite treat one another with disdain. The more subtle results can occur in the fourth and fifth situations. As far as the host is concerned the sought-after result is the elimination of the bacterium either by its own immune mechanisms or by outside intervention. As far as the bacterium is concerned it has found itself in a life or death situation. It reacts in a way to ensure its preservation. By ceasing to synthesize wall and other cellular components exterior to the cytoplasmic membrane the bacterium renders itself less foreign and hence less recognizable to the host. Antibody directed against the surface structures and antibiotics inhibiting biosynthesis of wall become ineffective against the adapted bacterium. It can escape other agents which cannot penetrate host cells by entering the cytoplasm of the host's cells. In doing so the bacterium loses its overt pathogenic actions on the host. While in residence in this state of true parasitism several outcomes could ensue. First, the organism could continue to exist and slowly multiply in this state resulting in no effect on the host. Or the organism can damage the chromosomes of the host cell nonlethally resulting in aberrations of host cell functions possibly even to the extent of causing on rare occasions malignant transformations. The presence of slowly multiplying organisms could constantly stimulate the formation of low levels of antibody. These antibodies would be directed against cellular components of the organism which have some relatedness to the host's own cellular components. Any sudden increase in the amount of antibody resulting from a new infection by a similar organism or an endogenous exacerbation of the existing infection could result in antibody–host cell interactions thereby producing what would appear to be an immunological disease. A specific example may be the streptococci and rheumatic fever or subacute glomerulonephritis.

Some of the organisms may not have been irreversibly transformed. Under appropriate conditions they may revert to the original bacterium with the resultant production of overt bacterial disease. In this situation mycoplasmas could be the key in explaining latency of infections and reservoirs of disease in which the obvious incriminating bacterium cannot be detected in the host prior to development of overt symptomatology. A specific example of circumstantial nature is the production of *Corynebacterium* infections in mice which harbor mycoplasmas upon stressing the animals with corticosteroids.

An example of the possible role of mycoplasmas in a disease of undetermined etiology might be atherosclerosis. Mycoplasmas are capable of concentrating lipids particularly sterols in artificial culture or as resting cells. This is seen visually as an accumulation of oily droplets around colonies or organisms. Mycoplasmas also are known to cause minute superficial petechial lesions on the surfaces of infected organs. Usually these lesions are self-limiting and heal spontaneously. Furthermore it is known that some species of mycoplasmas cause such lesions on the aorta of swine, an animal naturally afflicted in old age with atherosclerosis. Lipid plaques once formed are able to attract other lipids by virtue of their hydrophobic nature resulting in an increasing deposition of lipid. In the case of atherosclerosis the initial lesion may be a series of small mycoplasmal-infected areas on arteries. The organisms initiate a process of cholesterol deposition. When the infection spontaneously regresses, small lipid plaques remain on which can build more cholesterol resulting in the familiar lesions of atherosclerosis.

The foregoing thoughts are merely speculation, but speculation with some circumstantial basis. Experiments could be designed to test these ideas. Additional speculation could be made about other pathological processes. But only a few examples are necessary to broaden ideas of the nature of microbial infections beyond stereotyped classical infectious disease.

Author Index

Numbers in italics refer to the pages on which the complete references are listed.

Subject Index

A

Abscess
  in guinea pigs, 3
  in humans, 3, 4
  in mycoplasmal infections, 200
  in rats, 3, 200
Acholeplasma, 7
Actinobacillus ligneresi, 11
Active transport
  amino acids, 164
  model, 169
  M. fermentans, 163
  M. gallisepticum, 163–164
  M. hominis, 163–164
  M. laidlawii, 164–171
Acylated sugars
  changes during growth, 157
  M. gallinarum, 13, 115, 157
  turnover, 115
Acyl coenzyme A
fatty acid biosynthesis and, 114
  lipid metabolism, 109
  polyterpene biosynthesis, 121
Acyl coenzyme A dehydrogenases, 172
Acyl coenzyme A synthetases, 103, 121
Adenosine triphosphatase
  localization, 75
  in membrane fractionation, 82
  oxidative phosphorylation and, 176
  photodynamic inactivation, 188
  properties, 104
Aerobic environment
  effect of amino acid metabolism, 104
    on glucose metabolism, 100, 190
    on growth, 145, 190
Aeromonas hydrophila, 11, 209
Aerosol
  effect of relative humidity, 185
    of temperature, 185
    of ultraviolet light, 185
  infection of cattle by, 2, 200
    of humans by, 212
Agar gel diffusion

antigenic components, 207
  mycoplasmas and bacteria, 14
  technique, 214
Agglutination
  antibody type, 213
  diphtheroids, 14
  hemagglutination, 214
  indirect, 214
  latex, 214
  M. arthritidis, 14
  M. laidlawii, 13
  Streptococcus MG, 13
Agrobacterium tumefaciens, 12
Amino acids,
  active transport, 164
  amino acyl lipids, 65–66, 118–119,
  dehydrases, 107
  induction of L-phase, 16
  in lipids, 30, 65–66, 71, 118
  of membrane proteins, 62
  metabolism, 30, 104–107
  permeability, 163–164
  requirements for growth, 127–131
Ammonia
  from amino acids, 103
  from arginine, 105
  from glutamine, 104
  pathogenesis and, 205
  production by mycoplasmas, 2
  from urea, 103
Anaerobic environment
  effect on amino acid metabolism, 104
  effect on glucose metabolism, 100, 190
    on growth, 145, 190
Antibiotics, *see also* specific antibiotics
  effects on mycoplasmas, 190–192
  membrane biosynthesis and, 84
  mutation to resistance, 177
  respiration and, 171–176
Antigens
  bovine arthritis strain, 12, 211
  effect of mycoplasmas on, 207
    of pH on, 189
  glycolipids, 12–13, 209–210

separation of lipid and protein, 81–82
uptake of polyterpenes, 125
Lysine
  biosynthesis, 112
  growth requirement, 128
  permeability, 164
Lysis
  complement induced, 215
  digitonin, 79, 197
  enzymes, 80, 196
  growth and, 155
  ionic strength, 77, 182–183
  M. laidlawii, 77, 182–183
  mycoplasmal infected cells, 205
  nutritional deficiency, 143–144
  polyene antibiotics, 79
  streptolysin 0, 78, 196
  surface active agents, 80, 195
Lysophospholipase, 107

M

M protein, 19
Mastitis, 2, 199
Membranes
  chemical composition, 61–73
  conductivity, 77
  density, 85
  dielectric constant, 77
  disaggregation, 80, 82
  effect of lipid deficiency, 78
  enzymes, 62, 75–76, 163
  fractionation, 82
  lipids, 62–73
  L-phase and mycoplasmas, 27
  M. gallisepticum, 55–56
  M. laidlawii, 56, 62–67, 78
  M. pulmonis, 57
  permeability, 162–171
  reaggregation, 83–84
  respiration, 171–176
  solubilization, 62, 80–82
  subunits, 57, 80–81
  ultrastructure, 54–57, 78
Metabolic inhibition
  antibody, 213–214
  antigen, 012
Methicillin, 16
Methylene blue reduction, 5, 171
Micromyces, 6
Mollicutes, 7

Monkey mycoplasmas, 5
Morphology
  cell aggregates, 150
  cellular, 8, 49–53
  colonial, 7, 42–48
  L-phase, 22–25, 27
  methods, 5
  M. agalactiae, 25
  M. gallisepticum, 25, 27, 55
  M. laidlawii, 78
  M. mycoides, 2, 25, 79
  reproductive process, 147–150
  size and sedimentation, 153
Motility
  M. pneumoniae, 149
  M. pulmonis, 60
Mouse
  carriers, 3
  exotoxin, 3, 200, 202
  motility of mycoplasmas, 60
  mycoplasmas in, 3, 5, 198
  polyarthritis, 3, 200
  respiratory infections, 198
Muramic acid
  in L-phase, 19, 29
  in mycoplasmas, 29
Murolytic enzymes, 16
Mutation
  to antibiotic resistance, 177
  induction by chemicals, 178
  L-phase, 19, 21
  temperature sensitive, 178
Mycoplasma
  M. agalactiae, 25, 57, 74, 86, 102, 186, 192, 199
  M. arthritidis, 10, 13, 14, 25, 33, 34, 50, 51, 54, 57, 62, 67, 70, 71, 74, 75, 86, 87, 99, 102–104, 106, 108–110, 112–114, 120, 121, 124–126, 128–132, 134, 136–139, 144, 145, 148, 149, 152, 153, 162, 163, 172–177, 179, 182–184, 186, 189, 190, 211, 213, 225, 226
  M. bovigenitalium, 74, 183, 198, 199, 212
  M. bovimastitis, 199
  M. bovirhinis, 74, 198
  M. bovis, 172, 174, 176
  M. canis, 74, 107
  M. felis, 74, 152
  M. fermentans, 74, 86, 107, 148, 149, 163, 164, 189, 211

Date Due